Electrical Applications 3

by the same author

Electrical Applications 2
Electrical Applications 2 Checkbook

Electrical Applications 3

David W. Tyler, CEng, MIEE

Formerly Senior Lecturer, Electrical Engineering
Reading College of Technology

Butterworth-Heinemann Ltd
Linacre House, Jordan Hill, Oxford OX2 8DP

OXFORD LONDON BOSTON
MUNICH NEW DELHI SINGAPORE SYDNEY
TOKYO TORONTO WELLINGTON

First published 1987
Reprinted 1990 (twice), 1992, 1993

British Library Cataloguing in Publication Data
Tyler, D. W.
Electrical Applications 3
1. Electric engineering I. Title
621.3 TK145

ISBN 0 7506 0648 7

Printed and bound in Great Britain by
Hartnolls Limited, Bodmin, Cornwall

Contents

Preface

Electrical Applications 3 covers fully the NIII level objectives of the BTEC National Course Electrical Applications (U86/330).

The NII level objectives of this course have been covered in my earlier book, *Electrical Applications 2.*

Some material from the level II book is reviewed in this volume, particularly in the area of machines and fuses. This may be used as revision material, and will be useful to readers who want to tackle the new material starting from perhaps only a basic knowledge of electrical principles.

I have endeavoured to cover the objectives in the liberal manner that is now encouraged by the new BTEC objectives format: in some instances extra material has been included – as in Chapter 7, for example, where transducers, cross-field machines, magnetic amplifiers and thyristors are discussed, all of these being capable of performing as an element in a servo system. Stepper motors seem not to have received the attention they merit and I hope that the section on these will stimulate interest and lead to further reading.

The work includes over 200 single line drawings and 150 review questions with numerical answers. I would encourage students to use diagrams wherever possible – the old adage that one good and relevant diagram is worth 500 words is very true.

I wish all my readers success in their studies and hope also that those who are not following a formal course will equally find the material in this book useful and interesting.

David W. Tyler

1 Transformers

Aims: At the end of this chapter you should be able to:

Explain the relationship between core flux, number of turns, frequency and the e.m.f.s in a transformer.
Discuss the losses which occur in a transformer and the methods employed to minimise them.
Draw the equivalent circuit diagram of a transformer using the information obtained from the open and short-circuit tests.
Calculate the efficiency of the transformer and determine the conditions of loading required to make this a maxim.
Determine the voltage regulation of a transformer.
Draw phasor and connection diagrams for three-phase transformers and to explain how a phase displacement is achieved between the input and output voltage phasors.

From Faraday we have the expression:

$$e = \frac{N\mathrm{d}\Phi}{\mathrm{d}t}$$

Where e = induced e.m.f. (volts)
$\mathrm{d}\Phi$ = change in magnetic flux linked (webers)
N = number of turns of a coil linked with the flux
$\mathrm{d}t$ = time interval during which the flux change takes place.

Wherever a conductor is situated in a region in which the magnetic field is changing, an e.m.f. will be induced in that conductor. In a generator, such as a vehicle alternator, the changing magnetic field is produced by rotating an electromagnet inside a high-permeability iron core on which coils of wire are wound. In the case of the transformer the changing magnetic field is produced by an alternating current flowing in a coil of wire called the primary winding. The changing magnetic field links with a second coil, the secondary. As with the generator, the flux paths lie within a high-permeability core. We are concerned in this chapter with power transformers and these are used to deliver power at a range of voltages to suit the application. For example, 25 V for safe lighting starting with a 240 V supply or to step up the voltage from a generator operating at 25 kV to 400 kV for long-distance transmission.

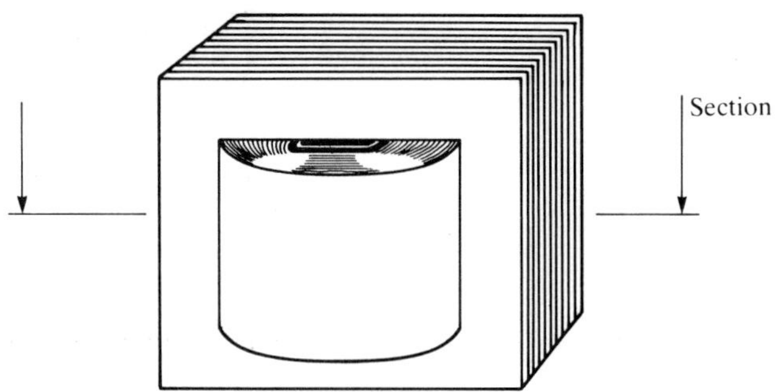

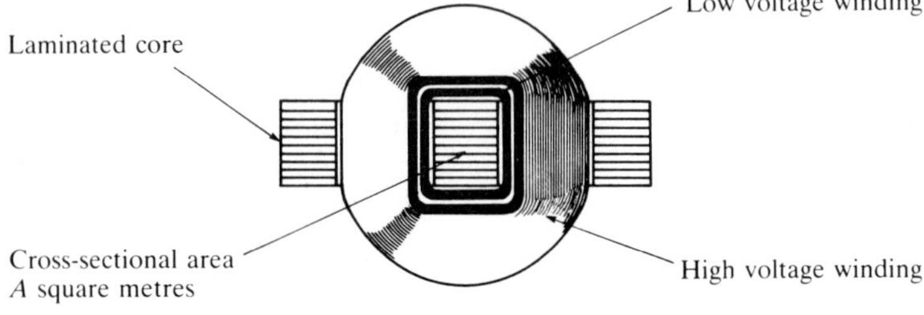

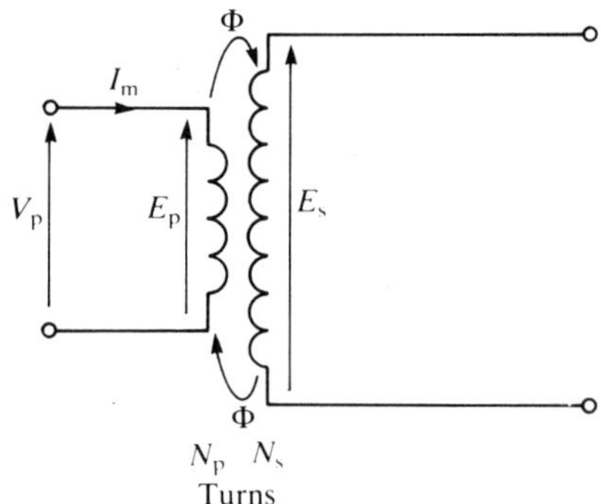

Figure 1.1

Figure 1.1 shows the basic construction of a single-phase transformer.

THE E.M.F. EQUATION

We have $e = \dfrac{N\mathrm{d}\Phi}{\mathrm{d}t}$

Since $\Phi = BA$, $e = \dfrac{N\,AdB}{\mathrm{d}t}$ volts

Where A = cross-sectional area of the core in square metres.
B = flux density in webers/m^2 or tesla (T)

Consider the transformer to be fed from an alternating supply of sinusoidal form and the flux density to vary sinusoidally, we may describe the flux variation in the form:

$B = B_{max} \sin \omega t$ tesla ($\omega = 2\pi f$ rad/s, f = frequency in hertz)

(Like describing a voltage: $V = V_{max} \sin \omega t$ volts.)

Hence: $e = \dfrac{N A \, d B_{max} \sin \omega t}{dt}$ volts

Performing the differentiation: $e = N A B_{max} \omega \cos \omega t$ volts
The maximum possible value of the induced e.m.f. is when $\cos \omega t = 1$

$\therefore E_{max} = \omega N A B_{max}$ volts Now for a sine wave $E_{(r.m.s.)} = 0.707 \times E_{max}$
$\therefore E = 0.707 \, \omega N A B_{max} = 0.707 \, 2\pi f N A B_{max}$ volts
$= 4.44 \, B_{max} A f N$ volts

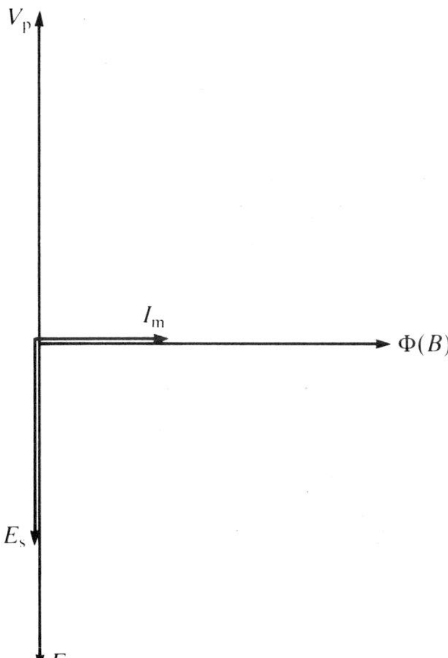

Figure 1.2

It should be noted that whereas the flux wave is a sine function, the induced e.m.f. is a cosine function. Since a cosine wave is a sine wave advanced through 90°, there is a 90° phase relationship between the phasors representing induced e.m.f. and flux.

Consider a perfect transformer. The primary winding has no resistance and therefore may be considered to be a perfect inductor. Applying a voltage V_p to the primary causes a magnetising current I_m to flow which lags the applied voltage by 90°. This is shown in *Figure 1.2.*

I_m magnetises the core creating flux density B tesla. The flux density is proportional to the instantaneous value of magnetising current and so varies sinusoidally. The magnetic flux links with both windings inducing voltages in them both. The induced e.m.f. in the primary is given by the expression:

$$E_p = 4.44 \, B_{max} A f N_p \text{ volts}$$

By Lenz's law, the induced e.m.f. in the primary winding, E_p will oppose the applied voltage V_p. Very closely $E_p = V_p$.

In the perfect transformer, all the flux created by the primary winding will link with the secondary so that the secondary e.m.f. will be given by:

$$E_s = 4.44 \, B_{max} A f N_s \text{ volts}$$

Dividing the first equation by the second all the common terms disappear leaving:

$$\frac{E_p}{E_s} = \frac{N_p}{N_s}$$

TRANSFORMER LOSSES

Good transformer design will provide the necessary power and output voltage with the smallest possible losses. Power transformers are generally between 98% and 99% efficient, but even at the higher value this means that 1% of the input is lost as heat. In a 500 000 kW transformer this means a heat loss of 5000 kW.

To have a high efficiency it is necessary that there shall be low power losses in the core and in the primary and secondary windings. In order that the output voltage shall not vary more than a specified amount as full load is applied and as the power factor of the connected load changes, there must be only limited magnetic flux leakage from the ideal path through the core. The winding resistance also affects voltage change but to a lesser extent and efficiency considerations will predominate.

Core losses

(a) *Hysteresis*. Ferrous materials are made up of *domains* which are groups of atoms of material. Each domain is a tiny magnet in its own right. In the non-magnetised state the domains form themselves into closed loops, north pole to south pole as one might imagine happening with a large number of permanent magnets thrown together in a box. Passing a current through a coil wound on a piece of ferrous material sets up a magnetomotive force which tends to break open the loops of domains causing them all generally to point in the same direction, along the axis of the coil. The core material exhibits strong magnetic effects at its two ends, a north pole at one and a south pole at the other. Breaking open the loops and aligning the domains requires energy as would be the case in the permanent magnet analogy above. When the coil carries alternating current the domains have all to be orientated in one direction during a positive half cycle and then in the opposite direction during a negative half cycle.

The amount of energy involved depends on how many of the loops are broken and to the extent that the domains are aligned. Externally this shows up as the strength of the magnetic flux density B tesla. The higher the external field strength, the more energy has been expended in re-orientating the domains. The energy used and flux density are not proportional, however.

The power involved is equal to the energy expended in setting up the domains in one direction and then reversing them multiplied by the number of times this occurs per second, i.e. multiplied by the frequency of the supply.

To sum up, the hysteresis power loss is:

(i) a function of maximum working flux density B_{max} as used in the e.m.f. equation and

(ii) directly proportional to frequency f Hz.

[An empirical formula developed by Steinmetz gives:

Hysteresis loss $= k_h B_{max}{}^n f$ watts

Where n = Steinmetz index which lies between 1.6 and 4 according to material

k_h = another constant concerned with volume of the core.]

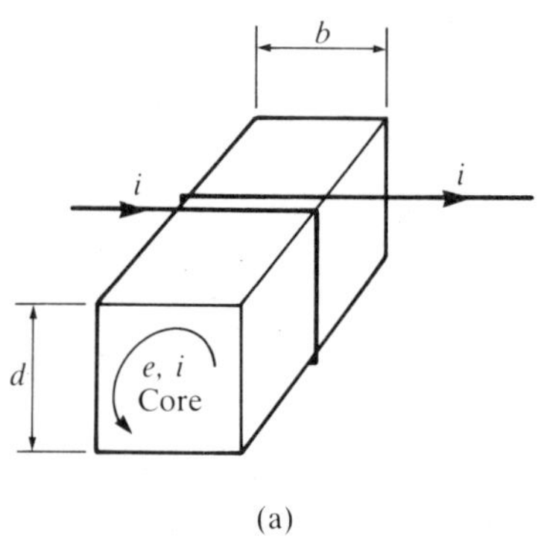

(a)

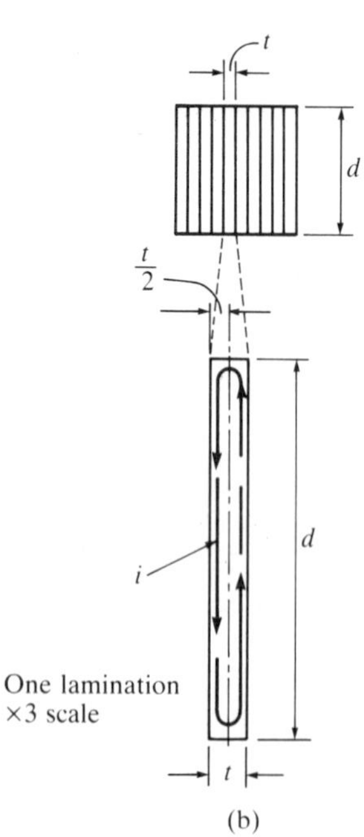

(b)

Figure 1.3

(b) *Eddy current losses. Figure 1.3(a)* shows a single turn wound on a solid conducting core. It is being fed from an alternating supply. An instant is chosen when the current in the coil is rising. The magnetic flux density is therefore rising and voltages are induced in the coil itself, in a secondary coil, if present, and since the core is made from conducting material, in the core itself. The e.m.f. induced in the core will drive a current which will generate heat. Core currents are known as eddy currents. The core is acting as a single turn and using $N = 1$ in the transformer equation the value of the induced e.m.f. is seen to be:

$E = 4.44\, B_{max}\, A f$ volts

Where $A = b \times d$

The eddy current losses are reduced by rolling out the core material into very thin strips called laminations. Power transformer laminations are approximately 0.4 mm thick and are insulated from each other. Reducing the thickness of material causes the large eddy current shown in *Figure 1.3(a)* to be broken up into many much smaller paths as in *Figure 1.3(b)*. Two effects are apparent: (i) the e.m.f. induced in each strip is less than with the solid core since the area per lamination is now $t \times d$ and (ii) the resistance of the current paths is increased since they are very much thinner. The ideal path for current is up one side of the lamination and down the other making the current path only 0.4/2 mm wide.

$$R = \frac{\rho \times \text{length of current path}}{\text{area}} \text{ ohms}$$

Where ρ = resistivity of the material.

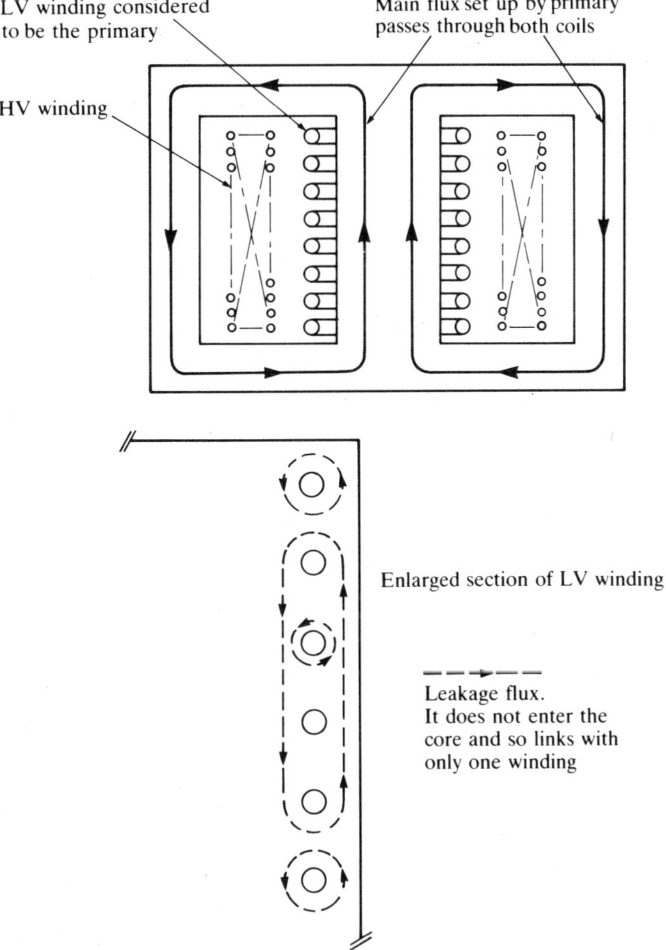

Figure 1.4

The power loss in the core $= E^2/R$ watts where R = resistance of the current path in ohms. The power loss in a lamination can therefore be expressed using a formula of the form:

$$\text{Power loss} = \frac{[4.44\ B_{max}\ A f]^2}{R} \quad \frac{[4.44\ B_{max}\ (t \times d)\ f]^2}{\rho l/\text{area}}$$

Since the actual current path cannot be predicted, we do not know the true area of the current path or that it will flow completely down one side (distance, d) before returning up the other side. The known quantities are B_{max}, t, f and ρ. Other quantities are lumped into an experimentally-determined constant k_e which will include a multiplier to allow for the number of laminations, i.e. the volume of the transformer core.

$$\text{Eddy current loss in a transformer core} = \frac{k_e[B_{max}\ t f]^2}{\rho}\ \text{watts}$$

The core losses have to be provided by the power supply and a current in phase with the primary input voltage will flow in addition to the magnetising current. (*Figure 1.2*) The loss current will be called I_{H+E}.

Winding losses

Both primary and secondary windings have resistance and there will be associated power losses. Calling the primary and secondary currents I_p and I_s respectively and the corresponding resistances R_p and R_s the transformer copper loss will be $I_p{}^2R_p + I_s{}^2R_s$ watts.

Winding leakage reactance

In practice, it is impossible to ensure that all the magnetic flux created by the primary winding links with the secondary. Some of it is set up in paths as shown in *Figure 1.4*. Similarly, when a load current flows in the secondary this creates a flux which ideally ought to link totally with the primary because it is this linkage which lowers the impedance of the primary allowing extra current, known as balancing current, to flow into the primary. If there is leakage flux, the input current is smaller than ideal so limiting the power output and the output voltage falls.

TRANSFORMER EQUIVALENT CIRCUIT

In order to be able to calculate the efficiency and output terminal voltage of a transformer on load we need an equivalent circuit diagram. At the heart of the diagram is a perfect transformer with no losses or imperfections. For the perfect transformer $V_p = E_p$, $E_s = V_s$ and:

$$\frac{E_p}{E_s} = \frac{N_p}{N_s}$$

The resistances of the primary and secondary windings, R_p and R_s respectively are shown external to the perfect transformer as shown in *Figure 1.5*.

Leakage is represented as two small reactances X_p and X_s in primary and secondary respectively. The combined value of these two components is determined in the short-circuit test. Considering

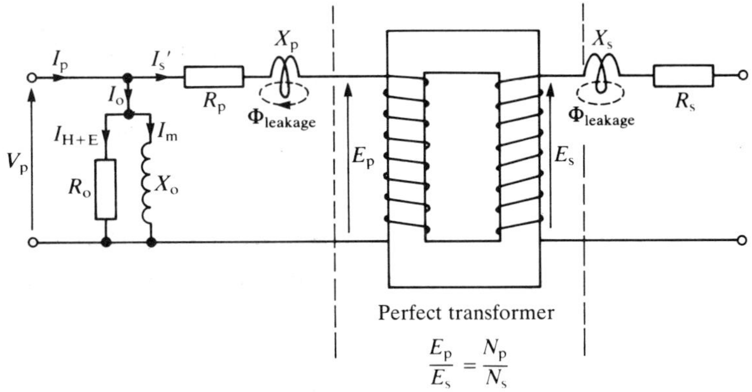

Figure 1.5

Figure 1.4 it is seen that most of the flux created by the primary lies within the core and so links with both primary and secondary coils. However, some of the flux links only the primary. Let us argue that 0.5% of the total flux takes up leakage paths and that the primary winding has 200 turns. The flux entering the core is 99.5% of that created by the primary winding. If the transformer were perfect and therefore the leakage flux did not exist, only 99.5% of the 200 turns would be needed, i.e. 199 turns. All the leakage is considered to be produced by the remaining single turn. In the equivalent circuit diagram the perfect transformer would be shown for this example as having 199 turns and the single turn producing only leakage (useless) flux drawn external to the transformer along with R_p. Since coils possess inductance and hence reactance, this external coil becomes X_p, the primary leakage reactance. The same argument can be applied to the secondary leading to the inclusion of X_s.

OPEN CIRCUIT TEST

The normal rated voltage is applied to one of the windings of the transformer while the other is connected to a high-resistance voltmeter. The input voltage, power and current are measured using suitable range instruments connected as shown in *Figure 1.6*. Since the second winding is delivering virtually no current and the current in the winding being fed is extremely small, the total input power to the transformer as indicated by the wattmeter may be considered to be the eddy current and hysteresis losses of the core only.

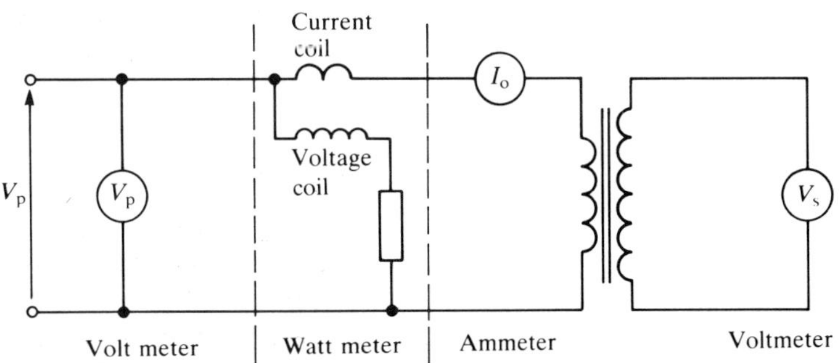

Figure 1.6

Using the results from this test we can construct the no-load phasor diagram and the no load section of the equivalent circuit diagram for the transformer.

Example 1. An open-circuit test on a 200 V:400 V single-phase transformer gave the following results with the 200 V winding connected to a 200 V, 50 Hz supply.

Input current = 2 A Input power = 69.44 W

Calculate: (a) The value of the iron loss current I_{H+E}
(b) The value of the magnetising current I_m
(c) The no-load power factor and phase angle
(d) The values of shunt components which can be used in an equivalent circuit diagram to simulate these results.

Draw a phasor diagram as in *Figure 1.2* and include I_{H+E}.

(a) The power input is regarded as core loss only. The core loss is therefore 69.44 W. It is being supplied from 200 V mains. Power can only be developed when a current flows which is in phase with the voltage.

$\therefore 200 \times I_{H+E} = 69.44$ W $\qquad I_{H+E} = 69.44/200 = 0.374$ A

(b) The input current on no load is called I_o; in this example $I_o = 2$ A. The magnetising current I_m lags the supply voltage by exactly 90°.

$\therefore \sqrt{[I_m^2 + I_{H+E}^2]}$ = total input current = 2 A (Pythagoras)

$$I_m = \sqrt{[2^2 - 0.374^2]} \qquad = 1.97 \text{ A}$$

(c) In a single-phase circuit, $VI \cos \phi$ = power
and $\cos \phi$ = power factor

200 × 2 × power factor = 69.44

$$\text{Power factor} = \frac{69.44}{200} \times 2 = 0.1736$$

$$\phi = INV \cos 0.1736$$
$$= 80°$$

(a), (b) and (c) answers are shown in *Figure 1.7*.

(d) The iron loss current being in phase with the voltage appears to be flowing in a pure resistance. This is called R_o.

$$R_o = \frac{200}{0.374} = 576\,\Omega$$

The magnetising current lags the applied voltage by 90° and hence appears to be flowing in a pure inductance.

$$X_o = \frac{200}{1.97} = 101.52\,\Omega$$

On no load the transformer draws the same current and power as a parallel combination of 576 Ω and inductive reactance of

101.52 Ω. Since I_{H+E} and I_m are independent of load, R_o and X_o are shown in the equivalent circuit diagram as connected to the constant voltage input, V_p (see *Figure 1.5*).

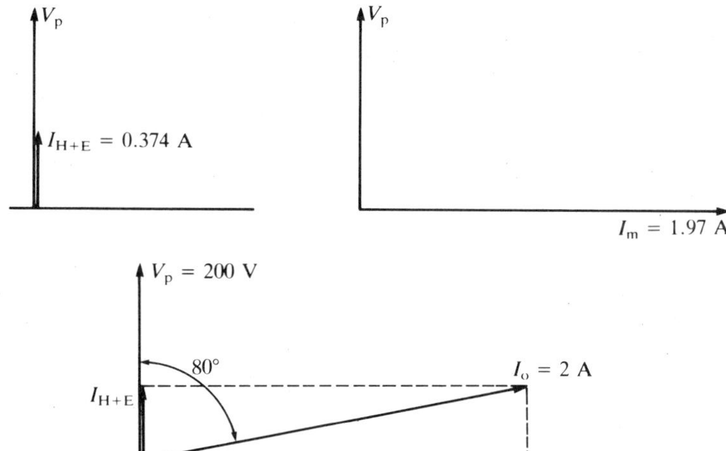

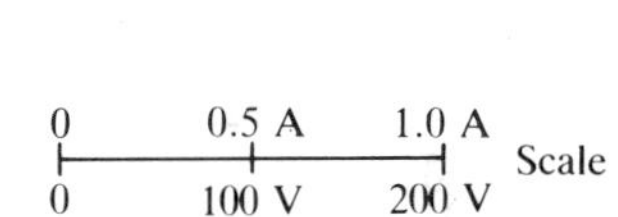

Figure 1.7

BALANCING CURRENT

Consider now the effect of connecting the secondary terminals of the transformer to a load so that a current I_s flows in the secondary winding. I_s amperes flowing in N_s turns produces a magnetomotive force which creates a magnetic flux which modifies the flux in the core set up by the magnetising current I_m flowing in the primary winding.

Since $E_p = 4.44\, B_{max}\, A f N$ volts, any change in core flux changes the value of E_p. The applied voltage V_p will differ from E_p and a current $I_s{}'$ will flow in the primary winding such that the extra magneto-motive force $I_s{}' N_p = I_s N_s$. This will restore the original value of E_p (closely).

Transposing, $I_s{}' = I_s \dfrac{N_s}{N_p}$

$I_s{}'$, the secondary current referred into the primary, is known as the balancing current. The balancing current flows in the primary winding at the same time as I_o so that in the phasor diagram for the loaded condition these two currents must be added.

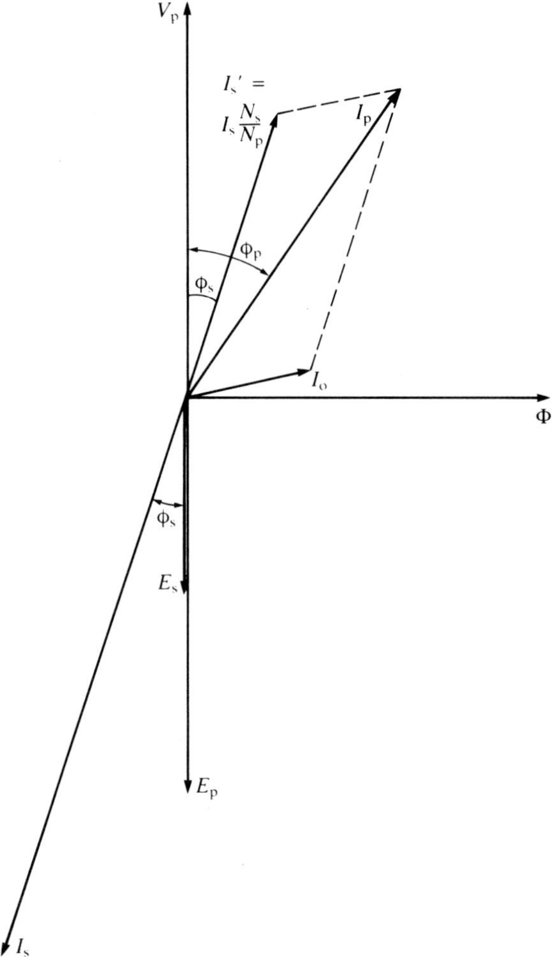

Figure 1.8

In *Figure 1.8*, I_s' is drawn to balance I_s and therefore lags V_p by the same angle as I_s lags E_s. Adding I_s' phasorially to I_o gives I_p, the total primary current. I_p lags V_p by an angle ϕ_p which is the operating power factor of the transformer for that particular load.

Example 2. A single-phase transformer with ratio 500 V : 100 V has a core loss of 200 W at full rated voltage. The magnetising current is 2 A in the 500 V winding. The transformer delivers a current of 50 A from its 100 V winding at a power factor of 0.75 lagging.

Determine: (a) The iron loss component of current
(b) The no-load current of the transformer
(c) The balancing current in the primary winding
(d) The total primary current
(e) The power factor of the primary input at this load.

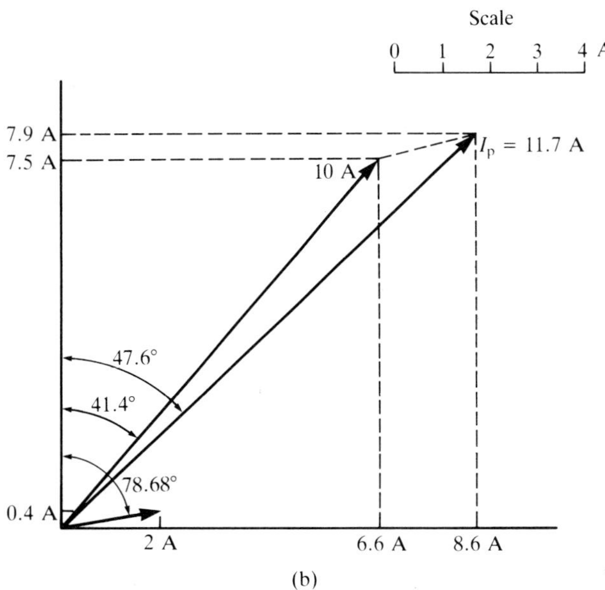

Figure 1.9

(a) From *Figure 1.9(a)* it may be seen that $I_{H+E}/I_o = \cos\phi_o$

$$\therefore I_{H+E} = I_o \cos\phi_o$$

But power input on no load = $V_p I_o \cos\phi_o$

$\therefore 500 \times I_{H+E} = 200$ W $\qquad I_{H+E} = 200/500 = 0.4$ A

(b) $I_o = \sqrt{I_{H+E}^2 + I_m^2}$ (pythagoras) $= \sqrt{0.4^2 + 2^2} = 2.039$ A

$$\cos\phi_o = \frac{I_{H+E}}{I_o} = \frac{0.4}{2.039} = 0.196 \quad \therefore \phi_o = 78.68°$$

(c) $I_s' = 50 \times \dfrac{N_s}{N_p} = 50 \times \dfrac{E_s}{E_p} = 50 \times \dfrac{100}{500} = 10$ A

(d) The load power factor = 0.75 so that I_s' lags on V_p by 41.4°.

These quantities are drawn to scale to *Figure 1.9(b)*. The value of I_p and the overall phase angle may be scaled from the diagram or calculated by resolving I_s' into vertical and horizontal components.

Vertical component of $I_s' = 10 \cos 41.4° = 7.5$ A
Horizontal component of $I_s' = 10 \sin 41.4° = 6.6$ A

Add vertical components: $I_{H+E} + 7.5 = 0.4 + 7.5 = 7.9$ A
Adding horizontal components: $I_m + 6.6 = 2 + 6.6 = 8.6$ A

By Pythagoras' theorem: $I_p = \sqrt{[7.9^2 + 8.6^2]} = 11.7$ A

$$\cos \phi_p = \frac{7.9}{11.7} = 0.675 \quad \therefore \phi_p = 47.6°$$

THE SHORT-CIRCUIT TEST

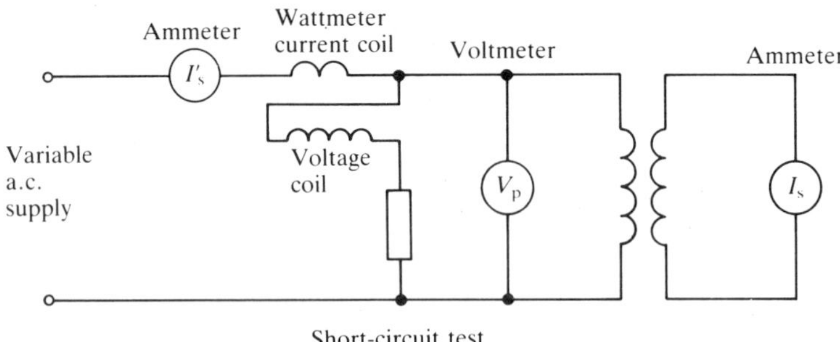

Figure 1.10

One winding of the transformer is short circuited through an ammeter while the other is fed from a variable-voltage supply through a wattmeter and ammeter as shown in *Figure 1.10*. The input voltage is raised in increments until a value is reached at which currents of the order of the full load values are circulating in both windings. Full load currents are generally not exceeded from overheating considerations. The voltage level to give these currents is usually in the region of 10 to 20% of the normal rated voltage. Now since $E = 4.44\, B_{max}\, A f N$ volts, the flux will only be between 10 to 20% of its normal working value. The hysteresis and eddy current losses are proportional to a power of B_{max} and so will both be extremely small. At 10% normal voltage the iron losses will be closely $(10\%)^2 = 1\%$ of those expected when working at full voltage. The losses as indicated on the wattmeter are therefore regarded as being due to the winding resistances only.

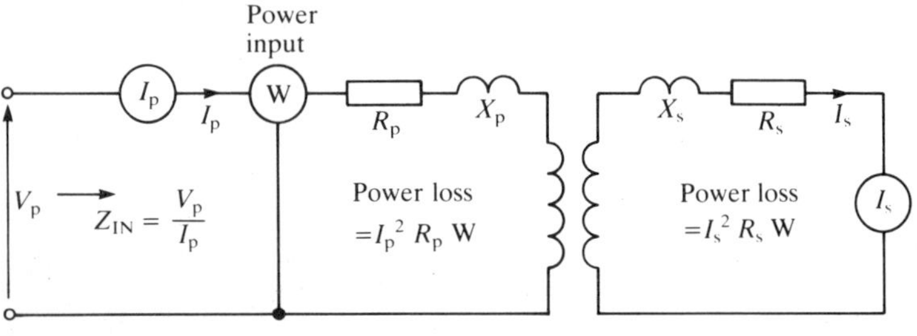

Figure 1.11

The series components for the equivalent circuit may be deduced from the short-circuit test results in the following manner with reference to *Figure 1.11*.

Power input as indicated on the wattmeter, $P = I_p^2R_p + I_s^2R_s$ watts

$I_pN_p = I_sN_s \quad \therefore I_s = I_pN_p/N_s$

Hence $P = I_p^2R_p + [I_pN_p/N_s]^2R_s$
$= I_p^2\{R_s + [N_p/N_s]^2R_s\} = I_p^2R_T{}^p$

The effective resistance as seen by the input voltage on the primary side is thus given by:

$R_T{}^{primary} = \{R_p + [N_p/N_s]^2R_s\}\ \Omega$

From the short-circuit test:

$$\frac{\text{Power input}}{I_p^2} = \{R_p + [N_p/N_s]^2R_s\} = R_T{}^p.$$

Where R = resistance
T = total
p or ^{primary} = as seen on the primary side.

Generally, we only know total values. We never need to know separate values for the primary and secondary.

$$\frac{V_p}{I_p} = \text{input impedance, } Z_T{}^{primary} \text{ or } Z_T{}^p.$$

and since $\sqrt{(R^2 + X^2)} = Z$ generally, $\sqrt{(Z^2 - R^2)} = X$
$\sqrt{[Z_T{}^p]^2[R_T{}^p]^2} = X_T{}^p$

$X_T{}^p$ = total leakage reactance of the transformer as seen by the primary.

Bringing the secondary quantities into the primary using $[N_p/N_s]^2$ is known as referring the secondary values into the primary. It is similarly possible to refer the primary values into the secondary.

$R_T{}^s = \{R_s + [N_s/N_p]^2R_p\} \quad X_T{}^s = \{X_s + [N_s/N_p]^2X_p\}$

Total values are referred from one winding to the other in exactly the same manner as is shown in Example 3.

When referring values from a low-voltage winding into a higher-voltage winding the values of resistance and reactance get *larger*.

When referring values from a high-voltage winding into a lower-voltage winding the values of resistance and reactance get *smaller*.

Remembering these statements should help in using the relationship N_p to N_s correctly.

Example 3. A short circuit test was done on a transformer with a turns ratio of 3:1 as shown in *Figure 1.11*. The low-voltage winding is short circuited through an ammeter. The primary applied voltage = 50 V. The primary input current = 100 A. The power input = 1987 W.
(a) Determine the values of: (i) $Z_T{}^p$, (ii) $R_T{}^p$, (iii) $X_T{}^p$.

(b) Using the turns ratio, refer the values in (i), (ii) and (iii) above into the secondary so finding (iv) $Z_T{}^s$, (v) $R_T{}^s$ and (vi) $X_T{}^s$.

(c) Verify that the calculated value of $R_T{}^s$ yields the same value of winding power loss as quoted above.

(a) (i) $Z_T{}^p = V_p/I_p = 50\ \text{V}/100\ \text{A} = 0.5\ \Omega$

(ii) $R_T{}^p = \text{power loss}/I_p{}^2 = 1987/100^2 = 0.1987\ \Omega$

(iii) $X_T{}^p = \sqrt{0.5^2 - 0.1987^2} = 0.4588\ \Omega$

(b) The turns ratio is 3:1. Referring into the lower voltage winding means using $[N_s/N_p]^2 = [1/3]^2 = 1/9$. (The values will be smaller.)

(iv) $Z_T{}^s = 0.5 \times 1/9 = 0.0555\ \Omega$

(v) $R_T{}^s = 0.1987 \times 1/9 = 0.0221\ \Omega$

(vi) $X_T{}^s = 0.4588 \times 1/9 = 0.051\ \Omega$

(c) $I_sN_s = I_pN_p \therefore I_s = I_pN_p/N_s = 100 \times 3/1 = 300\ \text{A}$

Power loss using secondary quantities, I_s and $R_T{}^s$:

$P = I_s{}^2R_T{}^s = 300^2 \times 0.0221$ watts = 1987 W (closely, since the resistance value was slightly truncated).

TRANSFORMER RATING

A transformer has a name plate rating which in effect informs us how much current the transformer windings can carry without overheating. The rating is quoted in volt-amperes (VA), at the full rated voltage. For example, a single-phase transformer with a rating of 10 000 VA and a ratio of 500 V : 100 V can carry 10 000/500 = 20 A in its 500 V winding and 10 000/100 = 100 A in its 100 V winding. If the voltage is lower than that specified on the name plate for any reason, the current may not be increased to give the original value of VA. Such an increase in current would increase the power loss in the windings and the transformer would overheat.

Example 4. Determine the rated current in each winding of a 1100 V : 240 V single-phase transformer with a rating of 25 kVA.

1100 V winding: $I = \dfrac{25\,000}{1100} = 22.72\ \text{A}$

240 V winding: $I = \dfrac{25\,000}{240} = 104.2\ \text{A}$

TRANSFORMER EFFICIENCY

The losses in a transformer are the eddy current and hysteresis losses in the core which are measured using the open-circuit test, and the conduction or copper losses which are determined in the short-circuit test.

$$\text{Efficiency} = \frac{\text{Output power}}{\text{Input power}} = \frac{\text{Output power}}{\text{Output power} + \text{losses}}$$

$$= \frac{\text{Output } VA \times \text{power factor}}{\text{Output } VA \times \text{power factor} + \text{core loss} + \text{winding loss}}$$

Example 5. A 240 V:110 V transformer is rated at 15 kVA. On an open-circuit test at full rated voltage the power input was 400 W. On a short-circuit test the power input was 540 W at full rated current.

Determine: (a) $R_T{}^p$ regarding the 240 V winding as the primary.

(b) The efficiency of the transformer for each of the following loads: (i) full load at unity power factor, (ii) full load at 0.6 power factor lagging and (iii) one half full load at unity power factor.

(a) Full rated current in the 240 V winding $= \frac{15\,000}{240} = 62.5$ A

$I_p{}^2 R_T{}^p$ = total copper loss in the transformer = 540 W

$62.5^2 \times R_T{}^p = 540 \quad R_T{}^p = \frac{540}{62.5^2}$

$= 0.1382\ \Omega$

(b) (i) $\text{Efficiency} = \frac{15\,000 \times 1 \text{ (unity power factor)}}{15\,000 + 400 \text{ (core loss)} + 540 \text{ (copper loss on FL)}}$

$= 0.94$

(ii) $\text{Efficiency} = \frac{15\,000 \times 0.6}{15\,000 \times 0.6 + 400 + 540}$

$= 0.905$

(Observe that although the power factor has changed the full load current has not and so the copper loss is unchanged. A reduced power output and lower efficiency result from a poor power factor.)

(iii) On half full load, the current in the 240 V winding

$= 62.5/2$

$= 31.25$ A

Copper losses $= 31.25^2 \times 0.1382 = 135$ W

$\text{Efficiency} = \frac{7500 \times 1}{7500 + 400 + 135} = 0.93$

Example 6. A 480 V:240 V, 20 kVA single-phase transformer has a core loss of 200 W and a copper loss of 45 W when one

half of full rated current flows in the windings. Calculate the efficiency of the transformer when delivering:
(a) 10 kVA at 0.8 power factor lagging
(b) 20 kVA at unity power factor
(c) 15 kVA at 0.75 power factor lagging.
Half rated current in 480 V winding = 10 000/480 = 20.83 A
$R_T{}^p = 45/20.83^2 = 0.1037\ \Omega$. (480 V winding regarded as primary.)

$$\text{(a) Efficiency} = \frac{10\,000 \times 0.8}{10\,000 \times 0.8 + 200 + 45} = 0.97$$

$$\text{(b) Efficiency} = \frac{20\,000}{20\,000 + 200 + 41.66^2 \times 0.1037} = 0.98$$

$$\text{(c) Efficiency} = \frac{15\,000 \times 0.75}{15\,000 \times 0.75 + 200 + 31.24^2 \times 0.1037} = 0.974$$

TRANSFORMER REGULATION

When a transformer is loaded its output voltage changes. The change in voltage expressed as a percentage of its no-load value is defined as the regulation of the transformer.

On no load, since there is no output current, there are no voltages developed across R_p, X_p, R_s or X_s. This means that $V_p = E_p$ and $V_s = E_s$. Loading the transformer causes currents to flow in all the series elements mentioned and the output voltage will change.

$$\text{Percentage regulation} = \frac{\text{Change in output terminal voltage}}{\text{No load output voltage, } E_s} \times 100\%$$

$$= \frac{E_s(\text{no load}) - V_s \text{ (measured at a specified load)}}{E_s(\text{no load})} \times 100\%$$

Example 7. A transformer has a no-load output voltage of 240 V. When carrying full load at 0.8 power factor lagging the transformer regulation is 4%. What is the output terminal voltage at this load?

$$\text{Percentage regulation} = \frac{\text{Change in terminal voltage}}{\text{No load output voltage}} \times 100\%$$

$$4 = \frac{\text{Change in terminal voltage}}{240} \times 100$$

$$\text{Transpose: } \frac{4 \times 240}{100} = \text{Change in terminal voltage} = 9.6\text{ V}$$

$\therefore$ Output terminal voltage = 240 − 9.6 = 230.4 V

To calculate the value of regulation we need the short-circuit test results with the total resistance and reactance referred into the

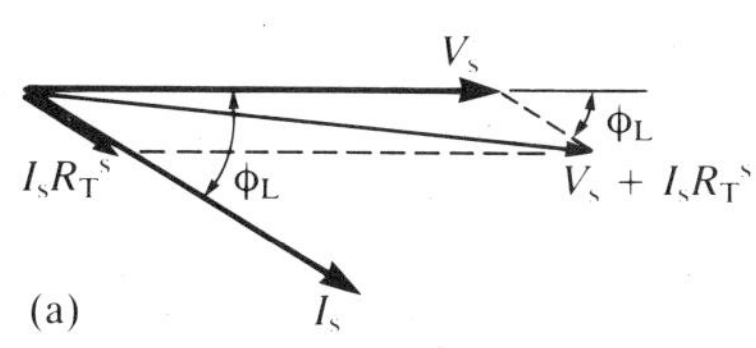

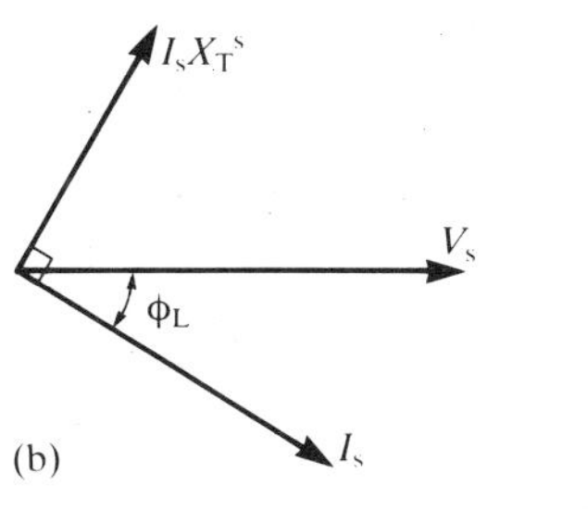

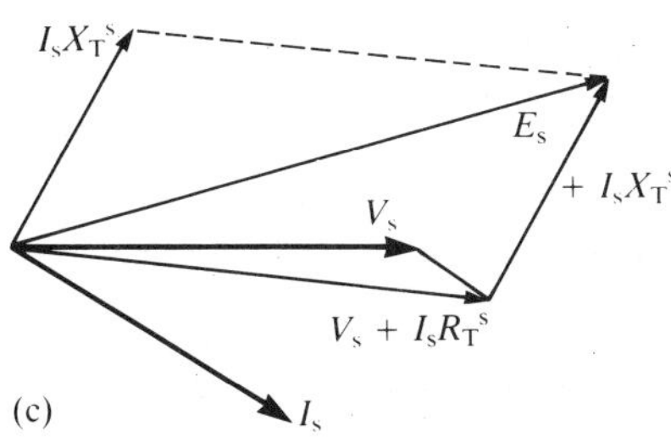

Figure 1.13

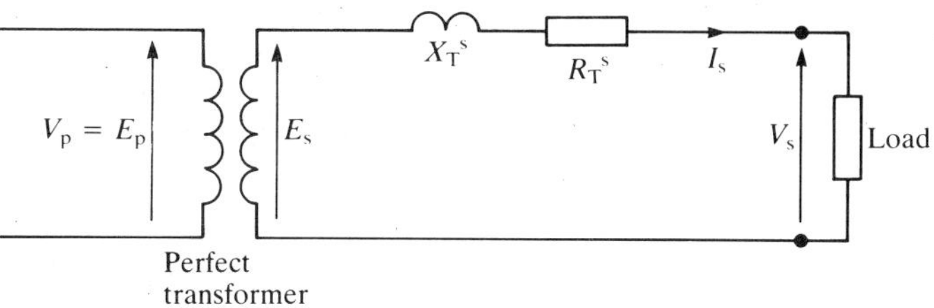

Figure 1.12

secondary. The equivalent circuit diagram becomes as shown in *Figure 1.12*.

On no-load $V_s = E_s$. When load current flows two internal voltages are developed, $I_sR_T{}^s$ and $I_sX_T{}^s$.

$V_s = E_s - I_sR_T{}^s - I_sX_T{}^s$ or transposing: $E_s = V_s + I_sR_T{}^s + I_sX_T{}^s$ taking into account the phase relationships.

The phasor diagram showing E_s in *Figure 1.8* is generally rotated to make V_s horizontal.

We will commence by considering a lagging power factor load. I_s lags V_s by an angle ϕ_L. In a resistance, the voltage and current are in phase therefore the voltage $I_sR_T{}^s$ is in phase with I_s. This is added to V_s as shown in *Figure 1.13(a)*. The voltage developed across a pure inductance leads the current by 90° so that the voltage $I_sX_T{}^s$ leads I_s by 90°. This is shown in *Figure 1.13(b)*. Finally, add $I_sX_T{}^s$ to the resultant $(V_s + I_sR_T{}^s)$ which gives *Figure 1.13(c)*. For the lagging power factor case illustrated V_s is less than E_s.

We require to know the change in voltage which occurs as the transformer is loaded, i.e. the difference between E_s and V_s.

In *Figure 1.14*:

$$\frac{x}{I_sR_T{}^s} = \cos\phi_L \qquad \frac{y}{I_sX_T{}^s} = \sin\phi_L$$

$$\therefore x = I_sR_T{}^s\cos\phi_L \quad y = I_sX_T{}^s\sin\phi_L$$

From the head of the V_s phasor to the point P the distance $= (x + y)$

$= I_sR_T{}^s\cos\phi_L + I_sX_T{}^s\sin\phi_L$ volts

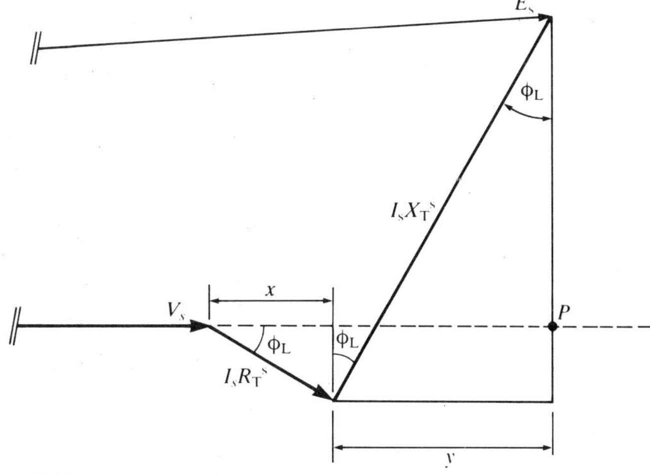

Figure 1.14

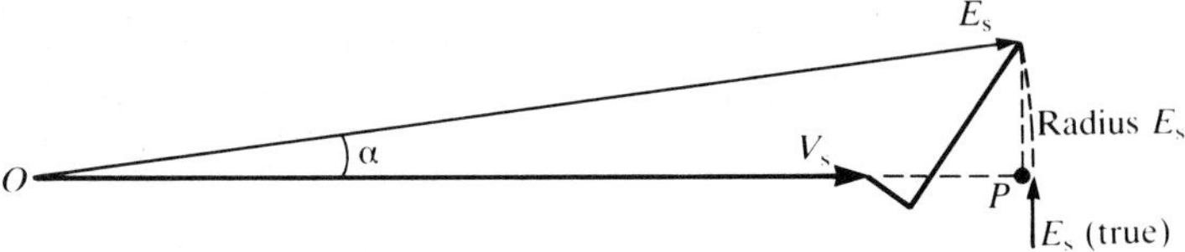

Figure 1.15

Looking at the same diagram drawn to a more realistic scale it can be seen that the length OP is very close to the value of E_s since the value of the angle α is very small. We are saying that in a right-angled triangle with a very small angle as illustrated, the hypotenuse is almost identical in length to the base. This being the case the change in voltage we are looking for is given by:

$$E_s - V_s = I_s(R_T{}^s \cos \phi_L + X_T{}^s \sin \phi_L)$$

$$\text{Regulation} = \frac{I_s(R_T{}^s \cos \phi_L + X_T{}^s \sin \phi_L)}{E_s} \times 100\%$$

Example 8. A short-circuit test was carried out on a 440 V: 110 V, 2.5 kVA single-phase transformer. The 110 V winding was short circuited and the input to the 440 V side was as follows:

Applied voltage = 45 V, input current = 6 A, power input = 51.84 W.

Determine the regulation of the transformer when operating as a step down transformer, the 440 V winding being energised using a 440 V supply, when carrying full rated current:
(i) at unity power factor
(ii) at 0.8 power factor lagging.

Using the short-circuit test data, calling the 440 V side the primary:

$Z_T{}^p = 45/6 = 7.5\,\Omega \quad R_T{}^p = 51.84/6^2 = 1.44\,\Omega$

$X_T{}^p = \sqrt{(7.5^2 - 1.44^2)} = 7.36\,\Omega$

Refer the quantities into the secondary. $N_p/N_s = 440/110 = 4$
$\therefore (N_s/N_p)^2 = 1/16$

$$R_T{}^s = 1.44 \times 1/16 = 0.09\,\Omega$$
$$X_T{}^s = 7.36 \times 1/16 = 0.46\,\Omega$$

Full rated current in the secondary (110 V winding)

$$= \frac{2500}{110} = 22.73\text{ A}$$

(i) At unity power factor $\cos \phi = 1$, $\phi = INV \cos 1 = 0°$
$\sin \phi = \sin 0° = 0$

$$\text{Regulation} = \frac{22.73[0\ 09 \times 1 + 0.46 \times 0]}{110} \times 100\%$$

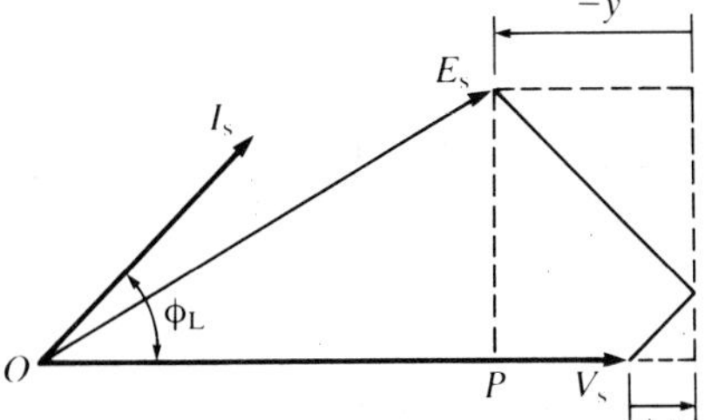

Figure 1.16

$$= \frac{2.046}{110} \times 100\%$$

$$= 1.86\%$$

(ii) At 0.8 lagging power factor $\cos\phi = 0.8$

$$\phi = INV \cos 0.8 = 36.87°$$

$$\sin\phi = \sin 36.87° = 0.6$$

$$\text{Regulation} = \frac{22.73[0.09 \times 0.8 + 0.46 \times 0.6]}{110} \times 100\% = 7.2\%$$

For leading power factor loads the phasor diagram in *Figure 1.16* is developed in the same manner as in *Figure 1.13*.

However it is seen that $V_s + x - y = OP$ (which is regarded as being equal to E_s).

Transposing: $E_s - V_s = x - y = I_s(R_T{}^s \cos\phi - X_T{}^s \sin\phi)$

V_s is larger than E_s. The output terminal voltage rises with leading power factor loads. The regulation expression gives a negative result. This may seem unreasonable to have positive regulation for falling output voltages and negative regulation for rising output voltages. However leading power factor loads are very rare so that falling voltages are the norm hence the regulation quoted as a percentage (positive) but without specifically writing the positive sign. The negative sign for rising voltages simply means the opposite of the normal; an abnormal situation. Large power transformers are sometimes subjected to leading power factor conditions due to the capacitance of the transmission and distribution system cables which have capacitance. When the consumer load is light, the capacitance of the network itself becomes significant and forms a large part of the transformer load when the system voltage rises as described above.

Example 9. A 440 V : 110 V transformer (as in *Example 8*) has the following parameters:

$R_T{}^s = 0.09\,\Omega \quad X_T{}^s = 0.46\,\Omega$

Determine its regulation and the value of the output terminal voltage when supplied at 440 V and delivering 18 A from its 110 V winding at 0.7 power factor leading.

$\cos\phi = 0.7 \quad \phi = INV \cos 0.7 = 45.6° \quad \therefore \sin\phi = 0.714$

$$\text{Regulation} = \frac{18[0.09 \times 0.7 - 0.46 \times 0.714]}{110} \times 100\%$$

$$= \frac{18 \times [-0.265]}{110} \times 100\% = -4.34\%$$

The negative sign indicates a rising voltage. The voltage rises by 4.34%

The output voltage = 110 V + 4.34% of 110 = 110 + 4.77
= 114.77 V.

CONDITION FOR MAXIMUM EFFICIENCY

The maximum efficiency of a transformer occurs at a load at which the winding copper loss is equal to the core loss.

Example 10. A single-phase transformer has a core loss of 150 W and a total referred resistance in the secondary of 0.23 Ω. Calculate:

(i) The value of current in the secondary which will cause the transformer to operate at its maximum efficiency.

(ii) The value of the maximum efficiency if the output terminal voltage when supplying the current in (i) above at 0.85 power factor lagging is 237 V.

(iii) The efficiency of the transformer at the same power factor when supplying one quarter of the value of current in (i) above, assuming that the terminal voltage does not change significantly from its value in (ii)?

(i) $I_s^2 R_T^s$ = total copper loss in the transformer. For maximum efficiency this must equal the core loss.

$$\therefore I_s^2 \times 0.23 = 150 \quad I_s = \sqrt{150/0.23} = 25.54 \text{ A}$$

(ii) $$\text{Efficiency} = \frac{\text{Output}}{\text{Output} + \text{core loss} + \text{winding loss}} \times 100\%$$

$$= \frac{237 \times 25.54 \times 0.85}{237 \times 25.54 \times 0.85 + 150 + 150} \times 100\%$$

$$= 94.5\%$$

(iii) One quarter of the current = 6.385 A
Copper loss = $6.385^2 \times 0.23 = 9.38$ W

$$\text{Efficiency} = \frac{237 \times 6.385 \times 0.85}{237 \times 6.385 \times 0.85 + 150 + 9.38} \times 100\%$$

$$= 88.9\%$$

THREE-PHASE TRANSFORMERS

Three-phase transformers are essentially three single-phase transformers wound on a single core. The primary and secondary windings for one phase are arranged as shown in *Figure 1.1*. There are three such pairs of windings, one for each phase, disposed on either a three limb or a five limb core as shown in *Figure 1.17*.

In a three-phase system, provided that the currents are balanced over the phases, the sum of the three currents is zero at any instant in time. Since each of the three currents produces a magnetic flux it

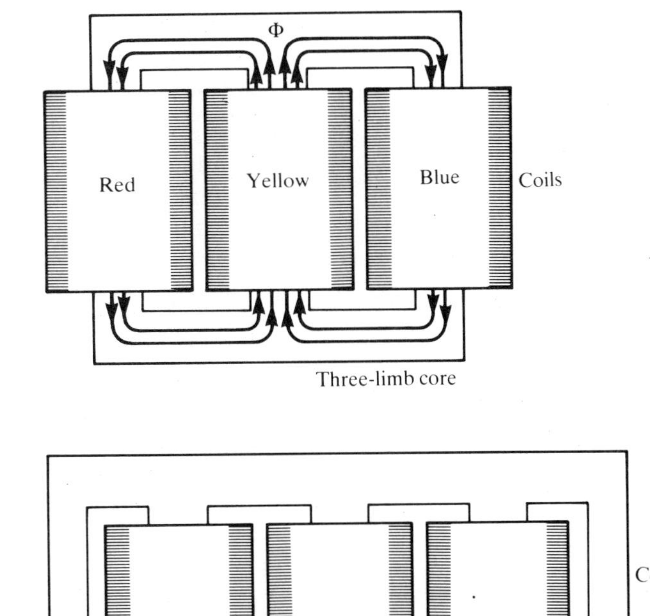

Figure 1.17

follows that at any instant the sum of the three fluxes is zero. In *Figure 1.17(a)* an instant has been chosen at which the yellow phase current is a maximum and is producing a flux upward in the centre limb as drawn. At this instant the current in each of the other two phases will be of opposite polarity and have a magnitude of one half that of the yellow current. Hence one half of the centre limb flux passes down through each of the outer limbs. At any instant in time this balance of fluxes will obtain. Where currents are not balanced the sum of the three fluxes will not be zero and a path for out-of-balance flux can be provided using the five-limb core.

BS 171: 1970 POWER TRANSFORMERS

D.5 Terminal markings

When a voltage V_p is applied to the primary winding, two induced e.m.f.s appear, E_p in the primary and E_s in the secondary (see *Figure 1.1* and the section on e.m.f. equation). E_p and E_s are induced by the same flux and are therefore in phase. The directions of these induced e.m.f.s are shown in *Figure 1.18*. British Standard 171 indicates the direction of these induced e.m.f.s by using the number 1 at the start of the arrow and number 2 at the head of the arrow. The polarity of the induced e.m.f. is from 1 to 2.

The phases are denoted using letters, upper case letters for the high-voltage winding and lower case letters for the low-voltage winding.

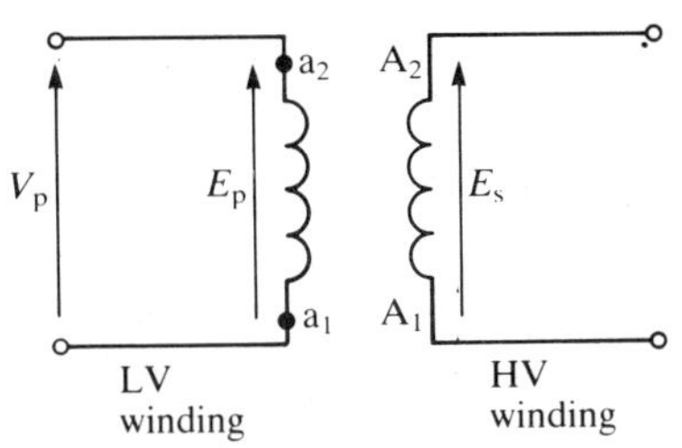

Figure 1.18

The *red* phase is denoted by 'A' or 'a'.
The *yellow* phase is denoted by 'B' or 'b'
The *blue* phase is denoted by 'C' or 'c'.

Figure 1.18 is therefore drawn for the red phase. The primary is the low-voltage winding. The start and finish of the arrow, the direction of the induced e.m.f. phasor, is from a_1 to a_2. The secondary is the high-voltage winding and the direction of the induced e.m.f. phasor is from A_1 to A_2.

There can be no circumstances under which E_p is not parallel to and in the same direction as E_s since they are produced by the same flux. Hence the direction from a_1 to a_2 must always be the same as the direction from A_1 to A_2. By the same reasoning, b_1 to b_2 must be in the same direction and parallel to B_1 to B_2 and c_1 to c_2 is in the same direction as and parallel to C_1 to C_2. When drawing three-phase transformer phasor and winding connection diagrams these relationships must not be forgotten. Three-phase transformers may have their primary and secondary windings connected in star or delta. For purposes of identification a star winding is described as a Y or y winding and a delta winding is described as a D or d winding (from the Greek Δ [delta]). As with the terminal markings the upper case letters are used for the high-voltage winding and the lower case letters for the low-voltage winding. Thus a Yd transformer has a high-voltage winding connected in star and a low-voltage winding connected in delta.

THE STAR–DELTA TRANSFORMER (yD)

Phasor and connection diagrams

The phasors for a three-phase star system are shown in *Figure 1.19(a)*. The normal sequence is red followed by yellow followed by blue, the phasors rotating anti-clockwise as indicated by the arrow marked ω rad/s. Since the primary is the low-voltage side lower case letters are used. The red phase is 'a', yellow, 'b' and blue, 'c'. The phasor directions are from 1 to 2. Therefore, a_1, b_1 and c_1 terminals are common at the centre of the star. The actual winding connections can now be drawn as in *Figure 1.19(b)*. The inputs to the transformer are on terminals a_2, b_2 and c_2 being marked red, yellow and blue respectively (see *Figure 1.18*).

Now look at the secondary. The secondary induced voltage A_1 to A_2 must be in phase with a_1 to a_2. In *Figure 1.19(c)* this first phasor is drawn. Now B_1 to B_2 has to be parallel to b_1 to b_2, and to form a delta it has to be connected to one end of the A phasor. There are two possibilities (shown as broken lines) in *Figure 1.19(c)*. Finally C_1 to C_2 must be drawn parallel to c_1 to c_2. Again there are two possibilities (shown as dotted lines) in *Figure 1.19(c)*.

First, consider the upper of the two deltas. This has been redrawn in *Figure 1.20(a)*. The secondary (high-voltage) windings are shown in *Figure 1.20(b)*. In the phasor diagram we see that B_1 and C_2 are at the same potential since the head of one phasor is connected to the tail of the other. This must be so in the actual connections of the secondary phases. Join B_1 to C_2 (broken line). By similar reasoning

C_1 and A_2 are common (dotted line). Finally, in the last corner of the delta B_2 and A_1 are joined. The output from the transformer may be taken from the top or the bottom of the windings. Red output from A_2 or from A_1, yellow from B_2 or B_1 and blue from C_2 or C_1. In *Figure 1.20(b)* the outputs are shown being taken from the top ends.

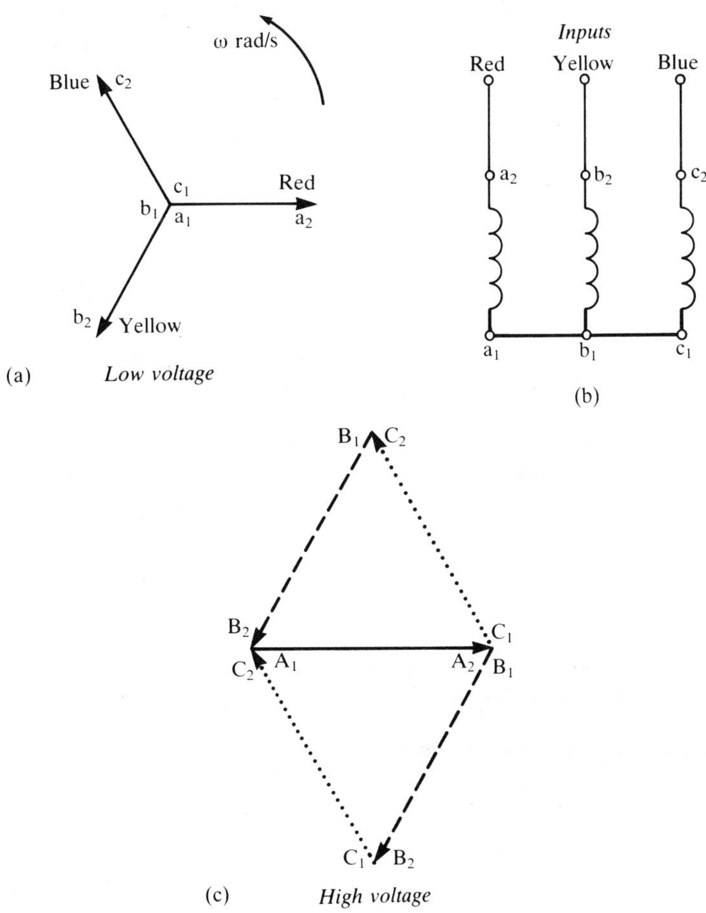

Figure 1.19

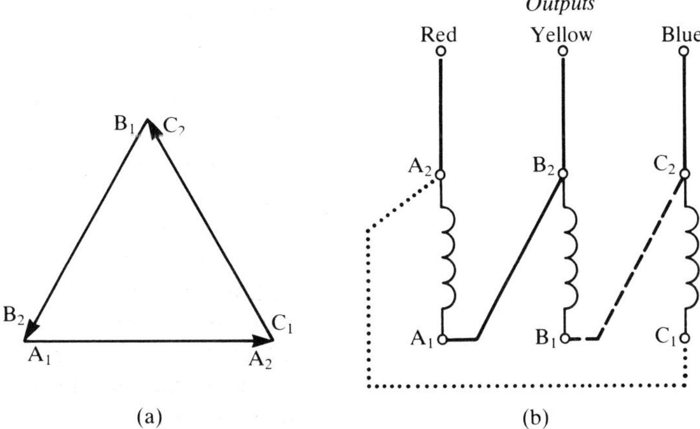

Figure 1.20

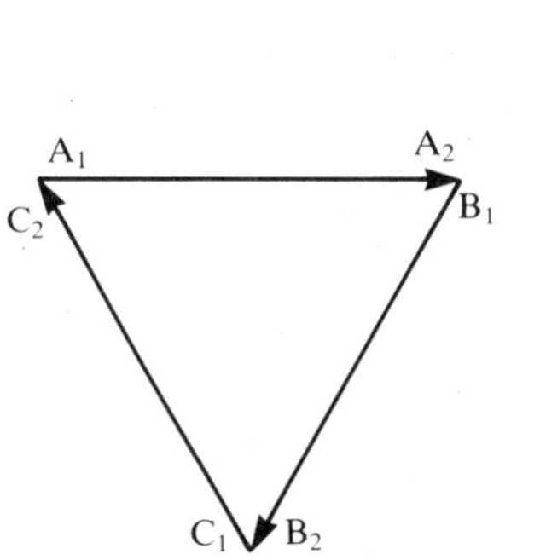

Figure 1.21

Similarly, the connection diagram may be deduced for the lower of the deltas in *Figure 1.19(c)*. This is shown in *Figure 1.21*.

Phase displacement

Most three-phase transformers deliver output voltages which are not in phase with input voltages. We say that the transformer gives a *phase displacement*. Each connection, e.g. Yd or Dy gives a different displacement and this is an important consideration when transformers are to be run in parallel or supplies are to be derived from different parts of the system. As an example we can consider a factory which is being fed from the 11 kV system. It is to have its supply reinforced by installing a transformer connected directly to the 33 kV system. If the output from the 33 kV transformer is to be in

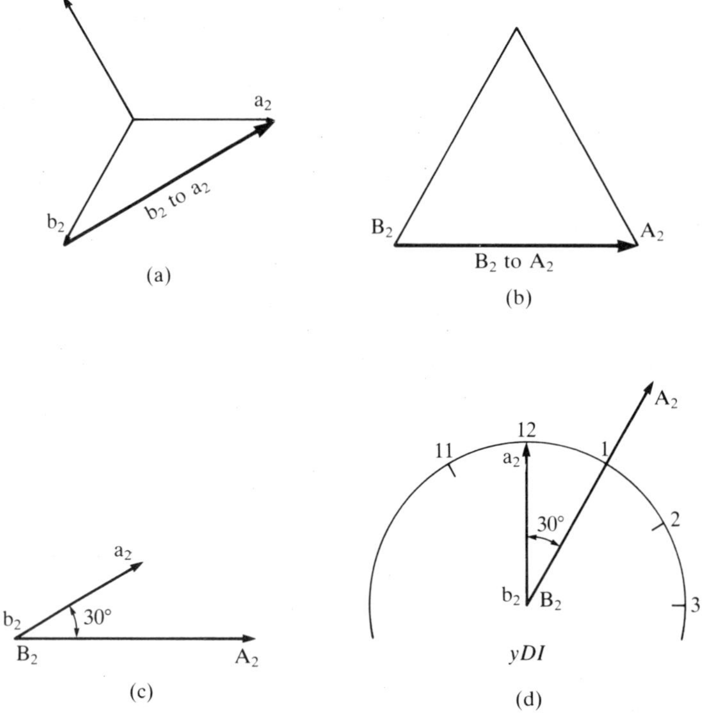

Figure 1.22

phase with the existing 11 kV supply so that the two can run in parallel two things have to be considered: (i) what is the phase relationship between the 11 kV system and the 33 kV system as it exists at the moment and (ii) what phase displacement will the new transformer introduce. The transformer has to be chosen to give an output in phase with the existing 11 kV supply.

Consider the input phasor and connection diagram for the transformer shown in *Figure 1.19(a)* and *(b)*. Choose a pair of line voltages, for example yellow to red. The yellow input is connected to b_2 and the red to a_2. In *Figure 1.22(a)* a phasor b_2 to a_2 has been drawn. This, to scale, would be the value of the yellow/red line voltage given that a_1 to a_2 was the red phase voltage to scale.

Now in *Figure 1.20(a)* and *(b)*, consider the output voltage between the same pair of lines. Yellow to red is again B_2 to A_2. *Figure 1.22(b)* shows this phasor. Superimpose the input and output phasors as in *Figure 1.22(c)*. We see that the output between yellow and red lines lags the input yellow to red voltage by 30°.

Transformers are grouped according to their phase displacements which is indicated by considering a clock face. The input phasor is turned around until it lies at 12 o'clock on the clock face. The output phasor, in this case, lies at 1 o'clock. This transformer had a low-voltage star input (y), a high voltage delta output (D) and the output is 30° behind the input (1 o'clock). It is described as a yD 1 transformer.

The same displacement is possible using a delta input and a star secondary. This would then be either Dy 1 of dY 1 according to which was the high voltage winding.

Consider the alternative delta in *Figure 1.21*. By the same process *Figure 1.23* can be drawn. Observe that although B_2 to A_2 is in a direction against the arrow in *Figure 1.21(a)*, when considering the

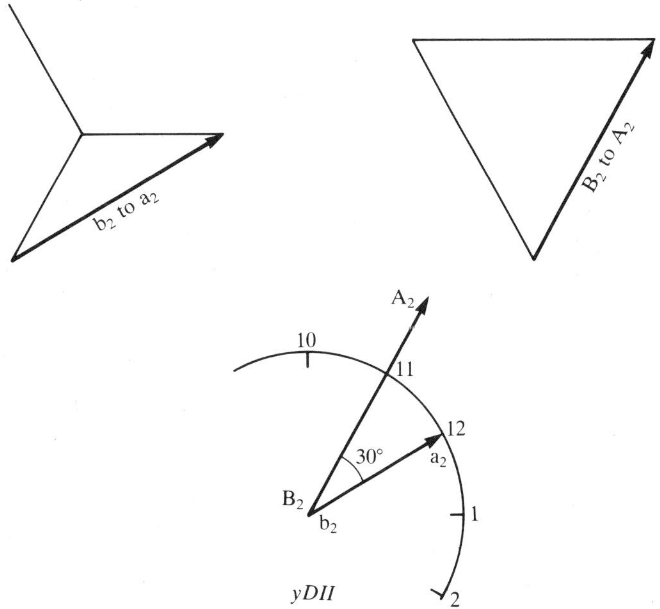

Figure 1.23

phase displacement to output phasor has to be drawn as described: from B_2 to A_2. (From yellow to red. Like must be compared with like and this is how the input was described. Any pair of inputs may be chosen and provided that the process is correctly carried out, the result is the same.) This transformer is a yD 11 since the B_2 to A_2 phasor lies at 11 o'clock on the clock face. It gives a +30° phase shift. This is also possible using the delta/star connection when the

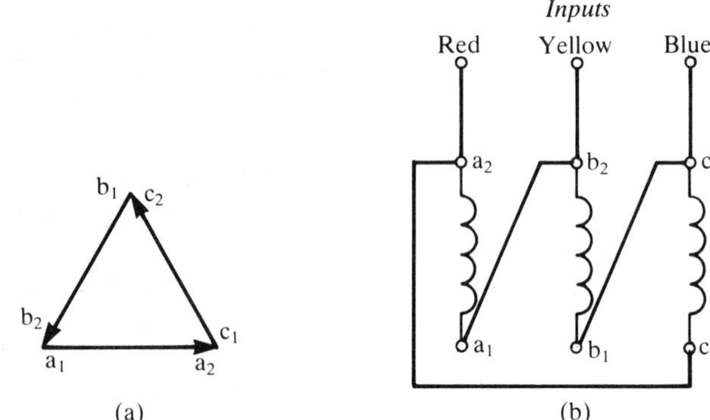

Figure 1.24

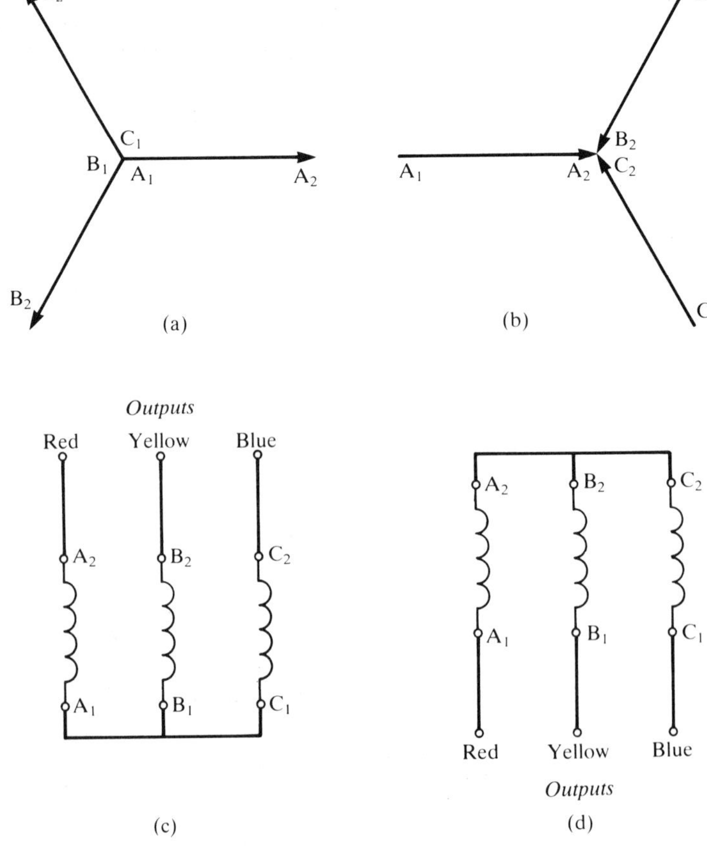

Figure 1.25

transformer would be described as Dy 11 or dY 11 according to which winding was energised from the higher voltage supply.

THE DELTA–STAR TRANSFORMER (dY)

Phasor and connection diagrams

Commencing with the delta as shown in *Figure 1.24(a)*, the winding connection diagram as in *Figure 1.24(b)* may be drawn. It follows the same construction as that for *Figure 1.20* except that in this case we are considering the delta to be the low voltage side of the transformer. Two possible star secondaries are possible. These are shown in *Figure 1.25(a)* and *(b)*. In both cases draw A_1 to A_2 parallel to a_1 to a_2; B_1 to B_2 parallel to b_1 to b_2 and C_1 to C_2 parallel to c_1 to c_2. The winding connections are shown in *Figure 1.25(c)* and *(d)*.

Phase displacement

In the primary (*Figure 1.24*) using any pair of line voltages the reference phasor may be drawn. We will use the yellow to red voltage as in the star-delta transformer above. Yellow to red is from b_2 to a_2 (*Figure 1.26(a)*). In the secondary, *Figure 1.25(a)* and *(c)*; yellow to red is from B_2 to A_2. (*Figure 1.26(b)*). Combining the two phasors in *Figure 1.26(c)* it is seen that the phase displacement is –30° and the transformer is described as a dY 11 transformer.

Using the secondary in *Figure 1.25(b)* and *(d)*, the output line voltage yellow to red is from B_1 to A_1. The transformer is a dY 5 transformer as shown in *Figure 1.26(d)* and *(e)*.

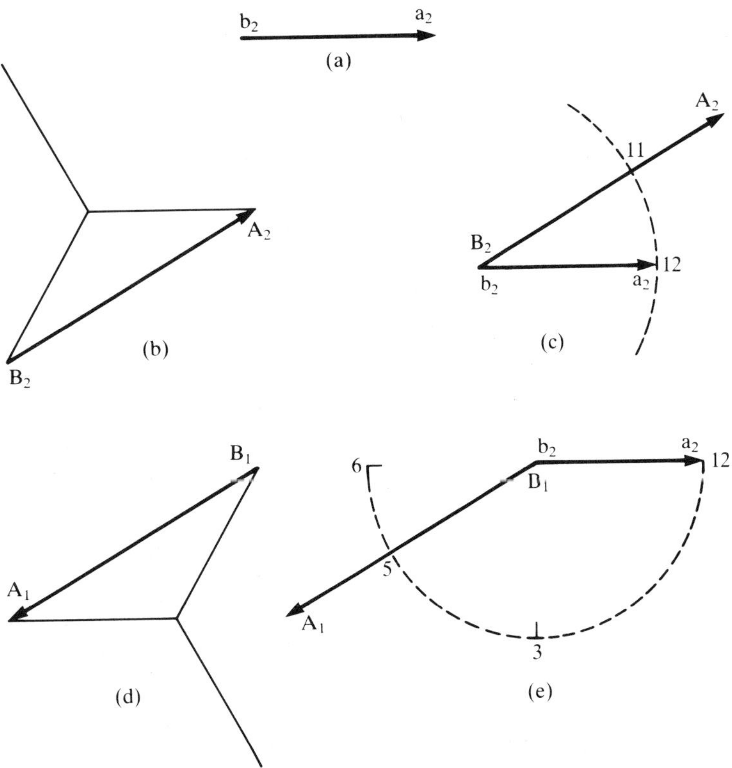

Figure 1.26

We have examined two possibilities for each case of dY and yD. However, other displacements are possible. With star-star or delta-delta transformers 0° or 180° are possible giving dD 0 or dD 6, yY 0 or yY 6. (Considering the input to be the lower voltage winding. For primary winding at the higher voltage upper and lower case letter positions are reversed.) Transformers which give zero phase displacement are said to be in Group 1. Transformers which give 180° phase displacement are said to be in Group 2. The other connections most commonly used give either −30°, Group 3; or +30°, Group 4. As seen in *Figure 1.26*, −150° is possible and, not demonstrated, +150° is also possible.

THREE-PHASE TRANSFORMATION USING THREE IDENTICAL SINGLE-PHASE TRANSFORMERS

It is possible to utilise three identical single-phase transformers to give three-phase transformation. It is an expensive method to employ since three, single-phase transformers weigh much more and are considerably more expensive than a custom-built three-phase transformer. There are instances where it is required that the three line currents in the three-phase system do not interact one with the others as is the case when all three windings are wound on a common core and therefore the single-phase transformers would be used.

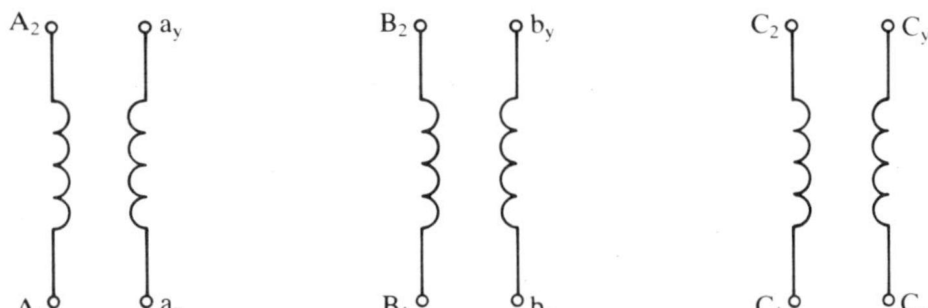

Figure 1.27

We will examine such use of single-phase transformers and discuss simple tests to ensure satisfactory operation. If the transformer terminals are marked 1 and 2 then there is no problem and primaries and secondaries may be connected to give the required phase displacement as described in the previous two sections. If, however, they are not marked or there is some doubt about the accuracy of the marking then the following procedure should be carried out. We will assume that the transformer is to be step-down so that upper case letters will describe the primary (input) side.

(i) Energise each transformer separately, using a single-phase supply and check to see that for the same input voltage they give identical output voltages (very closely).
(ii) Mark the pairs of primary terminals A_1, A_2; B_1, B_2 and C_1, C_2 at random. The selection of which terminal is called 1 and which 2 will be chance only. Mark the secondary terminals, again at random a_x, a_y, b_x, b_y and c_x, c_y as shown in *Figure 1.27*.
(iii) Connect the primary windings in the required input configuration, either in delta (see *Figures 1.20* and *1.21*) or in star (see

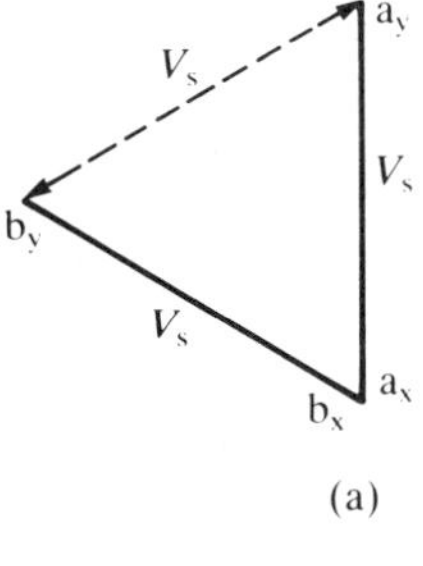

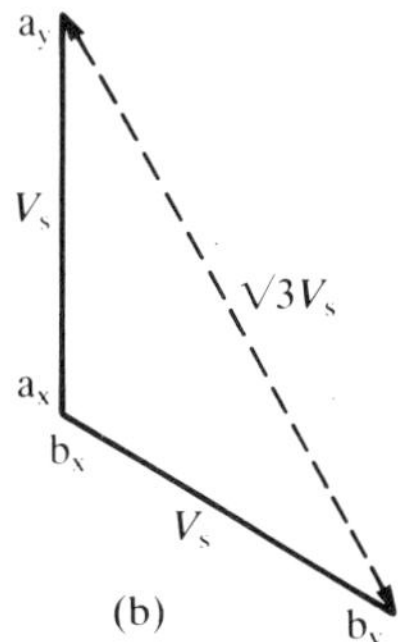

Figure 1.28

Figure 1.25(a) and *(b)*). Energise the primary from a three-phase supply and measure the voltage on the secondary between a_x and a_y. This is the secondary phase voltage, V_s volts (s = secondary).

(iv) Connect a_x to b_x. Measure the voltage between a_y and b_y. If this voltage is equal to V_s then the two secondary windings are forming the first two legs of a delta (*Figure 1.28(a)*. If the measured voltage is equal to $\sqrt{3}V_s$ then the two windings are forming the first two legs of a star (*Figure 1.28(b)*).

(v) If the secondary is of the form required then the third winding has to be connected. If the secondary is not of the form required, then reverse the (b) winding and re-check.

(vi) If the output is to be in star, connect c_x to the common point of the other two windings to form a star point. At the star point one end of all three windings come together. Measure the voltage from c_y to the output terminals of the other two windings. If the measured voltage is V_s then the (c) winding must be reversed. If the measured voltage is equal to $\sqrt{3}V_s$ then the connection is correct.

If the output is to be in delta, connect c_x to either of the open ends of the partly-formed delta and measure the voltage between c_y and the open end of the (a) winding. If this is very nearly zero all is well, the voltmeter may be removed and the connection made. If the voltage is large ($2 \times V_s$), the (c) winding must be reversed (see *Figure 1.29*).

Determination of the phase displacement achieved will need to be measured using a phase-sensitive voltmeter or a synchroscope.

PROBLEMS

11 A 50 Hz, single-phase transformer has a voltage ratio 11 000 V : 240 V. The core has a cross section 10 cm × 10 cm and operates with a maximum flux density of 1.5 tesla. Calculate the number of turns:

(i) in the 11 000 V winding

(ii) in the 240 V winding.

12 (a) Explain why (i) hysteresis losses and (ii) eddy-current losses occur in a transformer core.

(b) How are these losses minimised?

13 The iron losses in a transformer core operating at 50 Hz are as follows:
Hysteresis loss 40 W
Eddy current loss 35 W
Calculate new values for these losses for a frequency of 55 Hz assuming that the flux density has been held constant.

14 A single-phase transformer has a voltage ratio of 400 V : 100 V.
The results of short and open circuit tests were as follows:
Open-circuit test. 400 V winding energised at 25 V, 100 V winding short circuited. Input current = 10 A. Input power = 78.5 W.
Open-circuit test. 400 V winding energised at 400 V, 100 V winding open circuited. Input current 1.6 A at a power factor of 0.9 lagging.
(i) Draw an equivalent circuit diagram of the transformer including $R_T{}^p$, $X_T{}^p$, R_o and X_o.
(ii) Refer the values of $R_T{}^p$ and $X_T{}^p$ into the secondary (100 V winding) to give $R_T{}^s$ and $X_T{}^s$.

15 An open-circuit test on a 440 V : 240 V transformer gave the following results:
440 V winding energised at 440 V, 240 V winding open circuited.
Input current = 1.2 A
Input power = 79 W
Calculate the values of: (i) I_m, (ii) I_{H+E} and (iii) the no-load power factor.

16 A 240 V : 110 V transformer supplies a current of 26 A at a power factor of 0.85 lagging from its 110 V winding.
(a) Calculate the magnitude of the balancing current in the 240 V winding.
(b) If the no-load current of the transformer is 2.1 A at a power factor of 0.2 lagging in the 240 V winding, calculate (i) the magnitude of the total primary current and (ii) the overall power factor, when the transformer is carrying the load as in (a) above.

17 A 50 kVA single-phase transformer with ratio 6360 V : 240 V gave the following test results:
Short-circuit test 6360 V winding short circuited. 50 V applied to the 240 V winding. Current in the 240 V winding = 175 A. Power input = 2 kW.
Open-circuit test 6360 V winding energised with full-rated voltage. Input current = 1.572 A at 0.2 power factor lagging.
(a) Calculate the values of R_T, Z_T and X_T referred to the 240 V winding.
(b) Calculate the efficiency of the transformer when it is supplying full rated current at a power factor of 0.8 lagging.

18 A transformer draws a magnetising current of 9.9 A and an

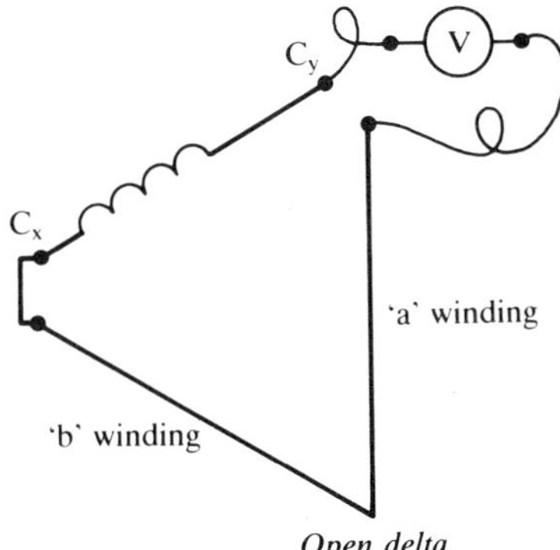

Figure 1.29

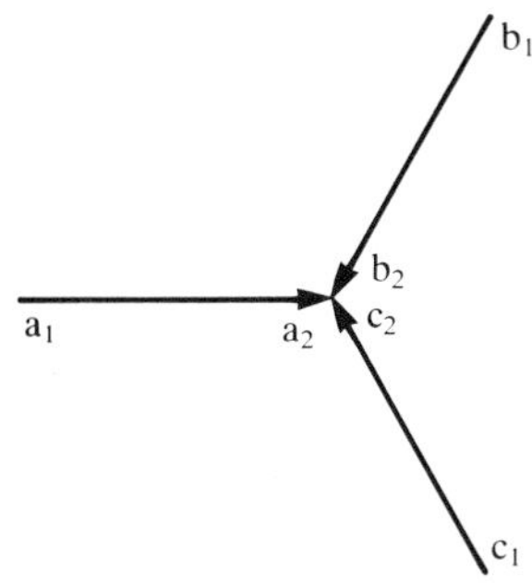

Figure 1.30

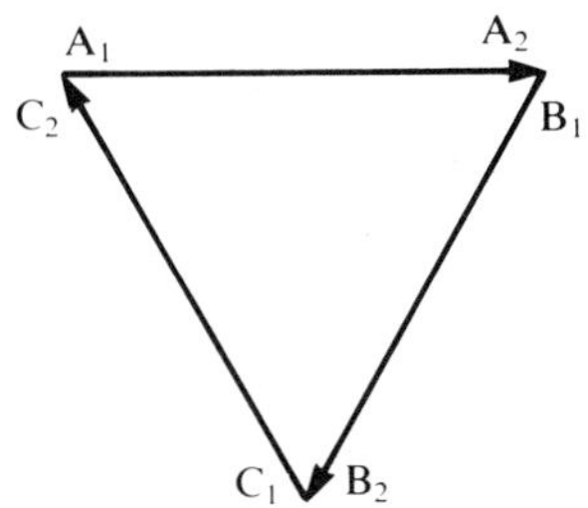

Figure 1.31

in-phase loss current of 1.1 A to supply hysteresis and eddy-current losses, when fed at full rated voltage. The ratio is 4:1 step down. Determine the value of the total primary current and the power factor when the secondary supplies a load of 20 A at 0.8 power factor lagging.

19 A transformer rated at 100 kVA has a voltage ratio 6600 V: 480 V. On a short-circuit test the following results were recorded:
6600 V winding short circuited. 480 V winding energised at 26 V. Input power = 1.52 kW. Input current = 175 A.
The core loss is 2 kW.
(a) Determine:
(i) the total resistance
(ii) the total impedance
(iii) the total reactance as seen in the 480 V winding.
(b) Consider the transformer to be supplied at 6600 V and delivering load current from its 480 V winding. Determine:
(i) the regulation when delivering its full rated current at a power factor of 0.85 lagging
(ii) the output terminal voltage
(iii) the transformer efficiency.

20 A transformer with ratio 440 V:240 V has a core loss of 96 W and a total resistance referred to the 440 V winding of 0.13 Ω.
Determine: (i) the current in the 440 V winding which will cause the transformer to operate at maximum efficiency; (ii) the value of this maximum efficiency if the operating power factor is 0.9 lagging.

21 The phasor diagram in *Figure 1.30* is for the star-connected primary of a three-phase transformer. Using BS 171 notation:
(a) Draw the winding connection diagram for the transformer primary.
(b) (i) Draw the phasor and connection diagrams for the *two* possible star-connected secondaries which could be formed using the above primary.
(ii) Describe the two transformers so formed using two letters and a number for each.

22 The phasor diagram in *Figure 1.31* is for the delta-connected primary of a three-phase transformer. Using BS 171 notation:
(a) Draw the winding connection diagram for the transformer primary.
(b) (i) Draw the phasor and connection diagrams for the *two* possible delta-connected secondaries which could be formed using the above primary.
(ii) Describe the two transformers so formed using two letters and a number for each.

2 Synchronous machines

Aims: At the end of this chapter you should be able to:

Describe the construction of both d.c. and a.c. machines and to discuss the differences in their design.
Deduce the relationship between the frequency of the supply, the number of poles and the speed of rotation for alternating current synchronous machines.
Discuss the types of rotor and the reasons for their use.
Sketch the open-circuit characteristic and explain its shape.
Discuss motoring and generating modes of operation.
Describe various starting methods.

A synchronous machine is one which is connected to an alternating system and runs at a speed which is precisely determined by the frequency of that system. It may be a motor, when it draws current from the system, or a generator when it supplies current to the system. Given that the mains frequency $= f$ Hz (cycles per second) the machine will run at a speed given by:

$$n = \frac{f}{P} \text{ rev/s}$$

Where P is an integer. We will see later that P is determined by the construction of the machine.

Hence, for a machine connected to a 50 Hz system the possible speeds are: 50/1 = 50 rev/s, 50/2 = 25 rev/s, 50/3 = 16.667 rev/s, etc.

Other types of alternating-current machines may have speeds related to mains frequency but which involve *slip*, a slight reduction from the synchronous values in the case of motors so that they can be designed to run at approximate values of 49.5 rev/s, 24 rev/s, 16 rev/s for example as compared with the corresponding values for the synchronous machines.

Direct current machines have speeds totally unrelated to mains frequency.

Most machines employing or generating alternating current have stationary windings which are connected to the mains system. These windings are wound on what is called the *stator*.

Direct current machines generally have their main d.c.-carrying windings on the *armature* which rotates and it is necessary to have relative motion between these windings and a magnetic field system which is energised using direct current. (A few very small machines have permanent-magnet field systems.)

Before studying the synchronous machine in detail we will look at some of the design features of the d.c. machine and examine the reasons for the design changes necessary to enable the development of alternating current machines capable of handling very large powers.

THE DIRECT CURRENT GENERATOR

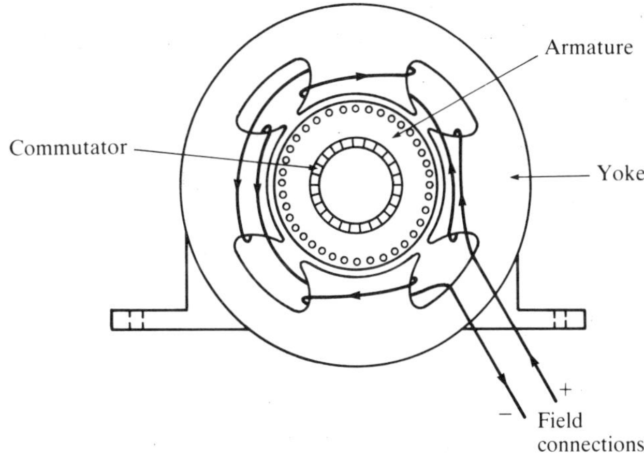

Figure 2.1

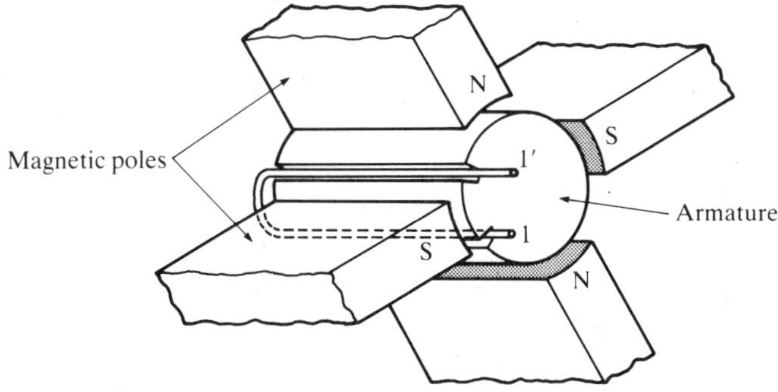

Figure 2.2

Figure 2.1 shows the electrically excited magnetic poles mounted within a steel yoke which supports them. Observe that the current directions in the pole windings is such as to produce poles of alternate polarity round the yoke, north followed by south etc. *Figure 2.2* shows one coil wound on the armature. The coil sides are marked 1 and 1′. The sides of the coil are spaced one pole pitch apart this distance being that from one edge of one pole to the corresponding edge of the next pole (see *Figure 2.3*).

Consider the armature to be driven in a clockwise direction as drawn, using an external engine. The convention is ⊗ for current flowing away from the viewer and ⊙ for current flowing towards the viewer. Using Flemming's right-hand generator rule the directions of induced e.m.f.s and currents are deduced as shown in *Figure 2.4.*

Starting with the conductors in the positions shown in *Figure 2.4(a)*, as conductor 1 moves from A to B and conductor 1′ moves from position B to position C a virtually-constant e.m.f. is induced since the magnetic field does not vary under the pole face. Current

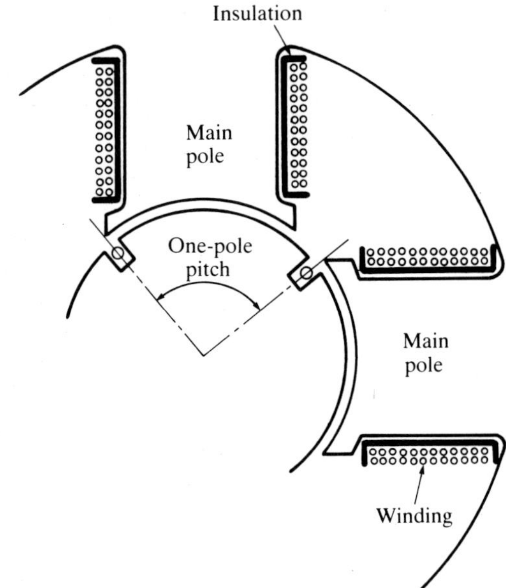

Figure 2.3

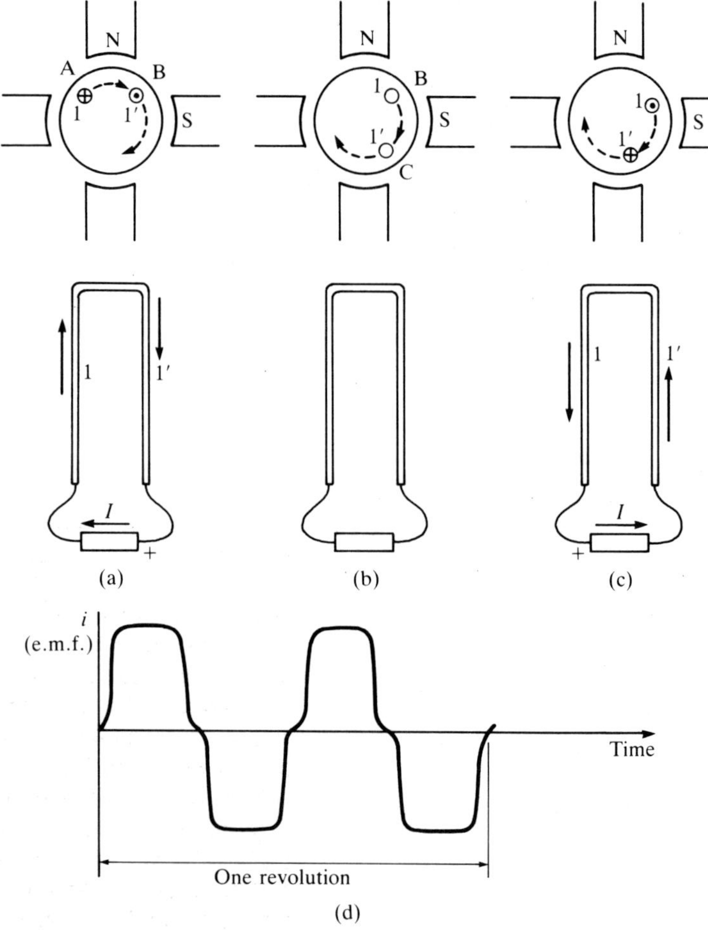

Figure 2.4

would leave the end 1′ flow in any external load, returning to conductor 1.

When the conductors are between poles as shown in *Figure 2.4(b)* there is no induced e.m.f. since in this position they are not cutting any flux.

As the conductors move on, conductor 1 from position B to position C and conductor 1′ from position C to position D the induced e.m.f.s and current is as shown in *Figure 2.4(c)*. Notice that the direction of current in the two coil sides has reversed. Current flows in the external circuit in the opposite direction to that in *Figure 2.4(a)*. The current in individual coils is alternating and during one revolution of the single coil the external current waveform is a flat-topped alternating wave as shown in *Figure 2.4(d)*. In order to make more use of the available space on the armature and to increase the output voltage it is necessary to employ more coils. Windings have been developed known as the *lap* and *wave* types. To cause a unidirectional current to flow in the external load it is necessary to incorporate some form of rectifying device in the circuit. In the normal direct current machine this is known as the *commutator* and this is shown in *Figure 2.5*.

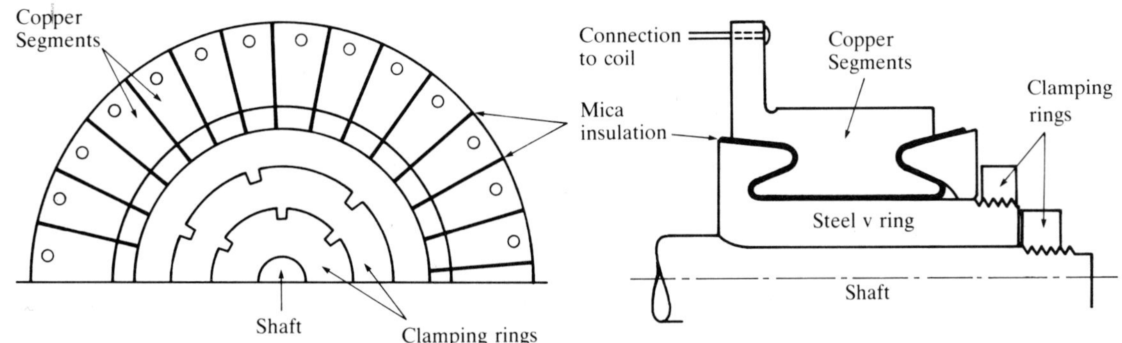

The Commutator

Figure 2.5

THE LAP WINDING

Each coil in the lap winding *overlaps* its neighbour. In *Figure 2.6* a lap coil is shown comprising two turns. It is coil number 1 and its two sides are marked 1 and 1′ respectively. Its two ends are connected to adjacent segments on a commutator and coil number 1 starts on segment number 1. The other end of the coil is connected to segment number 2. Coil number 2 is added and this starts on segment number 2 of the commutator. In *Figure 2.7* only one turn per coil is shown to make the diagram easier to follow. In fact there may be many turns making up one coil.

The coils are situated in slots in a laminated iron armature and *Figure 2.8* shows a part-wound armature. The complete winding is built up in this manner until all the slots in the armature contain two coil sides, one on top which starts at the commutator segment which carries its number (1, 2, 3, 4, etc.), and the other at the bottom which is the return coil side (1′, 2′, 3′, 4′, etc.). The armature rotates in a

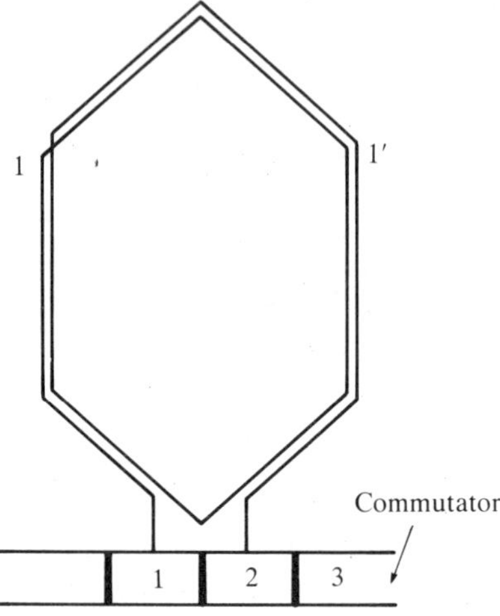

Figure 2.6

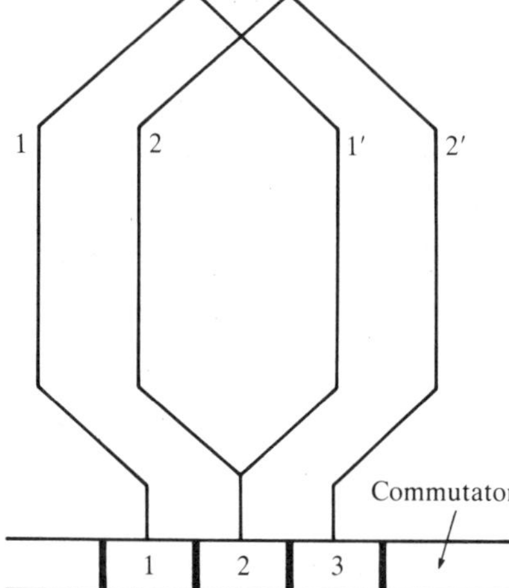

Figure 2.7

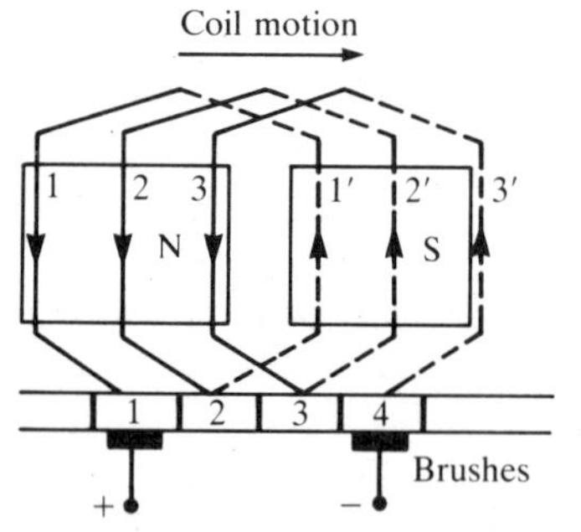

Figure 2.9

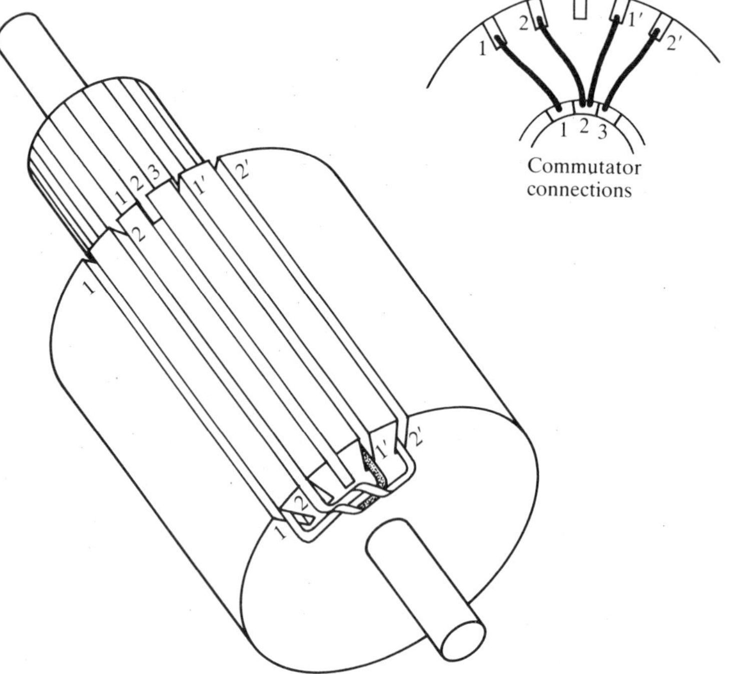

Figure 2.8

magnetic field. A typical four-pole arrangement being shown in *Figure 2.1*.

Consider the typical section of a lap winding under a north and south pole as shown in *Figure 2.9*. The view is from the centre of the armature looking outward through the winding and seeing the pole faces outside the winding. Using Flemming's right-hand rule, the directions of the induced e.m.f.s are as shown. Between the positive and negative brushes there are six conductors connected in series so that the e.m.f. between the brushes is six times the e.m.f. induced in a single conductor. The complete lap winding for a four-pole machine has four brushes, one for each pole, the brushes under like poles being connected together. There are four such groups of windings, as shown in *Figure 2.9*, to fill all the slots. This is shown in *Figure 2.10*.

The full winding for this machine therefore comprises twenty-four conductors (1–12 plus 1′–12′). There are four parallel ways through the armature, from brush B to C and to A and from brush D to C and A. Checking one route, from B to C, for example, involves conductors 4, 4′, 5, 5′, 6 and 6′.

Parallel ways each contribute current to the external circuit as would batteries connected in parallel. Conductors connected in series each contribute to the generated e.m.f. For the simple machine described, if the conductors were of such a size as to be able to carry 25 A without overheating, the generator could deliver $4 \times 25 = 100$ A. If the e.m.f. generated in each conductor was 20 V, then six conductors in series would give an output voltage of $6 \times 20 = 120$ V.

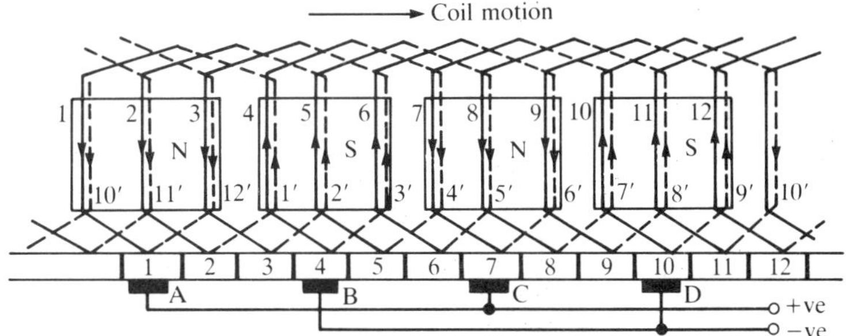

Figure 2.10

Example 1. A four-pole d.c. lap-wound generator has forty-eight slots on the armature. Each slot contains six conductors. When the speed of the armature is 750 r.p.m. the induced e.m.f. in each conductor is 5.6 V.

Calculate:

(a) The total number of conductors on the armature
(b) The total number of turns on the armature
(c) The number of conductors in series in each of the parallel groups
(d) The total generated e.m.f.
(e) The rating of the generator if each conductor can carry 15 A before overheating.

(a) Total number of conductors = number of slots × number of conductors in each slot
$= 48 \times 6$
$= 288$

(b) Two conductors form one turn. Number of turns =
$= 144$

(c) Since there are eight poles, there will be eight brushes and eight parallel ways through the armature.

$$\text{Number of conductors in series in each group} = \frac{288}{8} = 36$$

(d) Generated e.m.f. = e.m.f. per conductor × number of conductors connected in series in each group.

$= 5.6 \times 36$
$= 201.6\ \text{V}$

(e) Each conductor can carry 10 A and there are 8 parallel ways.

Total current from the armature $= 8 \times 10$
$= 80\ \text{A}$

Rating $= 201.6\ \text{V} \times 80\ \text{A}$
$= 16\,128\ \text{W}$

THE WAVE WINDING

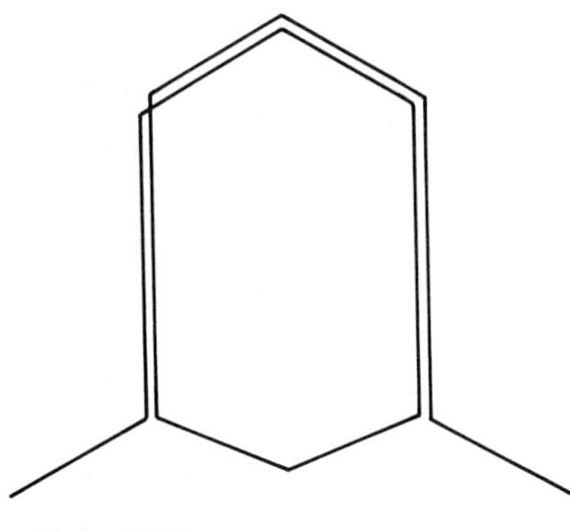

Figure 2.11

Figure 2.11 shows a coil for a wave winding. The ends of the coil are not connected to adjacent segments on the commutator but to segments some distance apart. Again using a four-pole machine as an example, a small section of the winding is shown in *Figure 2.12*.

Notice that commutator segments 2 and 3 are repeated at each end so that the commutator may be visualised in its circular form. There is an additional commutator segment, number 13 which causes the winding to progress in 'waves'.

Starting with the negative brush presently on segment 4, follow conductors 4 and 4′ to segment 11 and then conductors 11 and 11′ to segment 5. Four conductors are involved in progressing one segment along the commutator. The process may be continued, following four more conductors (not shown) so returning to segment 6. A further four conductors making twelve in all allows us to progress to segment 7 upon which the positive brush rests.

With this winding two parallel ways through the armature exist. One of them is as described and the other could be traced from segment 4 starting with conductor 10′ which passes under the south pole to the right of the diagram, returning to segment 7 eventually.

A wave wound machine has only two brushes and two parallel ways through the armature irrespective of the number of poles.

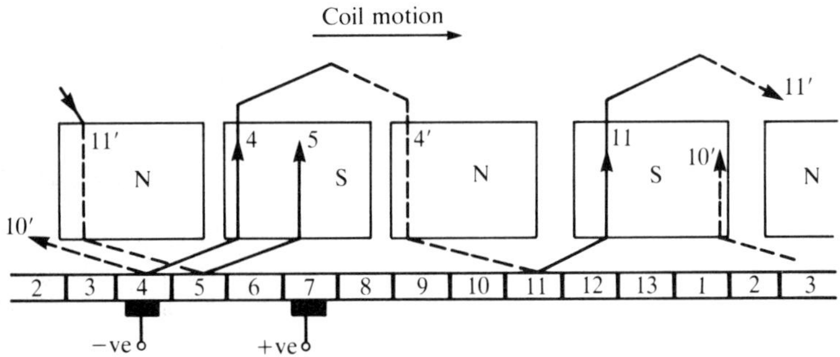

Figure 2.12

Example 2. A six-pole, wave wound d.c. generator has the following details:
Number of slots on the armature = 50
Conductors per slot = 6
Induced e.m.f. per conductor = 4.6 V
Maximum current per conductor = 10 A.

Determine: (i) the output voltage (ii) the maximum output current which the machine can safely deliver.

(i) Total number of conductors = $50 \times 6 = 300$

There are two parallel ways through a wave-wound armature.

$$\text{Number of conductors in series in each path} = \frac{300}{2} = 150$$

Induced e.m.f. = number of conductors in series × e.m.f. per conductor
= 150 × 4.6 V
= 690 V

(ii) Maximum output current = 2 × 10 = 20 A.

THE ACTION OF THE COMMUTATOR

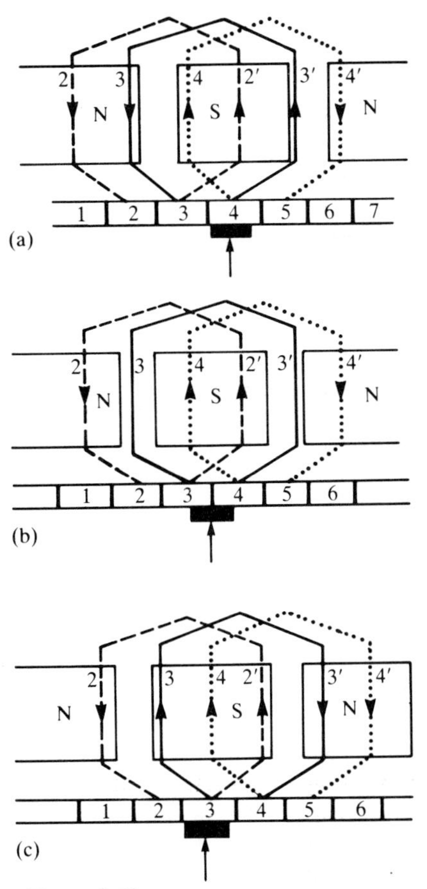

Figure 2.13

Figure 2.13 is based on the lap winding diagram shown in *Figure 2.10*. The arrows show the directions of induced e.m.f. and current in a generator (Flemming's right-hand generator rule). We are considering a negative brush which is returning current to the armature.

Look first at *Figure 2.13(a)*. Current entering the winding through the brush resting on segment 4 flows upwards as drawn in conductors 3′ and 2′. In particular, notice that the current in coil 3, 3′ is in an anti-clockwise direction as viewed, the direction of induced e.m.f. being downwards under a north pole and upwards under a south pole.

Now move on to *Figure 2.13(b)*. The armature has moved one half of the width of a commutator segment to the right. The brush spans segments 3 and 4. This brush has a low resistance so that this effectively puts a short circuit across coil 3, 3′. However, this is not important since both of these coil sides are out of the magnetic field and so the induced e.m.f. is zero at this instant. Current still enters the winding leaving segment 4 in coil side 4, and segment 3 in coil side 2′.

Finally, in *Figure 2.13(c)* the armature has moved on a further half width of the commutator segment. Coil side 3 is now under a south pole so that the current direction is upwards and 3′ is under a north pole and the current direction is downwards. The current direction in this coil has reversed from *Figure 2.13(a)* to *(c)*. Current enters the winding through coil sides 3 and 2′.

Every coil on the machine goes through this position during each revolution of the armature.

(i) The current in the external circuit is unidirectional (direct current).
(ii) The current in individual coils is alternating.
(iii) During the time taken for the armature and commutator to move the width of one segment, the current in the shorted coil reverses. This is known as *commutation*. Commutation has to take place while the associated coil sides are out of the magnetic field.

In the case of the generator, which we have been considering, the commutator is being used as a mechanical rectifier, causing the internally generated alternating e.m.f.s in the individual coils to drive a direct current into the external circuit (see also *Figure 2.4*).

THE DIRECT-CURRENT MOTOR

If instead of driving the armature of the d.c. machine using an external engine, the armature is energised from a direct power supply it will run as a motor delivering mechanical power to an external load. Assuming that the brushes and magnetic poles in *Figure 2.10* retain their polarities, current will enter the armature via brushes A and C and leave via B and D. The coil currents will reverse while the armature will run in the same direction as in the generating mode (Flemming's left-hand rule for motors). No modifications to the machine are necessary to change from motoring to generating or vice-versa.

THE SYNCHRONOUS MACHINE

Construction

Almost all electrical generation worldwide is done using synchronous generators. This is due to the ease with which voltage levels can be changed using the transformer and the subsequent savings which can be made in transmission costs.

Consider a power of 1000 kW (1 mega-watt [MW]). If it were necessary to generate this at 240 V, d.c. the current would be $1 \times 10^6/240 = 4167$ A. The cross-sectional area of transmission conductor to carry this current without substantial volt drop and copper loss would be of the order of 25 cm^2. Employing synchronous generators operating at 25.6 kV, the value of current required is substantially reduced and by the use of a step-up transformer to give a transmission voltage of 400 kV a further substantial reduction in current is achieved.

Synchronous generators are driven by engines (prime movers) using steam generated by burning coal or oil or by nuclear reactors, water falling from a higher to a lower level or aircraft engines burning oil or gas. A very small amount of generation is carried out using diesel engines.

In the direct-current machine unsurmountable difficulties arise with the commutator and the mass of the rotating armature which would need to carry conductors approximating to the size quoted above. First consider the commutator. It is necessary to collect the generated current from the surface of the commutator using carbon brushes.

Each square centimetre of rubbing surface on the commutator can collect approximately 20 A. The area of rubbing surface to collect large currents is achieved by employing a long commutator and using many brushes along its length. There is a limit to the number of brushes which can reliably be used since all their resistances will be very slightly different and the lowest-resistance brush tends to take more than its share of the current when it overheats and may eventually burn through its brush tail leaving the others to carry the extra load (see *Figure 2.14*). Increasing the generated voltage runs into trouble at only a few kilovolts since the insulation between the segments is very narrow. It tends to collect carbon dust from the brushes and a flashover between segments results.

Now consider the mass of the armature. To carry the required number of copper conductors to generate a modest output voltage each with a cross-sectional area many square centimetres to carry a large current requires a steel armature of considerable mass and diameter. This mass and its commutator has to be turned at fairly

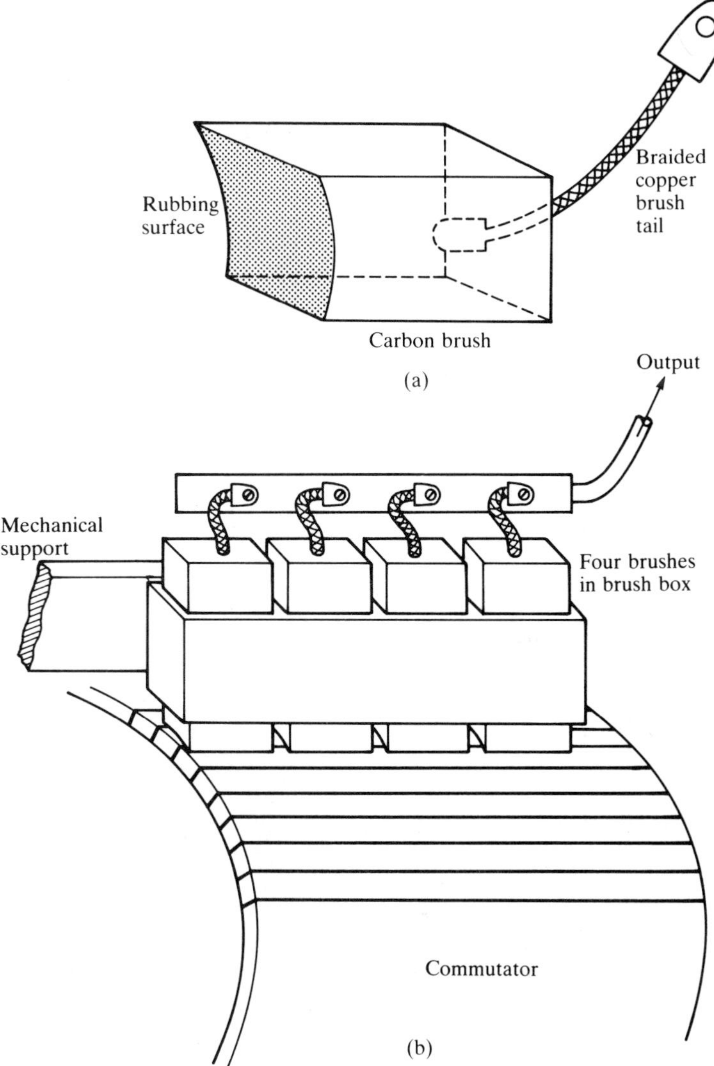

Figure 2.14

high speed carried on two supporting bearings without vibration inside the yoke of the machine which will itself be of very large external diameter.

D.c. machines with ratings up to about 2 MW have been built but with modern generators having ratings of 500 MW and upwards it would not be possible to contemplate the size of a direct current machine of this order.

When the output from a generator is to be alternating there is no need to employ the rectifying action of the commutator. We have seen that individual coils have alternating e.m.f.s generated in them leading directly to alternating currents. Since there is no need to have a commutator, there is no need to cause the armature to rotate. The armature could be stationary and the field system rotate. It would be a very difficult and pointless exercise to try and make the field system rotate while in the form of the d.c. machine (see *Figure*

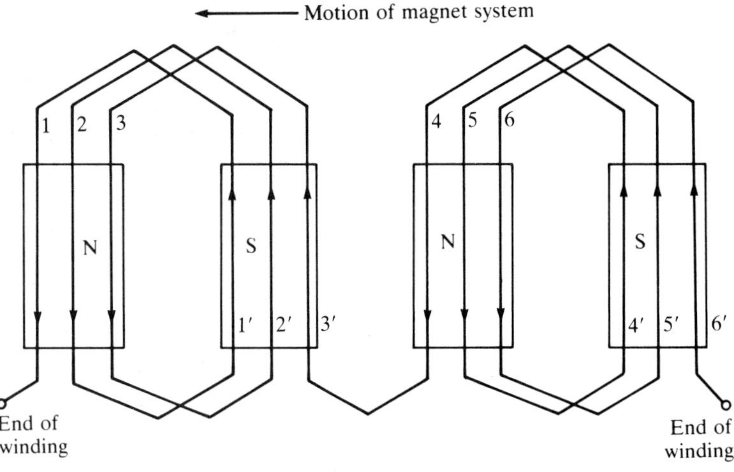

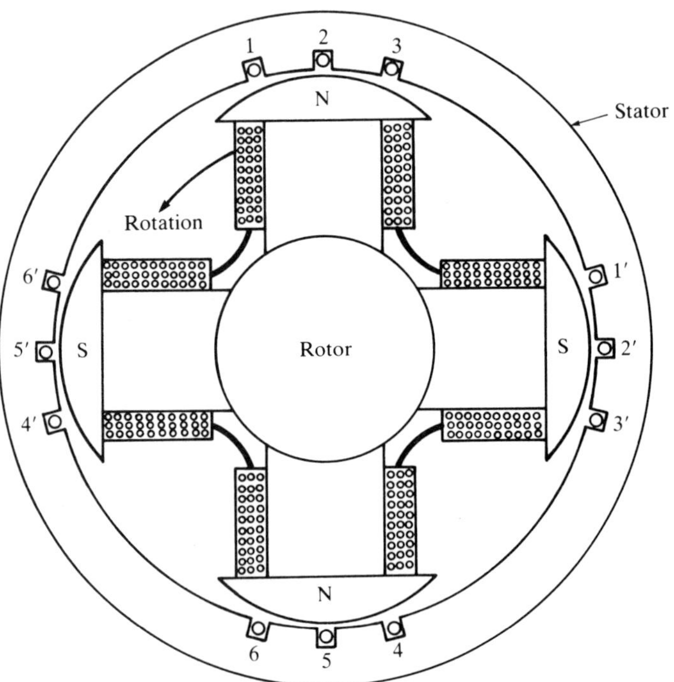

Figure 2.15

2.1). It is, however, quite simple to replace the external poles with internal poles. In *Figure 2.15* a slightly modified lap winding (*Figure 2.10*) is wound in slots inside a hollow armature and the pole faces have been re-shaped and rotate inside the conductors. The armature is now stationary and is referred to as the stator. The field rotates and is now generally referred to as the rotor. The rotor carries direct-current windings to create the field as in the d.c. machine. The direct current is fed on to the rotor using two slip rings which are continuous steel or bronze rings shrunk on to the shaft over mica insulating sleeves. Carbon brushes run on the outside of these rings feeding in and taking away direct current which is derived from a separate generator known as an exciter. The exciter may be driven by the main alternator shaft or by a separate motor.

The power necessary to produce the field is very small, typically about one thousandth of the total stator output, so that problems with the brushes are less than would be involved with collecting the whole of the electrical output from a rotating armature. The stator windings do not have to rotate and so can be as heavy as required. They are often formed from copper tube through which water is pumped to give direct cooling. The stator may weigh in excess of one hundred tons but this presents no problem except perhaps that of transporting it to the power station site.

In *Figure 2.15*, as a north pole sweeps past conductors 1, 2 and 3 a south pole is sweeping past the other sides of the coils, 1′, 2′ and 3′ inducing voltages which are cumulative. The same is true of conductors 4, 5 and 6, and 4′, 5′ and 6′. The output voltage is very nearly equal to the sum of the induced e.m.f.s from twelve conductors all in series. This is a single-phase alternator. It produces a single voltage between a pair of output terminals.

RELATIONSHIP BETWEEN NUMBERS OF POLES AND SPEED

Figure 2.15 shows a single-phase synchronous generator with four poles which has been developed from the d.c. machine shown in *Figures 2.1* and *2.10*. If we consider any conductor on the stator it will link with the magnetic flux of each of the rotor poles, two north poles and two south poles, during one revolution. The direction of induced e.m.f. in each conductor will reverse as it links with alternate poles and the voltage appearing at the output terminals will be alternating as shown in *Figure 2.4*. There will be two complete cycles of output per revolution of the rotor. Therefore, driving the rotor at 25 revolutions per second will cause the output frequency to be 50 Hz.

In the synchronous generator there will always be the same number of groups of conductors as there are poles. Looking at *Figure 2.15*, if the stator were effectively cut in half so removing conductors 4, 5, 6, 4′, 5′ and 6′ together with their associated poles and the remaining windings and poles were expanded into a circular form once more, a two-pole machine would result as shown in *Figure 2.16(a)*. During one revolution each conductor would link with one north pole and one south pole giving one cycle of output.

Generally, $n = \dfrac{f}{P}$ rev/s

Where n = speed in revolutions per second
f = frequency in cycles per second (Hertz)
P = *pairs* of magnetic poles.

Adding more groups of conductors and more poles while keeping the arrangement symmetrical makes a range of lower speeds possible. Steam turbines need to run at high speeds so that a one-pole pair rotor is employed. Some low-head water turbines need to run at low speeds and fifteen to twenty pole pair machines are found.

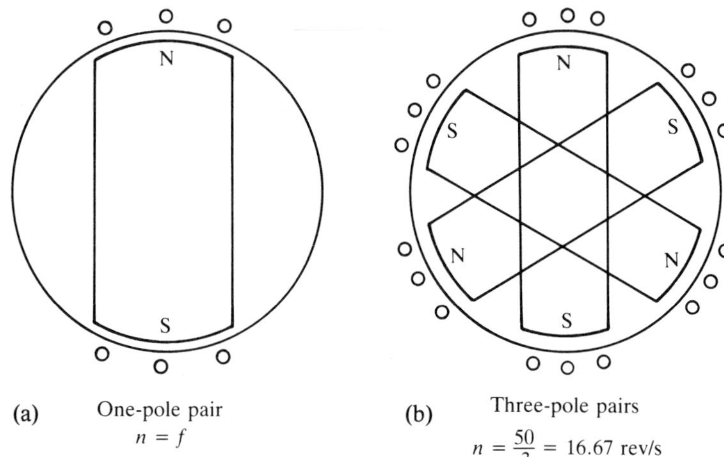

Figure 2.16

(Speeds $50/15 = 3.33$ rev/s and $50/20 = 2.5$ rev/s.) The arrangement of a three-pole pair machine is shown in *Figure 2.16(b)*.

TYPES OF ROTOR

In the d.c. machine the surface of the pole face was concentric with the surface of the armature creating an air gap of constant length across the pole face. With uniform air gap and hence uniform reluctance the flux density is constant and hence the induced e.m.f. in a conductor linking with this flux is constant during its passage under the pole. This leads to the very nearly square waveform of e.m.f. shown in *Figure 2.4*. The synchronous generator, however, is required to deliver an output which is of sinusoidal form. This means that the magnetic flux must vary sinusoidally as the pole moves under the conductor groups. As the leading edge of the pole approaches the conductors the flux must be weak giving a low output voltage. As the pole face sweeps by the flux must increase to cause the e.m.f. to increase to a maximum value and then fall as the pole leaves the conductor group.

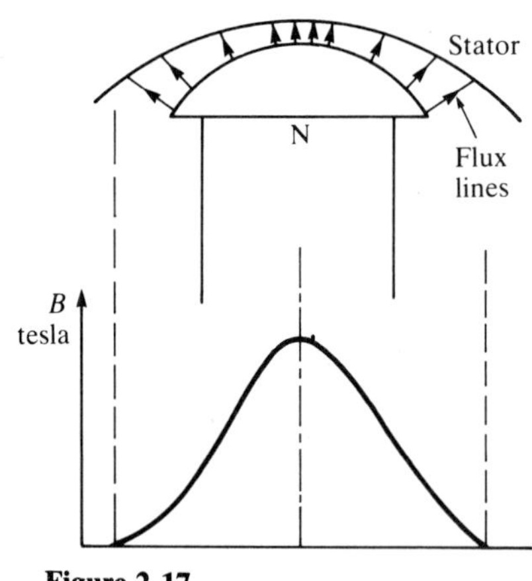

Figure 2.17

There are two types of rotor:

(i) The salient-pole rotor.
(ii) The cylindrical rotor.

We will consider each in turn.

The salient-pole rotor

Salient means sticking out. The machine in *Figure 2.15* has a salient-pole rotor. Mounted on the shaft of the machine there is a steel hub or 'spider' to which the required number of poles are bolted. Each pole carries a coil which excites it. The pole winding is described as a *concentrated* winding meaning that there are many turns on each pole, literally all in one place. The required flux distribution is achieved by profiling the pole face. The edges of the pole are some distance from the stator while its centre is much closer. Where the air gap is long the reluctance is large and the flux will be small. As the air gap reduces the flux concentration increases. The arrangement and the resulting flux distribution is shown in *Figure 2.17*. It will be observed that a pure sine wave is not achieved but the resulting output voltage is close to a sine wave.

The cylindrical rotor

A solid steel rotor has slots cut into its surface along its length. The slots are lined with insulating material and carry a winding formed from copper strip or square-section hollow copper tube to allow the passage of cooling gas. The form of the winding showing only four slots is shown in *Figure 2.18*. Several turns are included in each slot. The slot is closed using a bronze wedge which is driven in over the top of the winding (*Figure 2.19*). The coil is fed with direct current from the exciter. There are many slots distributed round the periphery of the rotor, for example thirty-two slots which would carry sixteen coils, eight used to create a north pole on one side of the rotor and the other eight to create a south pole on the other side. Because the winding is spread over the face of the rotor it is known as a *distributed* winding. In *Figure 2.20* four coils are shown on one side of the rotor. Each coil produces a magnetic flux of the form shown in *Figure 2.21*. Now in *Figure 2.20*, using five lines of force for each coil, the total field pattern is built up. The lines from coil 1, 1′ are distributed between the coil sides. The five lines from coil 2, 2′ are uniformly distributed between its coil sides. Similarly, for the coils 3, 3′ and 4, 4′. Where the force lines are closely packed the region of highest flux is found. The flux distribution with four coils is reasonably close to a sine wave, using eight coils per pole gives an

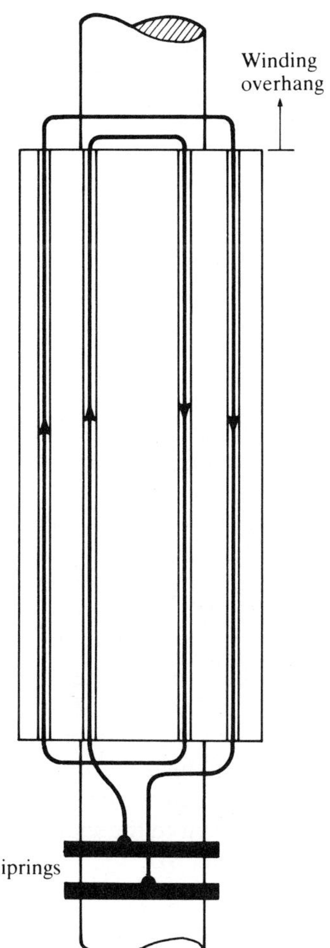

Figure 2.18

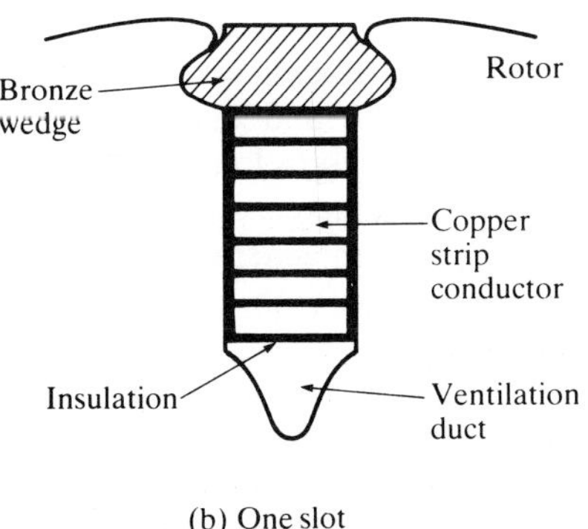

Figure 2.19

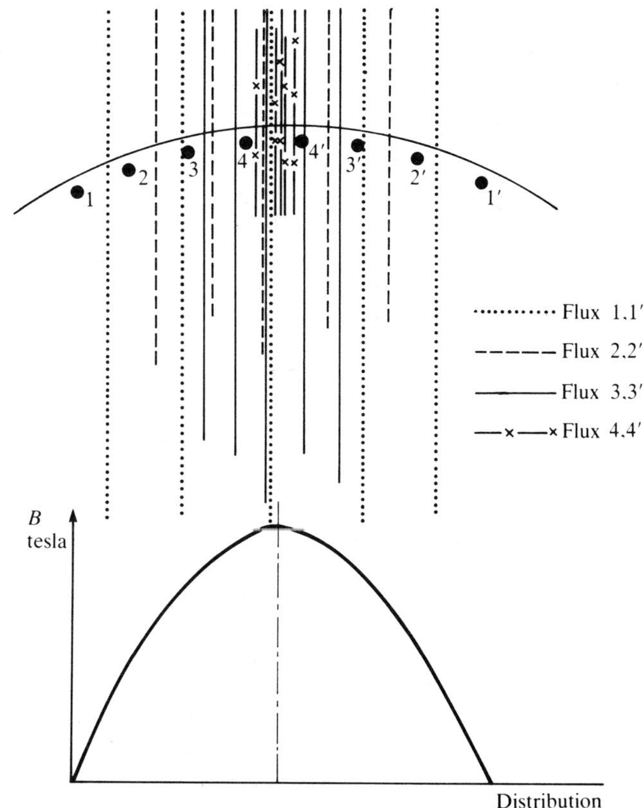

Figure 2.20

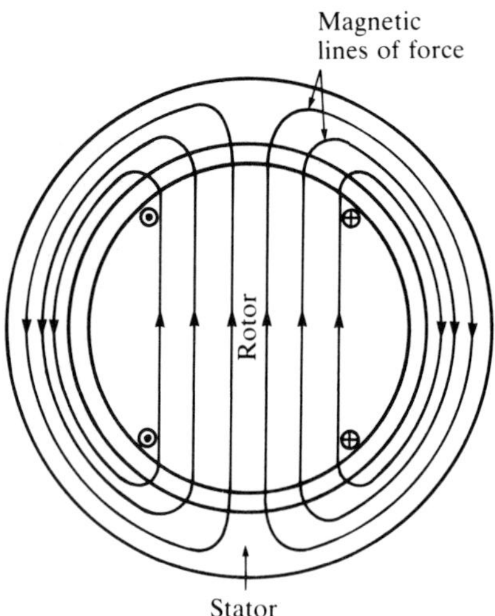

Figure 2.21

even better result. The coil sides are not in fact equally spaced and the designer has carefully to calculate the required spacing to give the best possible waveform.

The section of the rotor winding outside the slots is called the overhang. The winding ends are carefully packed with insulating material to eliminate any free space so restricting coil movement. A large steel ring or end bell is heated and shrunk on to a groove machined around the circumference of the end of the rotor completely surrounding the overhang. This ring prevents the windings being thrown outwards by centrifugal force. As the ring grips the end of the rotor it comes into contact with the ends of the slot wedges and the ends of copper strips beneath them so forming conducting paths along the rotor slot tops, through the end bells and back into other similar paths. This is equivalent to the squirrel cage rotor in the induction motor (see also Chapter 3).

Uses of the two types of rotor

In order to generate at 50 hertz, a one pole pair machine needs to run at a speed of 50 revolutions per second. The centrifugal forces on a mass rotating at this speed are a limiting factor in the design of the rotor. To limit these forces to a safe level the diameter of the rotor cannot be greater than about 110 centimetres. This generally rules out the salient pole rotor and the cylindrical type is used. The generated e.m.f. is a function of the magnetic flux linked and in order to generate high voltages, typically between 12 kV and 26 kV, a large flux is required. This is achieved by making the rotor long, the active length being of the order of five times its diameter. A long, small diameter, two-pole rotor is thus associated with generators operating at the highest speed possible associated with the required frequency.

Where lower-speed prime movers are to be used more poles are required. At the lower speed, diameters may be increased without critically increasing the centrifugal forces. The cylindrical construction can be employed to give two pole pairs but above this number the salient pole construction is employed. The diameter of the spider is increased to give an outer surface area great enough to carry the required number of poles. Since there are now a number of poles each producing flux and each linking with series-connected conductors in the stator the overall length of the machine can be reduced. Taking a slightly simplistic approach it might be envisaged that a rotor which was 5 m in length with one pole pair could be cut in half along its length and the mass of material formed into a four-pole rotor 2.5 m in length. The length has been reduced and the diameter increased. Multi-pole, salient pole machines have large diameters but very short lengths.

Cylindrical rotor machines are associated with steam, gas turbine and high-head water turbines. Salient pole machines are employed with diesel and low-head water turbine drives.

THE THREE-PHASE SYNCHRONOUS GENERATOR

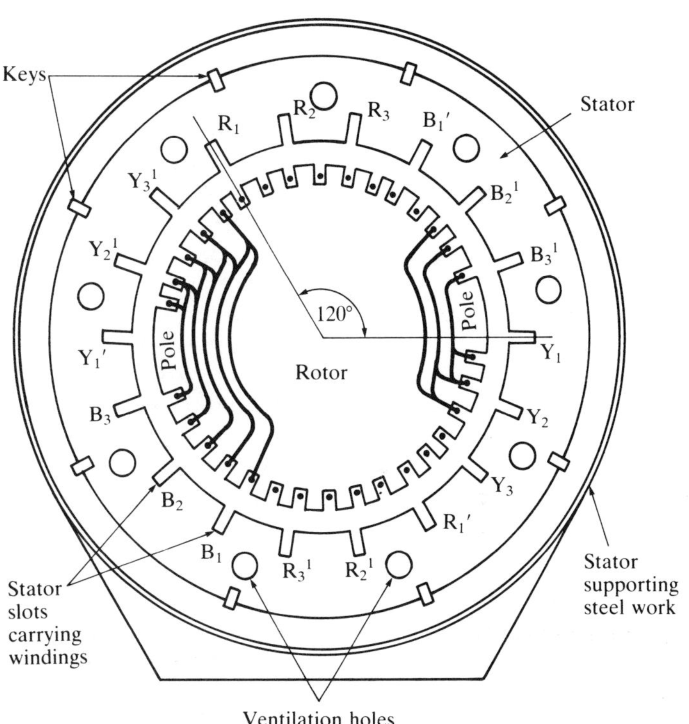

Figure 2.22

So far we have only considered the single-phase machine which has one set of windings per pole pair.

The three-phase machine is developed from this basic design by adding two other identical windings. The three windings are carried in slots which are uniformly distributed round the stator. *Figure 2.22* shows a one-pole pair, cylindrical rotor machine with a partly-wound rotor. The pole faces are to the left and right of the diagram. The red phase winding occupies six slots, 1, 1′, 2, 2′ and 3, 3′ with the prefix 'R' to indicate 'red phase'. The yellow phase winding is displaced 120° in a clockwise direction on the stator so that coil Y (1, 1′) is 120° from R (1, 1′). In the same way, the blue coils (B) are displaced by a further 120°. As the rotor turns in a clockwise direction

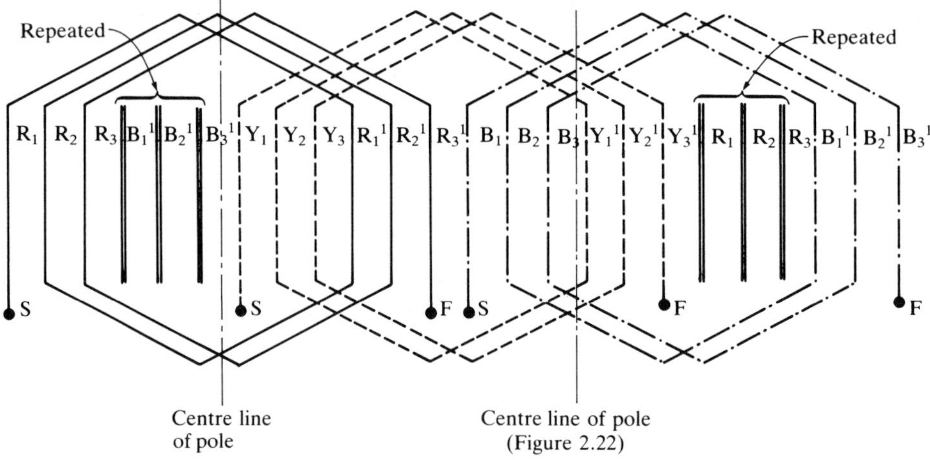

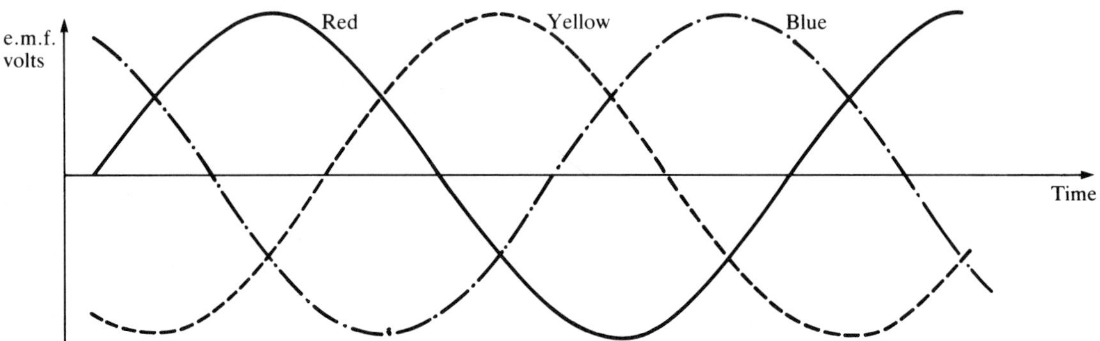

Figure 2.23

as drawn, it will induce identical e.m.f.s in each of the windings but at different times. To a regular sequence the maxima will occur in each of the windings in turn, first in the red winding then in the yellow winding and then in the blue winding.

The stator winding shown in *Figure 2.22* is shown developed in *Figure 2.23*. Observe that six slots have been repeated in the drawing to avoid conductors having to be shown starting on one side of the figure and re-appearing on the other. Envisage the flat drawing being wrapped round to form a cylinder. The pole centre lines relate to the static positions of the poles in *Figure 2.22*. As the poles sweep past the conductors, moving from left to right, the e.m.f. waveforms will be produced as shown. The ends of the windings are marked S indicating 'start' and F indicating 'finish'. All synchronous generators are connected in star so that either the three start terminals or the three finish terminals are connected together to form the star point which will be connected to earth, either directly in the case of low voltage machines, or via a fault-current limiting resistance in the case of high-voltage machines. The three-phase output is taken from the other three terminals.

THE E.M.F. EQUATION

Consider a synchronous machine with the following parameters:
Total magnetic flux per pole = Φ webers
Number of pairs of poles = P ($2P$ poles)
Speed = n rev/s
Total number of conductors in series per phase = Z

Consider a single conductor in a stator slot.

In one revolution the conductor is cut (or linked with) the flux of $2P$ poles.

At a speed of n rev/s, the conductor is cut by the flux of $2Pn$ poles/s

Time taken for the flux from one pole to cut the conductor

$$= \frac{1}{2Pn} \text{ seconds}$$

$$\text{Average e.m.f. induced in the conductor} = \frac{\text{Flux cut}}{\text{Time taken}} \text{ volts}$$

$$= \frac{\Phi}{1/2Pn} = 2Pn\Phi \text{ volts}$$

$$\text{Peak value of a sine wave} = \frac{\text{Average e.m.f.}}{0.636}$$

r.m.s. value of a sine wave = $0.707 \times$ peak value

$$= 0.707 \times \frac{\text{Average value}}{0.636}$$

$$= 1.11 \times 2Pn\Phi \text{ volts}$$

For Z conductors connected in series, the output voltage

$$= 2.22\, Pn\Phi Z \text{ volts}$$

Or since $n = \dfrac{f}{P}$ $\quad Pn = f \quad$ and output voltage = $2.22\, f\Phi Z$ volts

Example 3. A three-phase synchronous generator has sixteen poles.

It has a stator with 144 slots and there are ten conductors in each slot. The total flux per pole = 0.03 Wb which is sinusoidally distributed.

It is driven at a speed of 375 revolutions per minute. Determine:

(i) The frequency of the output.
(ii) The phase and line values of output voltage.
(iii) The number of slots on the stator under each pole per phase.

(i) $375 \text{ rev/min} = \dfrac{375}{60} = 6.25 \text{ rev/s}$

$n = \dfrac{f}{P} \qquad f = Pn \qquad$ and $P = \dfrac{16}{2}$ = eight pole pairs

$\therefore f = 8 \times 6.25 = 50 \text{ Hz}$

(ii) The machine has 144 slots in total.

$$\therefore \text{slots for each phase} = \frac{144}{3} = 48$$

There are ten conductors in each slot.
∴ conductors in series in each phase = $48 \times 10 = 480$
e.m.f. per phase $= 2.22\, f \Phi Z$ volts
$= 2.22 \times 50 \times 0.03 \times 480$
$= 1598.4$ V

Alternators are star connected so that line voltage
$= \sqrt{3} \times V_{phase}$
$= \sqrt{3} \times 1598.4$
$= 2768.5$ V

(iii) There are forty-eight slots per phase on the stator. The machine has sixteen poles. There are therefore $48/16 = 3$ slots under each pole for each phase. Three slots carry the red winding, three slots carry the yellow winding and three slots carry the blue winding. This was the case for the machine shown in *Figures 2.22* and *2.23*. When the number of poles is increased, a matching increase in the number of groups of slots is required. The number of slots in each group does not vary widely being typically 3 or 4. See also *Figure 2.16*.

THE OPEN-CIRCUIT CHARACTERISTIC

The synchronous generator

The open-circuit characteristic is a graph of the open-circuit e.m.f. against field (rotor) current for the machine running at its synchronous speed.

The open-circuit voltage may be measured directly on a low-voltage machine but for larger machines a potential transformer will be required as shown in *Figure 2.24*. This will have a ratio suitable to give a zero to 110 V output over the required range of voltages to be measured. The machine is run up to synchronous speed and the excitation increased from zero over a range so as to cause the output e.m.f. to vary from near zero to a little in excess of its normal rated value.

Large machines have wide air gaps between their rotor and stator some being of the order of 12 to 13 cm. Air has a much larger reluctance than steel and so before the steel saturates most of the magnetising force is used in setting up the magnetic flux in the air gap and only a little in setting up the flux in the stator steel. In air the relationship between flux density and magnetising force is linear so that the total flux in the machine is very nearly proportional to field current, any slight non-linearity being due to the relatively small effect of the steel. Since output e.m.f. is proportional to magnetic flux and magnetic flux is very nearly proportional to field current, the open circuit characteristic approximates to a straight line through the origin in *Figure 2.24(b)*. At the highest values of flux the

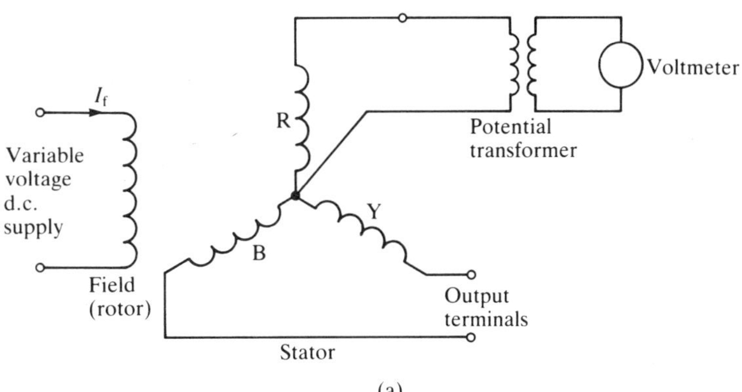

(a)

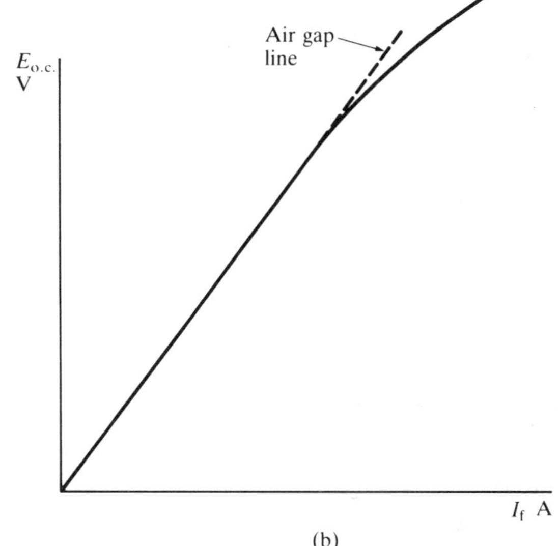

(b)

Figure 2.24

steel begins to saturate requiring larger increments of excitation current for a given increase in flux. The open-circuit characteristic becomes non-linear, the magnetic flux and e.m.f. rising more slowly for a given increment of excitation current. Because of the significance of the air gap the straight line in the open-circuit characteristic is called the *air-gap line*.

The direct-current generator

The direct-current generator may be separately excited, when the field current is derived from a separate source as is the case of the synchronous machine shown in *Figure 2.24(a)*, or it may be self-excited when it derives its field current from its own output terminals.

Large machines will generally be separately excited when the air gaps will be fairly long as already discussed for the synchronous machine. The long gaps are present to limit the effects of armature reaction which is the effect of the magnetic flux set up by currents in the armature on the main pole fields. These machines will have an open circuit characteristic similar to that of the large synchronous machine.

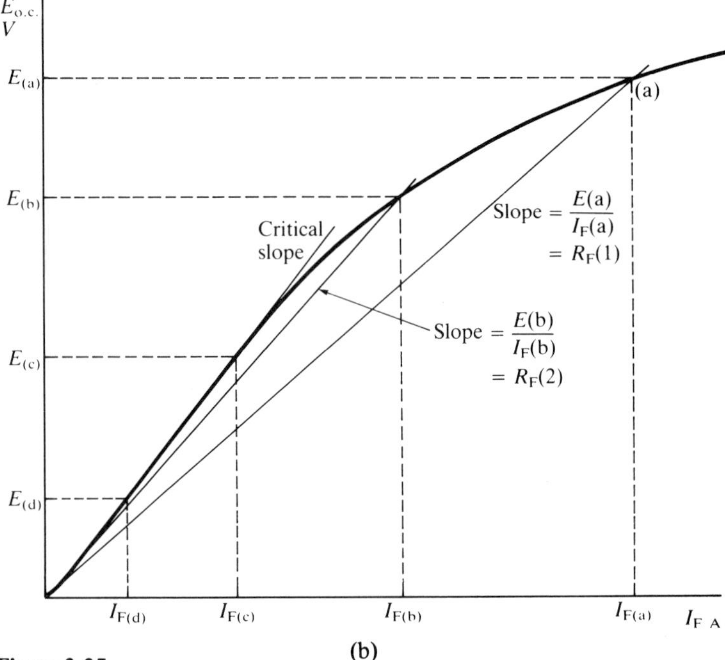

Figure 2.25

For smaller, self-excited machines, as shown in *Figure 2.25(a)*, the curve of the open circuit characteristic is significant as is now demonstrated.

Let the resistance of the field circuit be R_F Ω. Consider a point (a) on the characteristic shown in *Figure 2.25(b)*.

At point (a) $\frac{E_{(a)}}{I_{F(a)}} = R_{F(1)}$

In order to generate a voltage $E_{(a)}$ it is necessary to set the field rheostat to such a value that the total field circuit resistance $= R_{F(1)}$ Ω. In order to decrease the output voltage the resistance of the field circuit is increased. To generate a voltage $E_{(b)}$, the necessary field circuit resistance is given by:

$$R_{F(2)} = \frac{E_{(b)}}{I_{F(b)}} \text{ ohms}$$

Over a large section of the curve these relationships can be satisfied giving a unique value to the field circuit resistance.

However if the field resistance is increased to a value given by:

$$R_{F(3)} = \frac{E_{(c)}}{I_{F(c)}} \text{ ohms}$$

The generated e.m.f. becomes indeterminate since any point towards the origin such as $E_{(d)}/I_{F(d)}$ yields the same required field resistance value. The slope of the resistance line in this region is known as the *critical slope*. The output voltage slips back to zero (closely) under these conditions. It follows that the output voltage from a machine having a characteristic with a long linear section from the origin cannot be controlled over a large range extending down to near zero. A self-excited machine depends upon operating at flux densities high enough to give a degree of saturation at the lowest stable output voltage required from the machine, since it requires a non-linear characteristic over its controllable range in order to function.

GENERATING AND MOTORING MODES

When a synchronous machine is sufficiently excited and is running at synchronous speed it can be made to generate or to motor.

Generating. In the generating mode, the prime mover supplies energy which being applied to the rotor shaft causes it to attempt to rotate at a faster speed than synchronous. However the rotor is held in synchronism by the strength of the magnetic field. The energy input to the shaft is transferred by the magnetic linkage to the stator windings and it appears at the output terminals as electrical energy which is exported to the supply system.

Motoring. When a mechanical load is connected to the shaft of the synchronous machine the rotor will tend to slow down. Since it can only run at synchronous speed power is drawn from the supply to maintain this speed.

To function in either of these modes the machine must first be brought up to synchronous speed.

THE SYNCHRONOUS MOTOR

When the stator of a machine carrying a three-phase winding is energised from a three-phase supply a rotating magnetic field of constant amplitude is created which rotates within the stator at synchronous speed. The production of this field is demonstrated in *Figure 2.26*. Three stators for a one-pole pair machine are shown which have their phase windings reduced to the simplest possible form of one coil per phase per pole. Beneath the stators the waveforms of the supply currents are drawn.

At an instant in time t_1, the red phase current is at a maximum value going positive while the other two phase currents are at one half of their maximum values going negative. A positive going current will enter R_1 and leave R_1'. Using the right-hand screw or grip rule this current will cause a north pole to be created at right angles to the coil diameter, pointing to the left of the stator as drawn. The negative going yellow current will enter Y_1' and leave Y_1. This will create a north pole at right angles to the coil diameter but since the value of this current is only one half that of the red current the flux and the phasor representing it are correspondingly shorter. The same procedure is adopted for the blue phase. Adding the flux phasors gives a total flux which has a magnitude of 1.5 times that for the red phase alone. This addition is shown to a larger scale beneath the waveforms.

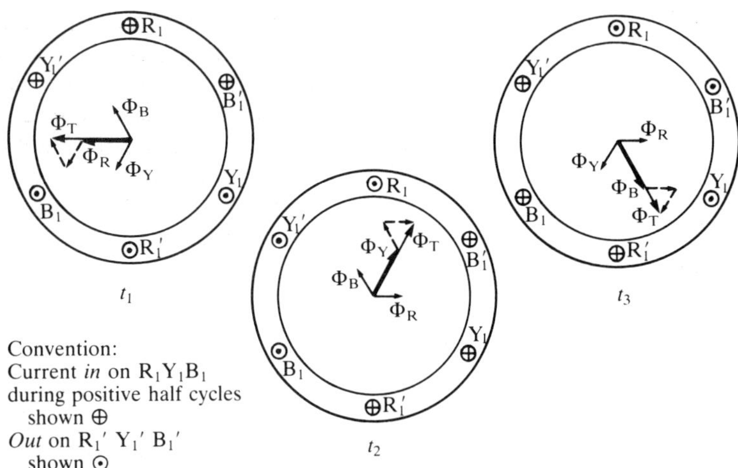

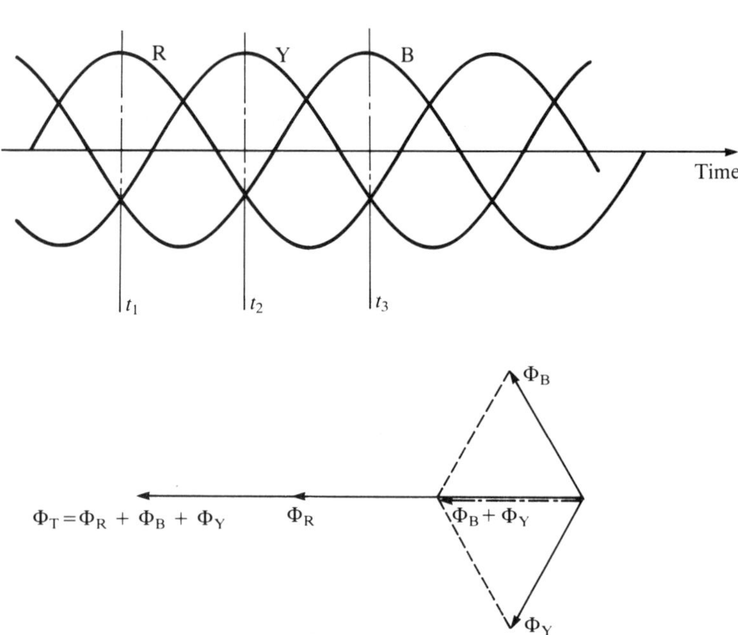

Figure 2.26

Two other instants in time, t_2 and t_3, are examined in the same way. The flux phasor representing the total flux is constant in magnitude. It is rotating in a clockwise direction in synchronism with the movement along the waveforms. When next the red current is at its maximum value, the flux phasor will have arrived back in its original position. Although not conclusive proof that the magnitude is constant, the reader might like to try any position on the current waveforms, drawing flux phasors of a magnitude to match the relative size of each of the currents, when it will be found that the total flux is always the same.

If the stator of a stationary synchronous machine is energised using a three-phase supply, a rotating magnetic field is produced. If the rotor is excited it has one or more pairs of stationary magnetic poles. As the rotating field passes the stationary poles forces will be set up since like poles repel each other and unlike poles attract each other. Every time the rotating north pole passes a rotor north pole there will be repulsion and then as it passes a rotor south pole there will be attraction. A rapidly pulsating torque will be produced which will generally cause the rotor to vibrate rather than begin to turn.

STARTING METHODS

1 As an induction motor. A machine which is purchased to operate specifically as a motor will have conductors incorporated into the rotor slots which will effectively create a squirrel cage. The machine may then be started as an induction motor. The main d.c. rotor winding is short circuited to prevent high alternating voltages being induced in it during the run up. *Figure 2.28* shows the field system of a synchronous machine, the field winding being shorted out by closing the field suppression switch. While the suppression switch is closed the exciter is isolated by opening the field switch. The stator is energised at full or reduced voltage when the machine will run up to near synchronous speed. The rotor is then excited by opening the suppression switch and closing the field switch when the machine will pull into synchronism with the system (see also Chapter 3 for a full explanation of induction motor starting).

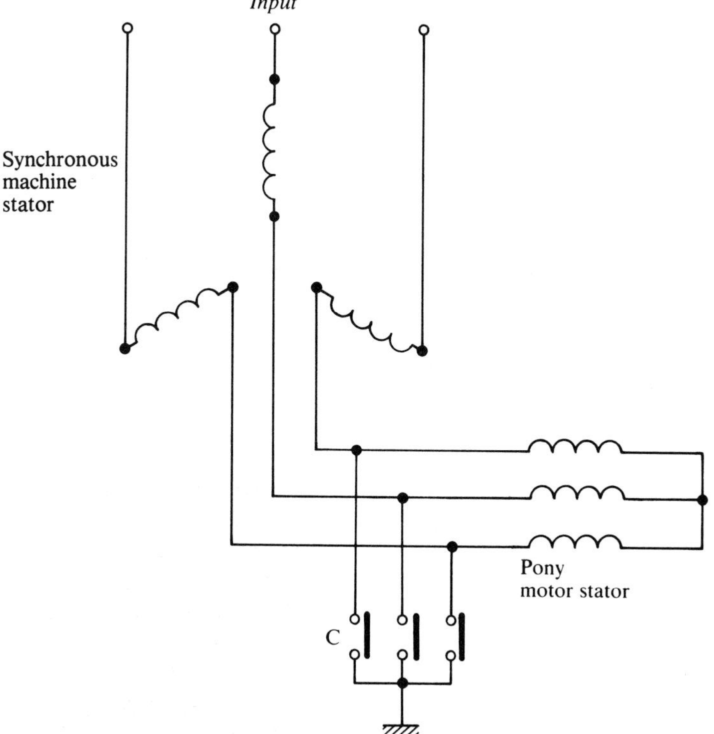

Figure 2.27

2 Using a pony motor. This is a short-time rated induction motor which is connected to the end of the shaft of the synchronous machine. It may be electrically independent of the main machine or, as shown in *Figure 2.27*, employ the synchronous machine itself as a series current limiting reactor. The circuit breaker *C* is opened, the field winding short circuited and the three-phase supply switched on to the input terminals. Current flows in the main stator producing some torque as described in 1 above and then in the induction motor stator producing more torque. The reactance of the synchronous motor stator is such that the input current is not excessive. When the machine is running near synchronous speed, breaker C is closed shorting out the pony motor, putting full voltage on to the main motor stator while earthing the star point. The main field is excited and the machine pulls into synchronism.
3 Using a driving engine. Large machines which may have a dual role acting either as generators or as a substitute for static capacitor banks to correct the power factor of a system are brought up to speed using their prime movers, for example a gas turbine or diesel engine. These will drive the machine through a clutch.

The main field is shorted out during the run up. The prime mover is used to bring the machine up to full speed, when the field is excited with a current sufficient to cause its terminal voltage to exactly match that of the running system to which it is to be connected. Two voltmeters are used for this purpose as shown in *Figure 2.28*. Fine adjustment of the speed is made to match that of the running system and an instant when the output voltage waveform of the incoming machine is in phase with that of the running system is detected using an instrument called a *synchroscope*. The main circuit breaker is then closed. Increasing the fuel input to the prime mover causes the machine to generate while disengaging the clutch and shutting down the prime mover leaves the machine running as a

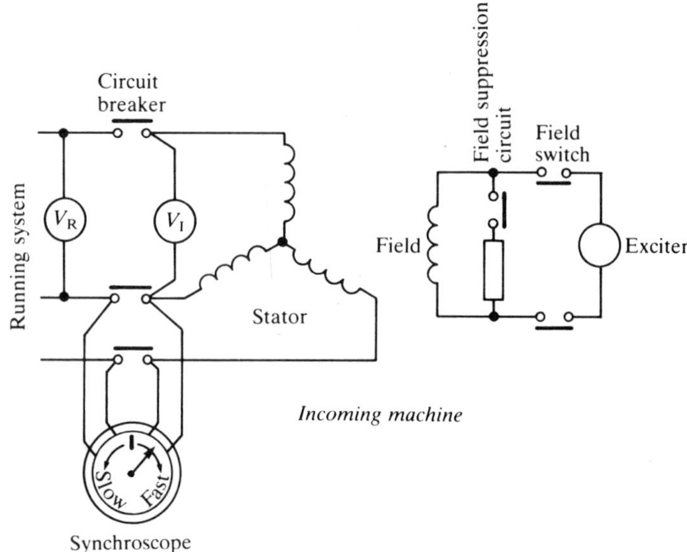

Figure 2.28

motor. The power factor at which it operates is a function of the excitation. Increasing the excitation current will cause the motor to draw leading VA_R from the supply so effecting power factor correction. The degree of correction is steplessly variable by varying the excitation.

Where an electrically independent pony motor is used to start a synchronous machine a similar procedure may be carried out if fine speed control is possible except that there will be no clutch, the pony motor remaining connected to the shaft after having been disconnected from the power supply.

USES OF THE SYNCHRONOUS MOTOR

Because the synchronous machine is not so readily started as the induction motor the usefulness of this type of motor is strictly limited. Once started, however, it runs at constant speed and draws a current from the supply with any desired power factor. In the industrial environment it is used to drive loads which need to run continuously, providing compressed air, ventilation or driving pumps while at the same time fulfilling its other role of correcting power factor.

PROBLEMS

4 In a d.c. machine, what is the function of the commutator?

5 What is the fundamental difference between a lap winding and a wave winding?

6 In a d.c. machine the pole faces are parallel to the face of the armature giving a uniform air gap width. Why can this not be so in an alternating-current generator?

7 What differences in the form of the commutator would you expect to find when comparing a machine dealing with small currents with one carrying very large currents?

8 What benefits are there to be gained by having a rotating field system in a synchronous machine as opposed to a rotating armature and fixed field?

9 At what speed would a twelve-pole synchronous machine have to run in order to generate a supply at (a) 50 Hz and (b) 60 Hz?

10 A three-phase synchronous machine has four slots per pole per phase and six poles. How many slots are there on the stator?

11 A six-pole synchronous machine has a stator with ninety slots and six conductors per slot. It revolves at 1000 rev/min. The flux per pole is 0.06 Wb. Calculate the values of phase and line e.m.f.s for the machine with its windings connected in star.

12 Describe the two types of rotor found in synchronous machines. Briefly discuss the uses and limitations of each type.

13 The bronze wedges which close the slots in a cylindrical rotor machine have two functions. What are they?

14 How is the direct current necessary to excite the field fed on to the rotor of a synchronous machine?
15 Why is it that the rotors in high-speed synchronous machines are long while those in low speed machines are very short?
16 Why is the open-circuit characteristic of a large synchronous machine very nearly straight while that for a small d.c. machine is distinctly non-linear?
17 Describe two methods which may be employed for starting a synchronous machine?
18 What is the function of a synchroscope?
19 What are the requirements to make a synchronous machine (a) generate; (b) perform as a motor?

3 Induction motors

Aims: At the end of this chapter you should be able to:

Describe the construction and action of the induction motor.
Deduce the relationship between slip, frequency, number of poles and speed of rotation.
Sketch the torque/speed relationship and explain its shape.
Describe various starting methods and their applications and limitations.
Describe the construction and benefits of the double-cage machine.
Discuss applications for induction machines.

The induction motor is an alternating current motor fed from a single- or a three-phase supply. It has a drooping speed/torque characteristic very similar to that of a d.c. shunt motor starting from a no-load speed slightly less than the synchronous value. There are basically two types: (i) *cage machines*, which have short circuited bars in slots on the rotor and need no external connections to the rotor. This is a relatively cheap method of construction which is very robust. (ii) *wound-rotor machines*, which carry windings on the rotor and need slip rings to provide a connection to external resistance banks. The latter arrangement provides the means to change the torque/speed characteristic while the former type can only run at essentially constant speed, with no simple means of speed variation. This chapter is concerned with the three-phase motor; Chapter 4 will look at the smaller, single-phase machines.

CONSTRUCTION

The three-phase induction motor has a stator which is identical to that of the synchronous machine. The two-pole arrangement is shown in *Figures 2.22* and *2.23*. If, instead of the winding occupying the complete stator, the slot spacing was compressed into one half of its circumference, another identical winding could be added to the machine. In the case of the synchronous machine this would require the use of an additional two poles on the rotor making it a four-pole machine. Although the induction motor does not have poles on its rotor, an induction motor with this winding arrangement is called a two pole pair or four pole machine. One phase of a four-pole stator winding is shown in *Figure 2.15*.

Compressing the original two-pole winding into one third of the circumference makes room for two identical sets of windings to be added. This would be known as a three-pole pair machine. Virtually any number of complete sets of windings may be wound on a stator involving the related number of poles.

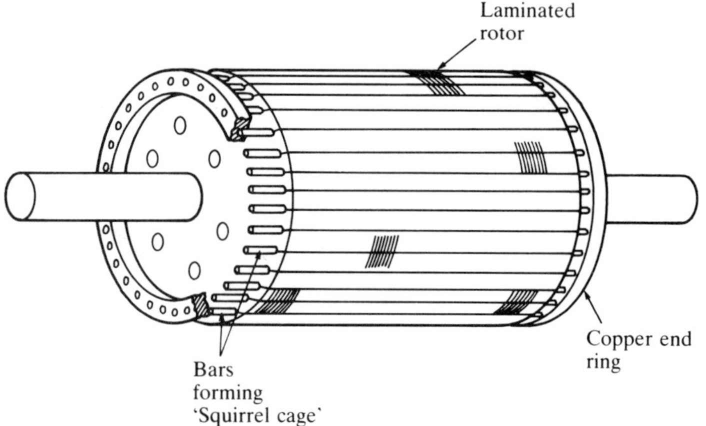

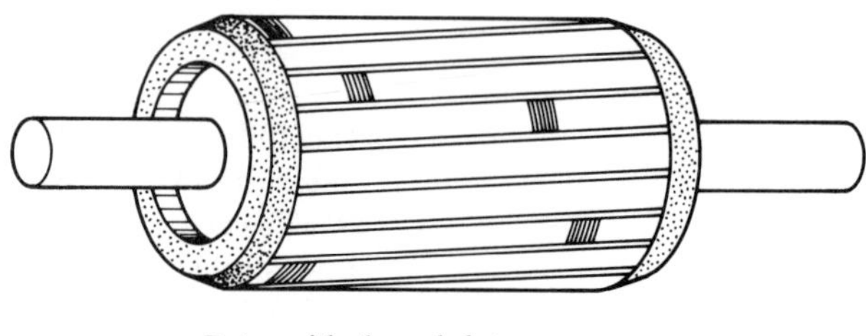

Rotor with skewed slots
cast aluminium bars and end rings

Figure 3.1

The cage rotor is built up from laminations of low reluctance steel, slots being provided to carry copper bars. The bars protrude at each end and a large cross-sectional area copper ring with holes drilled to suit is pressed on to the bars at each end. The bars are brazed into their holes to give a good electrical connection. The arrangement of bars and end rings is sometimes referred to as a *squirrel cage* since it resembles the exercise wheel used by small rodents kept in cages. The original motor was described by Nicola Tesla in 1889 and in Russia, so the story is told, squirrels could be seen employing such wheels. A cage rotor with the left-hand shorting ring partly sectioned is shown in *Figure 3.1*. In a cheaper form of construction found frequently in smaller motors, the rotor laminations are assembled and placed in a mould. Molten aluminium under considerable pressure is injected into the mould which fills the slots forming the bars and end rings simultaneously.

The wound rotor is also laminated and carries a three-phase, star connected winding. The starts of the phase windings are joined to form a star point while the three finishes are connected to slip rings which are shrunk on to the shaft but insulated from it. The slip ring brushes provides a means of connecting external resistance banks. The arrangement is shown in *Figure 3.2*.

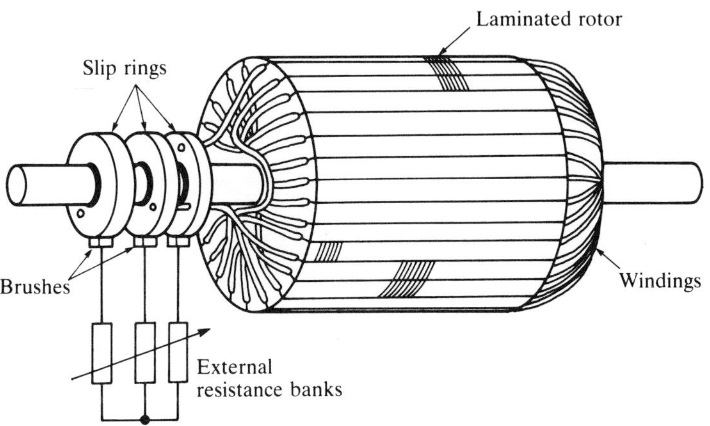

Figure 3.2

ACTION OF THE INDUCTION MOTOR

When the stator of the induction motor is energised from a three-phase supply a magnetic field is produced within the stator and which links with the rotor. This field rotates at synchronous speed (see *Figure 2.26*). As the field sweeps past the rotor conductors the bars have e.m.f.s induced in them and consequently currents flow. The action is that of a generator. Hence the name induction motor; it functions because of voltages induced in its rotor.

In *Figure 3.3*, consider that the stator has just been energised and the rotor has not yet had time to start turning. At this instant in time the stator produced field has a north pole towards the top of the stator as drawn and is rotating in a clockwise direction. The rotor bars have a relative motion backwards through the field. Put another way, if the field were stationary the bars would have to be moving anti-clockwise to give the same effect. Flemming's right-hand generator rule was formulated for d.c. machines in which the field was stationary while the conductors moved. Using the conductor motion through the field it may be deduced that the bar current is away from the viewer. This will set up a clockwise magnetic field around the bar which is shown in isolation in *Figure 3.3(b)*. In its slot this will result in bar field and stator field assisting each other to the left of the bar and opposing each other on the right of the bar. The resulting strong field to the left of the bar will produce a force causing it to move in the same direction as the rotating field.

There are many bars on the rotor all producing torque and the rotor will accelerate. If the rotor ever attained synchronous speed, that is to say if the bars ever moved at the same speed as the rotating field, the induced e.m.f.s and bar currents would fall to zero and there would be no torque. The rotor would slow down, the induced e.m.f.s would reappear and torque would again be produced. It follows therefore that for any particular load applied to the motor there is a speed at which the rotor currents will produce just enough torque to drive that load. With the rotor speed too small the induced e.m.f.s and resulting currents are large enough to produce an accelerating torque. If the rotor speed is too high, the rate of flux cutting, induced e.m.f.s and currents fall so reducing the torque and the rotor slows down. The speed/torque characteristic is therefore a

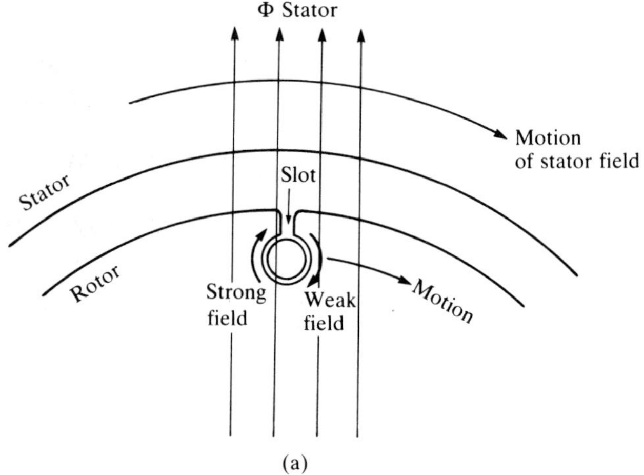

(a)

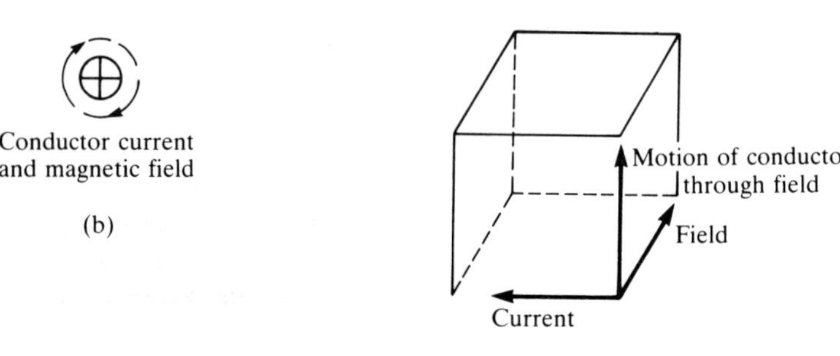

(b)

Flemming's right-hand generator rule

Right hand: thu*m*b = *M*otion
*f*irst *f*inger = *f*ield
se*c*ond finger = *c*urrent

(c)

Figure 3.3

slightly drooping one, an increase in torque causing a small decrease in speed.

In order to generate the rotating field, currents flow in the stator giving rise to copper losses (I^2R_{stator}) and iron losses. Rotor currents are matched with balancing currents in the stator. The various currents and losses may be compared directly with those in the transformer.

SLIP

The synchronous speed of the rotating field is given by:

$$n = \frac{f}{P} \text{ rev/s}$$

(See Chapter 2, 'Relationship between numbers of poles and speed'.)

The actual speed of the rotor = n_R rev/s

$$n - n_R = n_s$$

Where n_s is called the slip speed.
The slip speed expressed as a proportion of the synchronous is the fractional, percentage or per unit slip S.

$$\frac{n_s}{n} = S \quad \text{Transposing: } n_s = S \times n$$

A machine with a synchronous speed of 25 rev/s and running at 24 rev/s has a slip speed:

$n_s = (25 - 24) = 1$ rev/s.
$S = 1/25$, 4% or 0.04 p.u.

Now since $n - n_R = n_s$ Transposing:

$$\begin{aligned} n_R &= n - n_s \\ &= n - Sn \\ &= n(1 - S) \end{aligned}$$

FREQUENCY OF THE ROTOR CURRENTS

Considering the instant just as the supply has been connected to the stator and before the rotor has commenced to turn, the stator and rotor are in effect the primary and short-circuited secondary of a transformer. At this instant:

$n_R = 0$, and since $n - n_R = n_s$, $n_s = n$ and $S = 100\%$

Since, in a transformer, there can be no frequency change between primary and secondary, the frequency of the currents in the rotor is the same as the frequency of the supply to the stator.

$f_R = f$ Hz

Where f_R = frequency of the rotor currents
f = frequency of the supply

Consider now the rotor to be running at synchronous speed. The rotor bars are moving at exactly the same speed as the rotating stator field. There can be no induced e.m.f. as already discussed. The only way in which such a condition can be sustained without an external driving force is for the rotor to be energised with direct current. It would become a synchronous motor. The frequency of the rotor currents would be zero. For this condition:

$n_R = n$ and again, since $n - n_R = n_s$, $n_s = 0$ and $S = 1$

Between the two limits of $S = 0$ and $S = 1$, the frequency of the rotor currents falls from the supply value to zero.

$f_R = S \times f$

Example 1. An eight-pole induction motor connected to a 50 Hz supply runs with a slip of 5%. Determine: (i) the speed of the motor and (ii) the frequency of the currents in the rotor.

(i) $$n = \frac{50}{4} = 12.5 \text{ rev/s}$$

$$
\begin{aligned}
n_s &= Sn \\
&= 5\% \text{ of } 12.5 \\
&= 0.625 \text{ rev/s} \\
n_s &= n - n_R \\
\therefore 0.625 &= 12.5 - n_R \\
n_R &= 11.875 \text{ rev/s}
\end{aligned}
$$

Or directly, $n_R = n(1 - S) = 12.5(1 - 0.05) = 11.875$ rev/s

(ii) $f_R = Sf$
$= 5\%$ of 50 Hz
$= 2.5$ Hz

POWER AND TORQUE

Figure 3.4 shows a rotor on which there is a tangential force F newtons created by the rotating field.

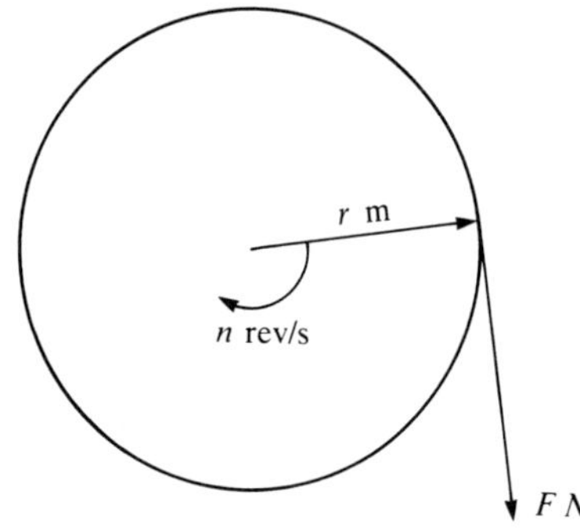

Figure 3.4

Work done = force × distance through which the force operates

In one revolution the force operates through the circumference of the rotor ($2\pi r$ metres).

Work done per revolution $= F \times 2\pi r$ Nm
At n rev/s, work done per second $= F \times 2\pi r \times n$ Nm/s
Now 1 Nm/s = power of 1 watt and $F \times r$ = torque T
Hence power $= 2\pi nT$ watts.

Suppose the torque supplied by the rotor of an induction motor = T Nm (This value includes the externally driven mechanical load and friction and windage on the rotor itself due to its bearings and cooling fan etc.)

The rotor is turning at n_R rev/s

$$
\begin{aligned}
\therefore \text{power developed by the rotor} &= 2\pi n_R T \text{ watts} \\
&= 2\pi(n - n_s)T \\
&= 2\pi n(1 - S)T \\
&= (1 - S)2\pi nT \text{ W}
\end{aligned}
$$

Now, the torque developed by the rotor = torque supplied by the stator. This must be true since if the stator torque were less than that demanded of the rotor, it would slow down until the currents in stator and rotor were sufficient to result in equilibrium at a new lower speed. If the stator torque was greater than that demanded of the rotor it would speed up until once again equilibrium would be restored.

The stator field revolves at synchronous speed n rev/s.
$\therefore$ Stator power $= 2\pi nT$ W (= power transferred to the rotor in the magnetic field)
Hence, power supplied to the rotor : power developed by the rotor

$$2\pi nT : (1 - S)2\pi nT$$

Which is a ratio $1 : (1 - S)$
The difference between the two quantities:

$$
\begin{aligned}
2\pi nT - (1 - S)2\pi nT &= S \times 2\pi nT \text{ W} \\
&= S \times \text{input power to rotor}
\end{aligned}
$$

The quantity S, the slip, is associated with rotor loss both in speed and in power. It follows that the lower is the value of slip, the lower are the rotor losses and the higher the efficiency of the motor will be.

Example 2. A ten-pole induction motor connected to a 50 Hz supply operates with a slip of 4.5% when the shaft power = 25 kW. Determine:
(i) The torque developed by the motor
(ii) The power being transferred from the stator to the rotor.
(i) $n = 50/5 = 10$ rev/s 4.5% = 0.045 p.u.

Power developed by the rotor

$$= 2\pi n_R T \text{ watts}$$
$$= (1 - S)2\pi n T$$
$$\therefore 25\,000 = (1 - 0.045)2\pi \times 10\,T$$
$$T = \frac{25\,000}{(1 - 0.045)2\pi \times 10} = 416.64 \text{ Nm}$$

(ii) Power supplied by stator $= 2\pi n T = 2\pi \times 10 \times 416.64$
$= 26\,178$ W

Or since power developed by rotor = $(1 - S)$ input to rotor

$$\text{Power input} = \frac{\text{Power developed by rotor}}{(1 - S)}$$

which yields the same result without having first to calculate the torque value.

THE TORQUE/SLIP CHARACTERISTIC

Consider the wound-rotor induction motor. This makes the concepts easier to understand but the principles involved apply to all induction motors.

With the rotor at *standstill*, i.e. $S = 1$, the e.m.f. induced in the rotor winding per phase, i.e. between the star point and one slip ring = E_R volts.

The value of this induced e.m.f. is directly proportional to the rate at which the stator flux is cut, that is to say, directly proportional to the slip S. As S approaches zero, the rotor approaches synchronous speed and the induced e.m.f. falls towards zero.

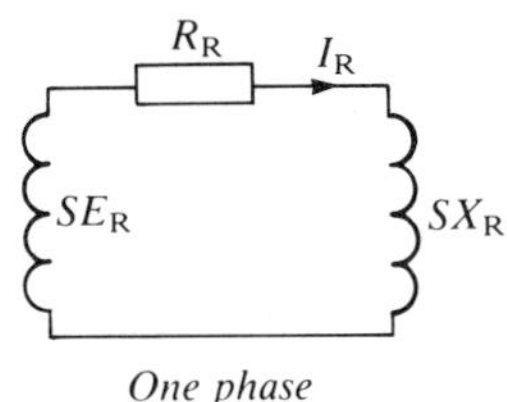

Figure 3.5

Rotor voltage at any value of slip $S = S \times E_R$ volts/phase.
Let the resistance of the rotor winding be R_R Ω/phase.

The rotor winding also has a large inductance since it comprises a number of turns on an iron core. Let the inductance be L_R H/phase.
At *standstill* the reactance $X_R = 2\pi f L_R$ Ω
At slip S, the frequency of the rotor currents falls to Sf Hz when:

$$\text{Reactance} = 2\pi(Sf)L_R = S(2\pi f L_R) = S \times \text{standstill value}$$
$$= SX_R \;\Omega$$

The electrical equivalent circuit for one phase of the rotor is as shown in *Figure 3.5*.

$$\text{Rotor current } I_R = \frac{V}{Z} = \frac{SE_R}{\sqrt{R_R^2 + (SX_R)^2}}$$

$$\text{Power loss in rotor} = I^2R_R = \frac{S^2E_R^2R_R}{(R_R^2 + (SX_R)^2)} \text{ watts}$$

But loss $= S \times$ power input to rotor. Divide the power loss expression by S

$$\text{Power input to rotor} = \frac{SE_R^2R_R}{(R_R^2 + (SX_R)^2)} \text{ watts per phase}$$

Using this expression, the torque/slip characteristic of a typical induction motor may be deduced.

Example 3. A three-phase induction motor has a synchronous speed of 25 rev/s, standstill rotor voltage of 100 V/phase, rotor resistance of 0.25 Ω/phase and standstill rotor reactance of 1.5 Ω/phase. Use these parameters to plot a torque/slip characteristic for the machine.
At standstill, $S = 1$.

$$I_R = \frac{1 \times 100}{\sqrt{0.25^2 + (1 \times 1.5)^2}} = \frac{100}{1.521} = 65.76 \text{ A}$$

$$\begin{aligned}\text{Rotor loss} = I^2R_R = 65.76^2 \times 0.25 &= 1081.08 \text{ W/phase}\\ &= 3 \times 1081.08 \text{ W in three phases}\\ &= 3243 \text{ W total rotor loss.}\end{aligned}$$

The rotor loss shows up as heat and cooling arrangements must be provided sufficient to keep the rotor cool.

$$\text{Input power} = \frac{\text{Power loss in rotor}}{S} = \frac{3243}{1} = 3243 \text{ watts}$$

$$\text{Input power} = 2\pi nT$$

$$3243 = 2\pi \times 25 \times T$$

$$T = \frac{3243}{2\pi \times 25} = 20.65 \text{ Nm}$$

At $S = 0.5$.

$$IR = \frac{0.5 \times 100}{\sqrt{0.25^2 + (0.5 \times 1.5)^2}} = 63.24 \text{ A}$$

Rotor loss $= 3(63.24^2 \times 0.25) = 3000$ W
Input $=$ loss/S $= 3000/0.5 = 6000$ W

$$T = \frac{6000}{2\pi \times 25} = 38.19 \text{ Nm}$$

The reader might care to work through the calculations for $S = 0.25$ ($T = 58.8$ Nm) and for $S = 0.05$ ($T = 35$ Nm).

At $S = 0.1667$,

$$I_R = \frac{0.1667 \times 100}{\sqrt{0.25^2 + (0.1667 \times 1.5)^2}} = 47.14 \text{ A}$$

$$\text{Power input} = \frac{3 \times 47.14^2 \times 0.25}{0.1667} = 10\,000 \text{ W}$$

$$\text{Torque} = \frac{10\,000}{2\pi \times 25} = 63.67 \text{ Nm}$$

The results of these calculations are plotted in *Figure 3.6*. The first observation from the graph is that the starting torque of the motor (when $S = 1$) is very low being only 20.65 Nm. The motor will be capable of running up to speed only if the applied torque at standstill is less than this value.

Because of the low starting torque induction motors are most often started with no applied load, this being applied when the motor is up to full speed, for example when driving machine tools where cutting operations only commence when the work is at full speed and centrifugal pumps which are started with their discharge valves closed, these being opened to commence pumping when at full speed.

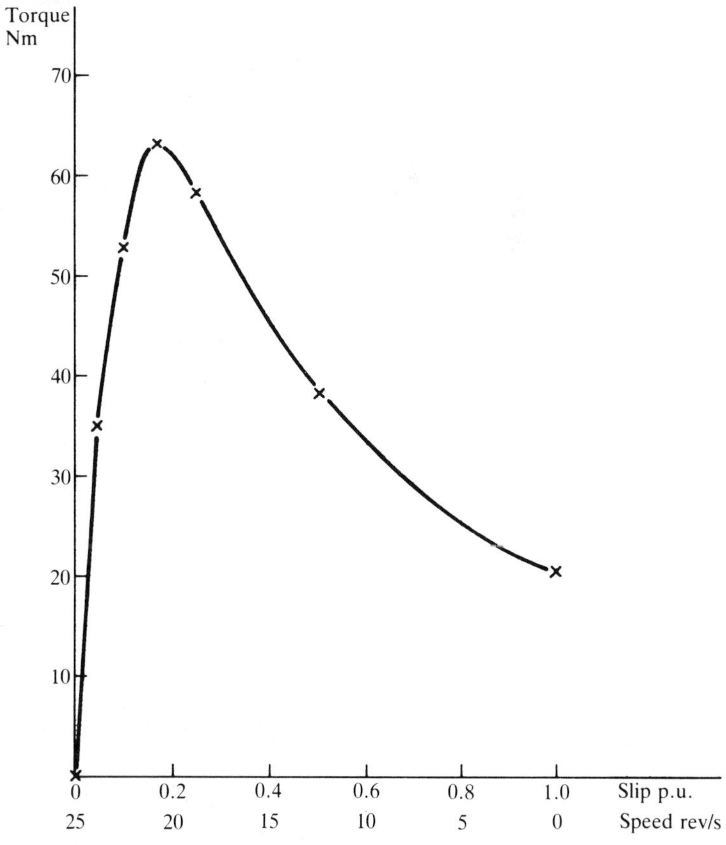

Figure 3.6

The second observation is the connection between R_R and SX_R at the maximum torque condition. Maximum torque occurs at $S = 0.1667$ p.u.

Investigating the relationship between R_R and X_R:

$$\frac{R_R}{X_R} = \frac{0.25}{1.5} = 0.1667$$

Maximum torque occurs at a value of slip given by R_R/X_R. This is clearly not a rigorous proof of the relationship, but the result is a valid one.

STARTING METHODS FOR CAGE MACHINES

1 Direct on line Cage motors may be started by connecting them directly to the supply employing a circuit breaker or contactor. The current input to the motor during the period taken for it to attain full speed is large being typically between five and eight times the normal full load value. Such a large current flowing in the power supply transformer and distribution network can cause an unacceptable reduction in supply voltage to other consumers. In an extreme case it might be envisaged that the voltage could fall to such a value as to affect the current input to the motor itself, substantially increasing the run-up time. Despite the extremely large current, the power input is not proportionally large resulting in a poor starting torque. This is due to the poor starting power factor.

$$\text{Power factor} = \cos\phi = \frac{R_R}{Z_R} = \frac{R_R}{\sqrt{R_R^2 + (SX_R)^2}}$$

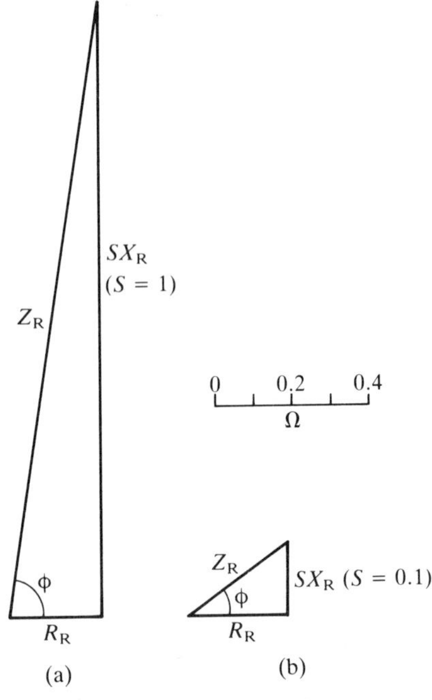

Figure 3.7

Using the data from *Example 3*, $R_R = 0.25\ \Omega$ and $X_R = 1.5\ \Omega$. Then using $S = 1$ for starting (standstill) conditions:

$$\text{Power factor at standstill} = \frac{0.25}{\sqrt{0.25^2 + 1.5^2}} = 0.164$$

As the motor runs up to speed the value of slip decreases so that (SX_R) decreases causing the power factor to improve.

Figure 3.7 shows the impedance triangles for the induction motor rotor for two conditions.

In some circumstances direct-on-line starting is acceptable, for example a motor in a factory which is fed from its own, probably large, supply transformer. The high current is supplied without causing undue voltage drop or affecting other consumers. Elsewhere, where the distribution system is less robust, small motors with correspondingly low starting current requirements and a short run-up times may be started direct on line, the limit on size can only be determined by the effect on the electrical system.

2 Star-delta starting The motor is started with the stator windings connected in star then when the rotor is close to full speed, they are reconnected in delta.

In *Figure 3.8*, the main contactor is closed together with contactor S which provides a star point. The motor runs up to speed connected in star when contactor S is opened. Contactor D is closed which joins winding starts to finishes in sequence and each winding across the line voltage so creating the delta connection. Contactors S and D

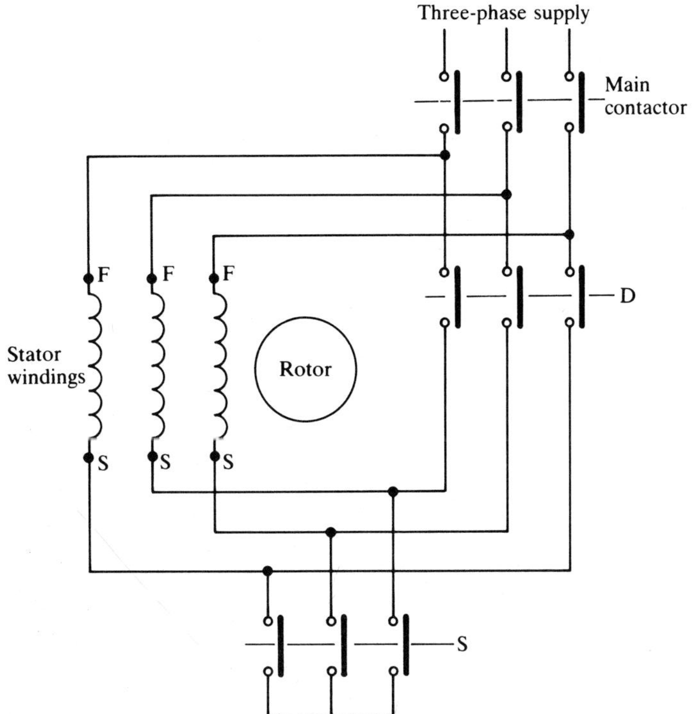

Figure 3.8

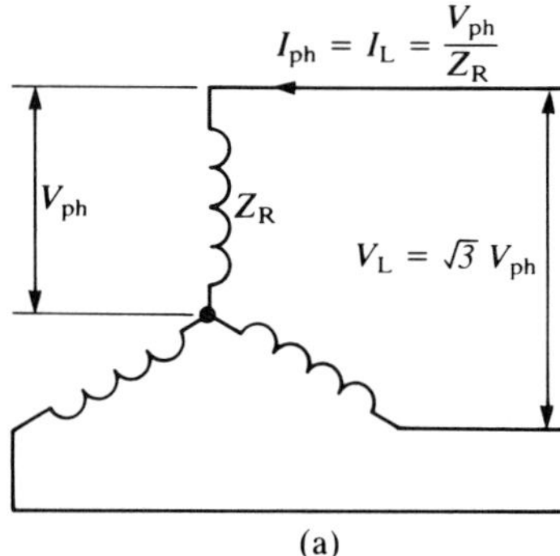

(a)

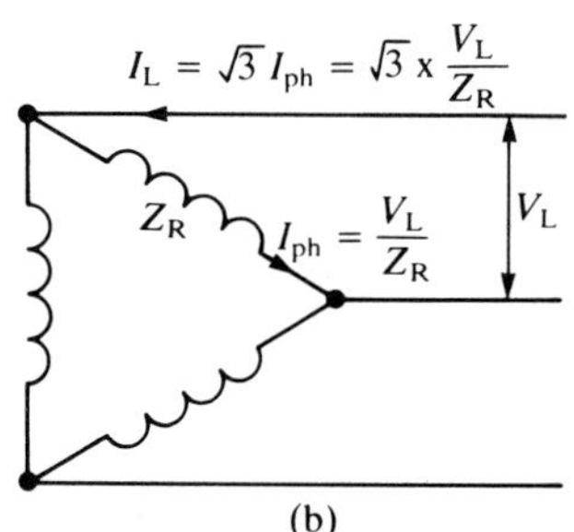

(b)

Figure 3.9

have to be interlocked to ensure that it is impossible to close both simultaneously. This method of starting reduces the current inrush and starting torque in proportion.

With reference to *Figure 3.9*:

Given a motor with standstill impedance Z_R Ω/phase

When started in star the phase current $= \dfrac{V_{phase}}{Z_R}$ A

In a star-connected system, $I_{phase} = I_{line}$

Starting the motor in delta the line voltage is applied to each phase winding.

$$I_{phase} = \frac{V_{line}}{Z_R} \text{ A}$$

In a delta-connected system, $I_{line} = \sqrt{3} \times I_{phase}$ and $V_{line} = \sqrt{3} \times V_{phase}$

$$\therefore I_{line} = \frac{\sqrt{3} \times V_{line}}{Z_R} = \frac{\sqrt{3} \times \sqrt{3} \times V_{phase}}{Z_R} \text{ A}$$

$$\frac{I_{line}(\text{starting in star})}{I_{line}(\text{starting in delta})} = \frac{V_{phase}/Z_R}{\sqrt{3} \times \sqrt{3} \times V_{phase}/Z_R} = \frac{1}{3}$$

By starting the motor in star the current inrush is reduced to one third of the value which would be drawn by the motor if started in delta. This reduction in current brings about a corresponding reduction in input power and hence torque. Using this method of starting the starting torque of the motor is only one third of what it would have been if started while connected in delta. The delta-connected starting torque is itself small (see *Figure 3.6*) so that this method of starting must be limited to motors which can be started off load.

The method of starting illustrated in *Figure 3.8* can give rise to current and voltage surges as contactor S is opened and contactor D is closed. This is because of the inductances of stator and rotor in which, as the currents change, voltages may be induced giving rise to excessive currents sometimes larger than those which would have

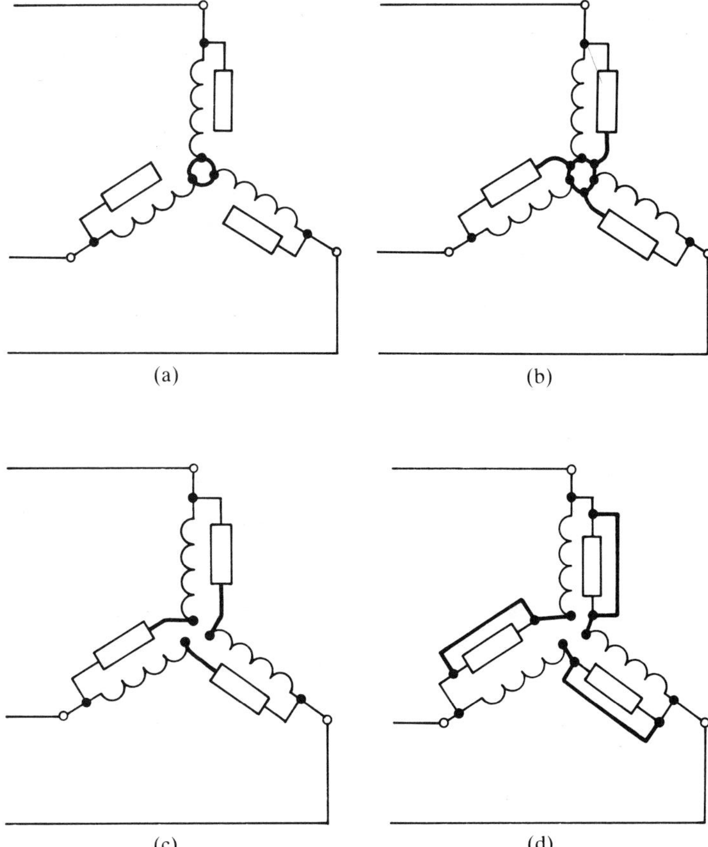

Figure 3.10

occurred employing direct-on-line starting. A better arrangement for large motors is shown schematically in *Figure 3.10.*

Figure 3.10(a) shows that the supply is connected to the motor while a contactor forms a star point at the centre of the diagram. *Figure 3.10(b)* shows further contactors connect external resistances in parallel with the motor windings which are still in star. *Figure 3.10(c)* shows further contactor operation results in each of the motor windings being connected in series with a resistor giving a delta formation and *Figure 3.10(d)* shows the resistors are shorted out leaving the motor windings connected in delta. The method gives a smooth transition from the star to the delta configuration without disconnecting the windings at any time.

3 Auto-transformer starting With star/delta starting the stand-still current inrush was reduced by re-connecting the windings so that the voltage on each was less than the normal running value when connected in delta. The reduction in voltage could only be that value dictated by the phase/line voltage relationship, i.e. $\sqrt{3}$ or 1.732.

With the auto-transformer method, the motor remains connected in delta at all times while the reduction in voltage is achieved by the use of the transformer.

In *Figure 3.11*, the auto-transformer is star connected. Its output voltage per phase is V_s so that the output line voltage which is applied to the motor is $\sqrt{3} \times V_s$ volts which is called V_m. When starting, the contactor is switched to the position shown in *Figure 3.11*. When the motor approaches full speed the contacts are moved to the top (run) position. The motor is now directly connected to the supply, the transformer being redundant. The transformer tapping may be adjusted to give any starting voltage required. As with star–delta starting it should be observed that a reduction in voltage with its corresponding reduction in current gives reduced starting torque.

In the motor, $I_{phase} = \dfrac{V_m}{Z_R}$ A and $I_{line} = \dfrac{\sqrt{3} \times V_m}{Z_R}$ A

The transformer voltage ratio $= \dfrac{V_L}{V_m} : 1$

$\therefore$ current ratio (inverse to voltage ratio) $= \dfrac{V_m}{V_L} : 1$

Hence, line input current to the transformer $= \dfrac{V_m}{V_L} \times \dfrac{\sqrt{3}\, V_m}{Z_R} = \dfrac{\sqrt{3}\, V_m^2}{V_L Z_R}$ A

When started direct on line, the input line current $= \dfrac{\sqrt{3}\, V_L}{Z_R}$ A (see *Figure 3.9*)

$$\frac{\text{Line input to the auto transformer}}{\text{Line input to motor, direct on line}} = \frac{\dfrac{\sqrt{3}\, V_m^2}{V_L Z_R}}{\dfrac{\sqrt{3}\, V_L}{Z_R}}$$

$$= \frac{V_m^2}{V_L^2}$$

With this type of starting, the current inrush to the auto transformer is V_m^2/V_L^2 times that which would flow in the same motor if it were started direct on line. The power input to the motor is reduced in the same proportion as is the starting torque. This method is therefore only suitable for off load starting of induction motors.

STARTING THE WOUND ROTOR INDUCTION MOTOR

See *Figure 3.2* and the section on 'Construction'.

Using this type of motor provides for starting against a large load torque while limiting the current inrush. It also considerably improves the starting power factor as compared with that achieved by the methods for starting cage machines described above.

In *Example 3* the relationship between rotor resistance R_R, rotor reactance SX_R and torque was briefly examined. Maximum torque is developed by an induction motor when the relationship $R_R = SX_R$ is satisfied. The brushes running on the slip rings provide the means whereby sufficient resistance may be added to the rotor circuit to balance this equation at any value of slip. This will cause maximum torque to be developed at any particular speed between standstill and its normal slightly sub-synchronous value.

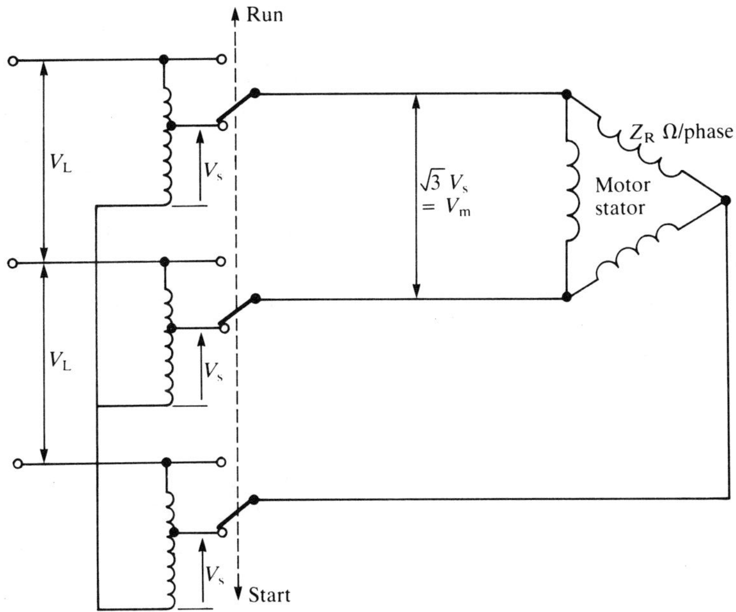

Figure 3.11

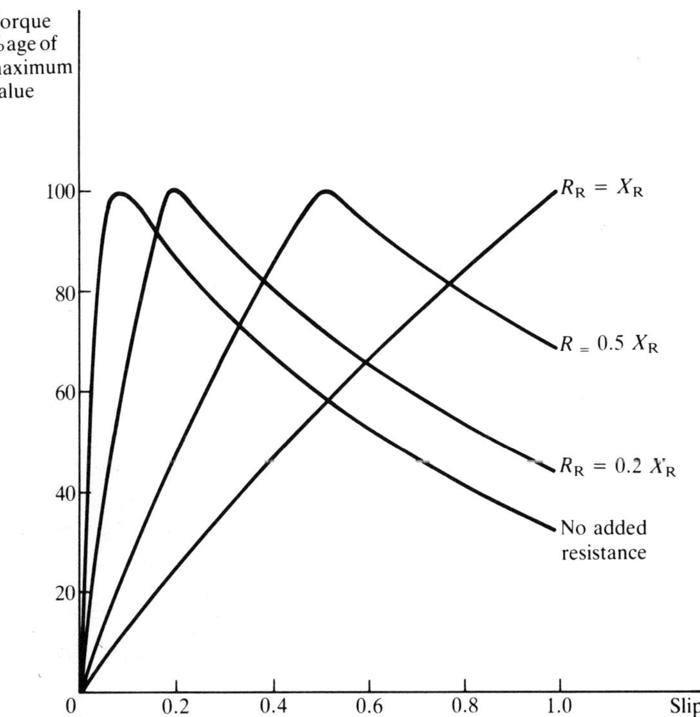

Figure 3.12

In *Figure 3.12* four possible torque/slip curves are shown. The first envisages the rotor circuit resistance being increased to match the value of the standstill reactance.

Then, since $R_R = SX_R$ for maximum torque and $R_R = X_R$, maximum torque must occur at S = 1, i.e. at standstill. The motor develops its maximum torque at starting and the characteristic is seen to be falling towards zero as the slip decreases that is to say as the motor speed increases.

With added external resistance to bring the total up to a value equal to one half of the rotor standstill reactance, for R_R to equal SX_R, the slip S must be 0.5. The same general shape of characteristic as shown in *Figure 3.6* may be plotted for this case with its maximum torque at S = 0.5.

For R_R increased to a value 0.2 times the standstill reactance, the maximum torque occurs at S = 0.2 and this curve is also shown in *Figure 3.12*. The final curve with no added resistance is that already shown in *Figure 3.6.*.

Using this method to start the motor, the stator is energised with as much resistance in the rotor circuit as is required either to give the required starting torque or to limit the inrush current to a specified level. As the motor speed increases the rotor resistance is eliminated in stages using contactors or a manual arrangement similar to a face-plate starter for a d.c. machine. A measure of speed control may also be achieved by leaving sufficient resistance in the rotor circuit to produce a given load torque at a substantially sub-synchronous speed. This is not to be recommended, however, because of the amount of energy dissipated in the resistance bank with subsequent low efficiency.

Example 4. A 50 Hz, four-pole, wound-rotor induction motor has the following parameters:
Rotor resistance $R_R = 0.1\ \Omega$/phase
Rotor standstill reactance $X_R = 0.5\ \Omega$/phase
Rotor standstill voltage $E_R = 65$ V/phase

(a) For starting purposes the rotor circuit resistance is increased to match the rotor standstill reactance. For the instant of starting (S = 1) calculate: (i) the magnitude of the rotor current/phase (ii) the rotor power factor and (iii) the torque developed by the rotor.

(b) During the run up the rotor circuit resistance is reduced to 0.25 Ω/phase. Re-calculate the values in (i), (ii) and (iii) above for S = 0.5.

(a) (i) $$I_{\text{rotor/phase}} = \frac{SE_R}{\sqrt{R_R{}^2 + (SX_R{}^2)}} = \frac{65}{\sqrt{0.5^2 + 0.5^2}} = 91.92 \text{ A}$$

(ii) $$\text{Cos}\ \phi = \frac{R_R}{Z_R} = \frac{0.5}{\sqrt{0.5^2 + 0.5^2}} = 0.707 \text{ (see } \textit{Figure 3.7}\text{)}$$

(iii) Rotor loss = $3\,I^2R_R = 3 \times 91.92^2 \times 0.5 = 12\,674$ W
At S = 1, loss = input. $n = 50/2 = 25$ rev/s

$$\text{Torque developed} = \frac{12\,674}{2\pi \times 25} = 80.68\ \text{Nm}$$

(b) (i) $I_{\text{rotor/phase}} = \dfrac{0.5 \times 65}{\sqrt{0.25^2 + (0.5 \times 0.5)^2}} = 91.92\ \text{A}$

(ii) $\text{Cos}\ \phi = \dfrac{0.25}{\sqrt{0.25^2 + (0.5 \times 0.5)^2}} = 0.707$

(iii) Rotor loss = $3 \times 91.92^2 \times 0.25 = 6337$ W

$$\text{Rotor input} = \frac{\text{loss}}{S}$$

$$\frac{6337}{0.5} = 12\,674\ \text{W}$$

$$\text{Torque developed} = \frac{12\,674}{2\pi \times 25} = 80.68\ \text{Nm}$$

This example demonstrates that by making reductions in the rotor circuit resistance as the motor runs up to speed, the current, power factor and torque may be maintained at substantially constant values.

DOUBLE-CAGE MACHINES

In order to combine the advantages of the cage machine in that it needs no electrical connections to its rotor with those of the wound rotor machine which develops high torque at starting various different arrangements of rotor bars have been developed. One of these arrangements involves the use of two separate cages and is called the *Boucherot* rotor.

From Faraday, we have the formula: induced e.m.f. $e = \dfrac{N\Delta\Phi}{\Delta t}$ volts

We have also a formula for the induced e.m.f. in terms of inductance:

$$e = L\frac{\Delta i}{\Delta t}\ \text{V}$$

$\therefore L\dfrac{\Delta i}{\Delta t} = \dfrac{N\Delta\Phi}{\Delta t}$ And cross multiplying; $L = \dfrac{N\Delta\Phi \times \Delta t}{\Delta i \times \Delta t} = \dfrac{N\Delta\Phi}{\Delta i}$ H

Where N = number of turns
$\Delta\Phi$ = flux change in webers
Δt = time interval in seconds
Δi = change in current
L = inductance measured in henry

Thus, if a current changes by an increment Δi and the resulting change in flux linkages $N\Delta\Phi$ is known, the inductance of the circuit can be found.

A conductor which is surrounded with a high-permeability or low-reactance material such as steel has high inductance since, for a given conductor current a large magnetic flux is created or expressed in another way, for a given current change, the field change is large.

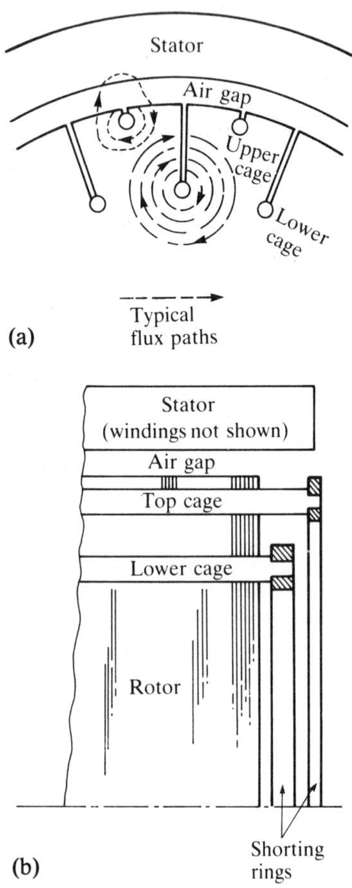

Figure 3.13

A conductor situated totally or partly in air will have a much lower inductance since air has a very much lower permeability.

Figure 3.13(a) shows the arrangement of slots in a double-cage rotor. The bottom cage is situated deep down in the steel and the flux paths are largely in the steel, having only to cross the narrow slot. Its inductance is therefore high. This cage is constructed using materials with low resistance. The flux paths associated with the current in the upper cage have to pass through a large length of air, leaving the rotor, crossing the air gap into the stator slots. This cage has low inductance and is formed using materials with relatively high resistance. The general arrangement of the bars and shorting rings is shown in *Figure 3.13(b)*.

Using typical values of resistance and reactance, the action of the rotor may be investigated.

For the top cage, $R_R = 1\,\Omega$, $X_R = 1\,\Omega$.
For the bottom cage, $R_R = 0.2\,\Omega$, $X_R = 5\,\Omega$

Consider the rotor at standstill, $S = 1$.

The impedance of the top cage $= \sqrt{1^2 + 1^2} = 1.414\,\Omega$

The impedance of the bottom cage $= \sqrt{0.2^2 + 5^2} = 5.004\,\Omega$

Because of its lower impedance much more current will flow in the top cage than in the bottom cage. It will be observed that since $R_R = X_R$ for the top cage it will produce its maximum torque at standstill.

Now consider the speed to have risen such that $S = 0.1$.

The impedance of the top cage $= \sqrt{1^2 + (0.1 \times 1)^2} = 1.005\,\Omega$

The impedance of the bottom cage $= \sqrt{0.2^2 + (0.1 \times 5)^2} = 0.54\,\Omega$

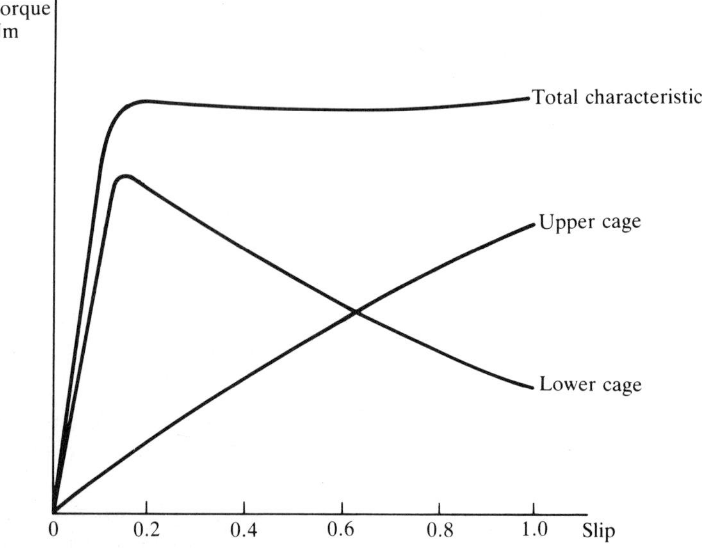

Figure 3.14

At this value of slip twice as much current flows in the bottom cage as in the top cage. As the speed increases the current in the high resistance cage decreases while that in the low resistance cage increases. The characteristic of the motor is the combination of that of a wound-rotor machine for starting changing over to that of a normal, low-resistance cage motor for running. The total characteristic is developed in *Figure 3.14*.

Motors are available with three cages employing various methods of interconnecting them resulting in differing characteristics to suit particular loads.

USES FOR INDUCTION MOTORS

Cage induction motors are used wherever a drive with virtually constant speed is required. This includes fans, pumps, compressors, conveyor drives and the range of machine tools which employ a gearbox to provide the work drive as in, for example, the centre lathe or milling machine.

Wound-rotor motors are used to start high-torque loads and to provide limited speed control. An example is the passenger lift. The rotor resistance is cut out in stages giving controlled acceleration of the cage which could be heavily loaded. Permanent low speed running of a load could be achieved using this method but is very inefficient and other methods possibly employing solid-state control would be preferable.

Multiple-cage induction motors are available which have two separate stator windings or the possibility of re-grouping the stator windings into series/parallel groups. These motors have two distinct permanent running speeds. A use is found in driving boiler forced draught fans. On loading up to say half full load the low speed winding is used, fine control being by damper. For loads beyond this and up to full load, the high-speed winding is employed again fine control being by damper.

A number of methods of controlling speed of induction motors have been developed employing solid-state electronics in particular, the thyristor and the gate turn-off thyristor (GTO). However, every development which makes this technology cheaper does the same for the control of direct-current motors which can be readily controlled from a crawl up to full speed so that the future choice of variable-speed machine types is not at all clear.

PROBLEMS

All the examples relate to three-phase machines.

5 Describe the construction of three types of induction motor rotor.

6 Why can the induction motor not run at synchronous speed?

7 What is the speed of an induction motor with eight poles when connected to a 50 Hz supply and running with a slip of 4%?

8 What is the value of slip for a six-pole induction motor connected to a 50 Hz supply when it is running at 16 rev/s?

9 What is the frequency of the currents in the rotor of a four-pole induction motor connected to a 60 Hz supply when it is running at a speed of 28.5 rev/s?

10 A six-pole induction motor connected to a 50 Hz system runs with 3% slip. It develops a torque of 53 Nm. Determine: (i) the power being transferred across the air gap from the stator to the rotor and (ii) the shaft power.

11 Sketch the torque/slip characteristics of induction motors with the following parameters:
(i) $R_R = 0.1\,\Omega$, $X_R = 0.4\,\Omega$
(ii) $R_R = 0.5\,\Omega$, $X_R = 0.5\,\Omega$
(iii) $R_R = 0.25\,\Omega$, $X_R = 0.6\,\Omega$

12 Explain why the rotor power factor of a cage machine improves as the rotor runs up from standstill to near synchronous.

13 What are the advantages of using a wound-rotor induction machine over a cage machine?

14 Describe two methods of starting cage induction motors which reduce the starting current inrush. What possible disadvantage is there in using these methods?

15 An eight-pole induction motor connected to a 50 Hz supply has the following parameters:
Standstill rotor voltage per phase, $E_R = 53$ V
Rotor resistance per phase, $R_R = 0.08\,\Omega$
Rotor standstill reactance per phase, $X_R = 0.42\,\Omega$.
Determine, for a slip of 5%, (i) the rotor power factor (ii) the torque developed by the shaft.

16 An induction motor develops a starting torque of 146 Nm when started direct on line with its stator windings connected in delta. What would be the expected values of starting torque if started: (i) using the star/delta method and (ii) using an auto transformer giving a line voltage ratio of 415 V/375 V.

17 What advantages has a multiple-cage induction motor over a single-cage machine?

18 What advantages has a multiple-cage induction motor over a wound-rotor machine?

4 Small motors

Aims: At the end of this chapter you should be able to:

Describe the construction of the single-phase induction motor and explain how rotation is obtained using only a single phase supply.

Discuss the applications and limitations of the shaded pole and universal commutator motors.

Describe the construction and operation of three types of stepper motor.

Describe the construction of permanent magnet and printed circuit d.c. motors.

THE SINGLE-PHASE INDUCTION MOTOR

The rotor of the three-phase induction motor turns due to the torque produced by the interaction between its cage and the rotating magnetic field set up by the stator windings. The magnetic field associated with a coil carrying current derived from a single-phase supply only pulsates; it builds up in one direction as the current increases during a positive half cycle, dies away to zero and then builds up with opposite polarity and decays as the negative half cycle progresses.

To understand how the single-phase induction motor functions it is necessary to examine the magnetic field set up by a two-phase

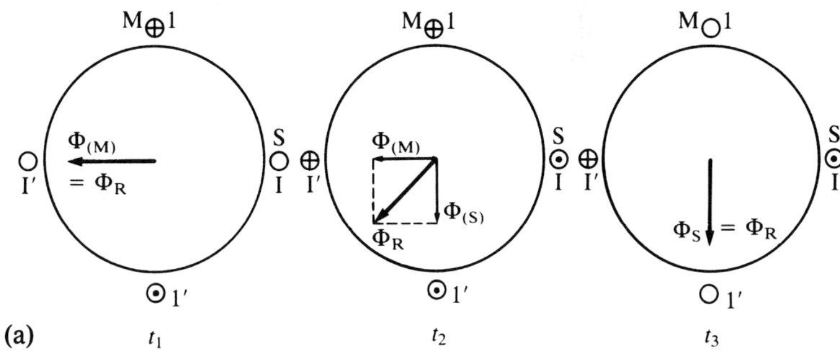

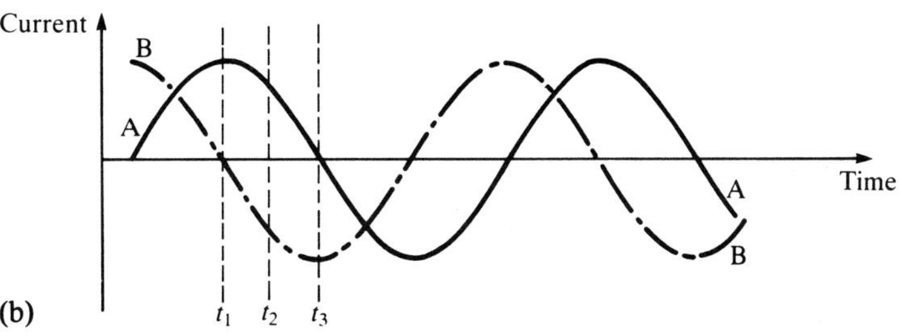

Figure 4.1

system. Such a system has two voltages which, instead of the 120° displacement associated with a three-phase system, are displaced by only 90°.

Consider these two voltages driving current waves labelled A and B as shown in *Figure 4.1(b)*. Current wave B leads current wave A by 90° since as wave A is passing through a zero going positive, wave B is already at its maximum positive value. An induction motor stator in basic form with slots reduced to only four in number is shown in *Figure 4.1(a)* for three time instants, t_1, t_2 and t_3. The top and bottom slot carries one coil marked M, starting on 1 and returning through 1′. The left- and right-hand slots carry one coil marked S, starting on 1 and returning on 1′. Coil M is fed with current wave A and coil S with current wave B.

During positive half cycles current enters coil side 1 and leaves by 1′. During negative half cycles current enters coil side 1′ and leaves by 1.

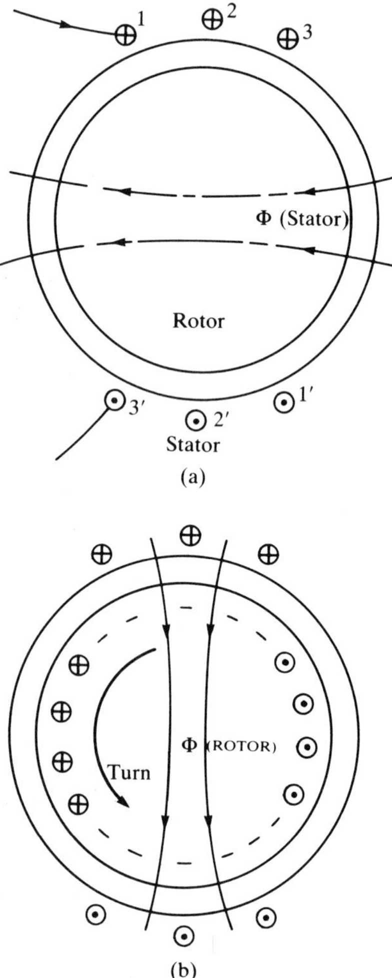

Figure 4.2

At time instant t_1 current A is at its maximum value positive. The magnetic field will be at right angles to the plane of the coil, and using the right hand grip or screw rule its polarity can be deduced as being north pole to the left. Current A is zero at this instant and coil S carries no current. The resultant field Φ_R is equal to $\Phi_M + 0$).

At time instant t_2, current A has a magnitude of 0.707 of its maximum value, still positive while the current B has a magnitude of 0.707 of its maximum value but negative so that current enters on S, 1′ and leaves on 1. The two resulting magnetic fields are shown in *Figure 4.1(a)*: (t_2). The flux phasors are drawn 0.707 times as long as that for time t_1, the resultant flux being $\Phi_R = (\Phi_M + \Phi_S)$ which it will be observed is the same length as that at time instant t_1.

At time instant t_3, current B has a maximum negative value while current A is zero. Current enters S, 1_1 and leaves on S, 1 creating a north pole vertically downwards. Current A is zero and so produces no flux. At this instant, the resultant field $\Phi_R = (\Phi_S + 0)$.

Between time instant t_1 and t_3 the waveforms have progressed by 90° and the resultant flux phasor has moved through 90°. Although only three particular instants have been chosen, any other instants would yield a resultant flux of the same magnitude. The flux phasor rotates within the stator at synchronous speed and with constant magnitude.

A laminated induction motor stator carrying only one winding is shown in *Figure 4.2(a)*. Applying a single-phase voltage to this winding will cause an alternating current to flow and a pulsating magnetic flux will be set up as shown. As current enters on 1 and leaves on 3′ the lines of magnetic force will be directed from right to left as drawn and will reverse as the current reverses.

A cage rotor will have currents induced in its bars in such a direction as to create an opposing flux (Lenz's law). The interaction of these fluxes will cause the rotor to vibrate but there will be no rotational effort. If, however, the rotor is turned by external means, the rotor bars cut the stator-created flux. Voltages will be induced in the bars and rotor current will flow resulting in a vertical magnetic field as shown in *Figure 4.2(b)*.

We now have two magnetic fields physically displaced by 90° as if they were produced by the two sets of coils shown in *Figure 4.1*. The ratio of reactance to resistance in the rotor winding is large and so the current in the rotor winding lags the induced voltage by a large angle, approaching 90°. The conditions are then almost perfectly correct to produce a rotating magnetic field, the axes of the fields are physically displaced by 90° and the phase angle between the currents is also 90° (almost). This is virtually a two phase system and once started, the rotor will continue to rotate and will pick up to almost synchronous speed.

The difficulty is that the rotor will run equally well in either direction and a small impulse in either direction causes it to set off. For some applications direction is not significant but in most cases correct rotation must be ensured. In addition, it may not be practical to give a starting impulse, consider owning a washing machine that needed a sharp pull on a starting handle as, for example, with a petrol motor mower.

THE SPLIT-PHASE SINGLE-PHASE MOTOR

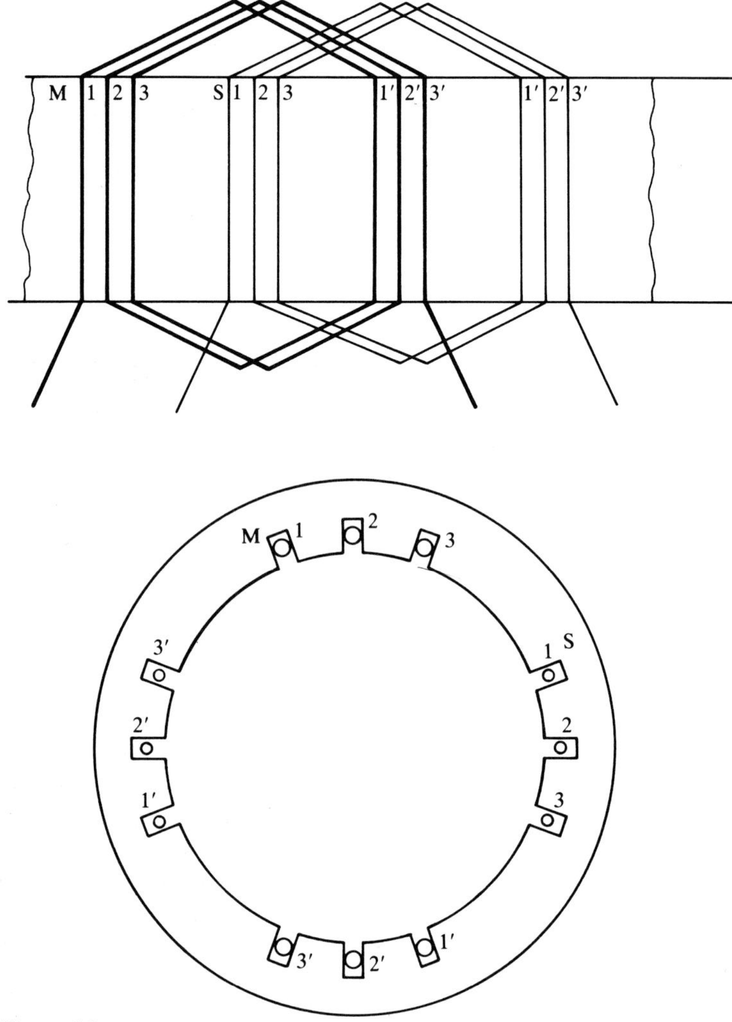

Figure 4.3

One method of starting the single-phase machine is to wind the stator as a two-phase machine. In *Figure 4.3* the *M* or *main winding* has three coils marked 1, 1′, 2, 2′ and 3, 3′ which are formed using relatively large diameter wire. The resistances of these coils will be low while their reactances at standstill will be fairly large. The phase angle between the applied voltage and the current in the M winding will be quite large as indicated in *Figure 4.4*. The S or *start winding* with coils similarly marked is formed using smaller-diameter wire so that their resistances are higher and the associated phase angle will be smaller. The actual physical displacement between the two sets of coils is 90° and the phase displacement between the two currents I_{START} and I_{MAIN} while not ideal, is sufficient to give some torque and the motor will start in the correct direction. Once started, because of the small diameter of the start winding conductors which would therefore rapidly overheat, and because of the non-ideal phase displacement which would give very uneven torque, the start winding must be disconnected once the rotor has commenced to turn.

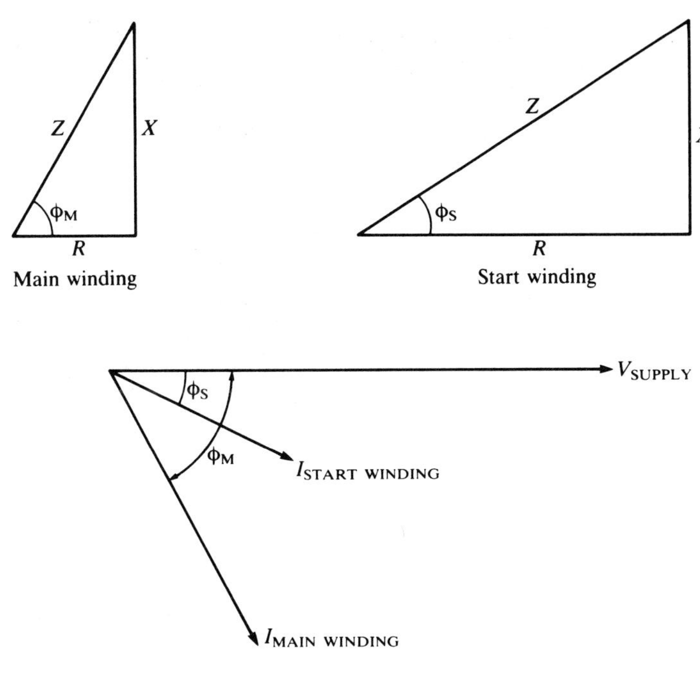

Standstill phasor diagram

Figure 4.4

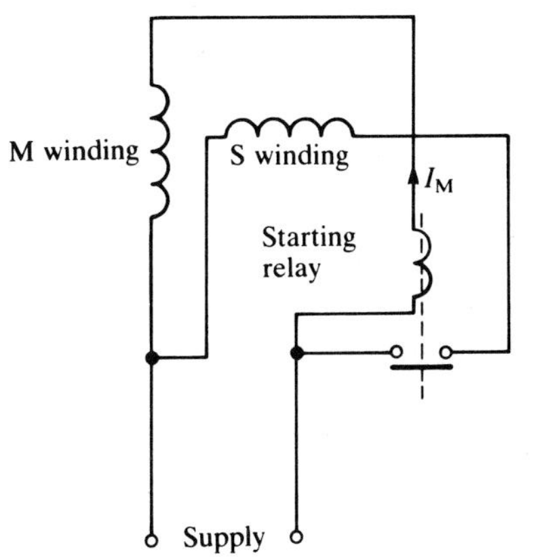

Figure 4.5

This may be achieved by means of a centrifugal switch mounted on the end of the rotor. One or more small metal weights are attached to a ring fixed to the shaft. Springs maintain these weights in a particular position while the rotor is stationary. A pair of fixed contacts on the motor casing which are closed while the motor is stationary or running at low speed are opened as the weights are displaced by the centrifugal force created by the accelerating rotor. This mechanism interrupts the current in the start winding as the rotor approaches full speed. There are various patented methods of ensuring that the switch operates with a snap action so avoiding undue contact burning.

An alternative method used in refrigerators where the motor is immersed in the refrigerant fluid employs an external solenoid.

This is shown in *Figure 4.5*. The main supply is switched on to the circuit using a thermostat when the current inrush to the main winding of the stationary motor is large enough to pull on the starting relay. This energises the start winding. As the motor runs up to speed, the current in the main winding and starting relay falls and at a preset value the starting relay drops off so interrupting the current to the start winding. The relay is external to the motor and is mounted on the refrigerator chassis which makes for easy replacement without depressurising the refrigerant system.

THE CAPACITOR MOTOR

If the stator shown in *Figure 4.3* is wound with two identical windings, it is possible to obtain 90° phase displacement between the two currents by connecting one of them in series with a capacitor.

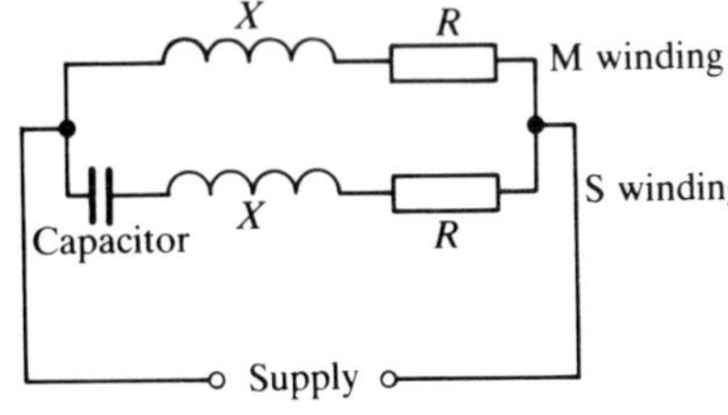

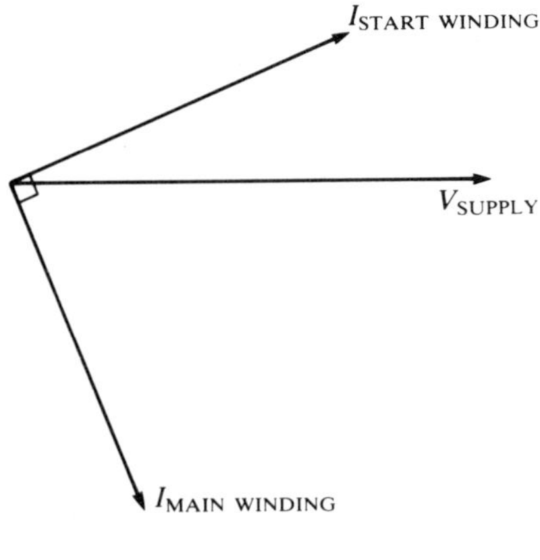

Standstill phasor diagram

Figure 4.6

The current in the main winding lags the supply voltage by a fairly large angle as in *Figure 4.6*. The capacitor in series with the start winding is slightly larger than would be required to give resonance so that the current in this winding leads the supply voltage by a small angle. At standstill, by careful choice of capacitor, the phase angle between the two currents may be made to be closely 90°. As the motor runs up to speed the phase angles and current magnitudes change and a capacitor which has the correct size for starting the motor will not maintain the ideal phase relationship between the two currents when the rotor is at full speed.

The capacitor is used in one of three ways:

(i) For starting only. The capacitor is used to give the correct phase angle between the currents during starting. Once the rotor is running, a centrifugal switch disconnects the capacitor as in the split-phase arrangement.

(ii) For starting and running. A smaller-than-ideal capacitor is permanently connected in series with S winding. The phase angle between the two winding currents is always less than the ideal value, but sufficient torque is developed to start the motor on light loads. When running, the capacitor reactance limits the current in the S winding and the running phasor diagram is similar to that of the split-phase machine at starting but with smaller currents.

(iii) For starting and running employing two capacitors.

During the run-up period two capacitors in parallel are used to give the correct phase angle in the S winding. As the rotor runs up to speed, a centrifugal switch cuts out one of the capacitors leaving the other permanently in circuit. This is of the correct size to give the ideal phase angle under full-load conditions. This type of motor, shown in *Figure 4.7*, gives good starting and running torque.

As with three-phase induction motors and alternators the synchronous speed of the single-phase induction motor is a function of the number of poles. The winding shown in *Figure 4.3* is that of a two-pole machine and its synchronous speed will be 50 rev/s when connected to a 50 Hz supply. By duplicating the winding, a four-pole machine is made with a synchronous speed of 25 rev/s. Most single-phase machines have a synchronous speed of 25 rev/s and an

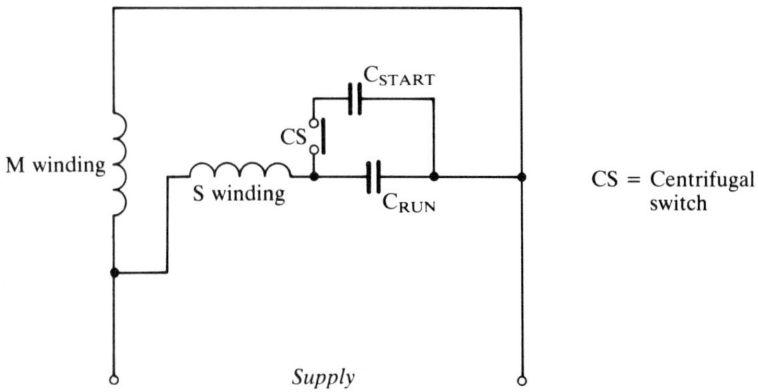

Figure 4.7

actual rotor speed of 24 rev/s. They run with greater slip than three-phase induction machines and are generally less efficient. A very few single-phase machines have been built with ratings up to 40 kW but the large majority of this type of motor have ratings of up to 1 kW.

THE SHADED-POLE MOTOR

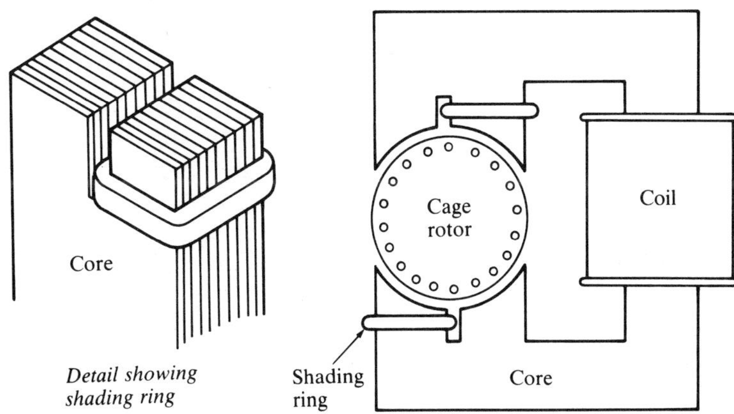

Figure 4.8

The shaded-pole, single-phase motor comprises a laminated core and a cage rotor. Each pole face carries solid heavy gauge copper ring as illustrated in basic form in *Figure 4.8*. The main coil is fed from an alternating supply, an alternating current I_{COIL} flows setting up an in-phase alternating magnetic flux Φ_{CORE}. Some of the core flux links with the shading rings inducing an e.m.f. in each of them. There is a 90° phase displacement between core flux and induced e.m.f.s as there is between the secondary e.m.f. and core flux in a transformer. The rings, having large cross section have low resistance and being near the pole face, low inductance. The induced e.m.f.s drive substantial currents in the rings producing magnetic fluxes in the shaded pole faces. There are now two distinct fluxes taking different paths: (i) that part of the core flux which bypasses the shading ring and crosses the air gap into the rotor and (ii) the flux in the shaded part of the pole. Adding that part of the main flux which passes through the shading ring to that produced by the shading ring current gives a resultant flux which differs in size and phase to that in (i).

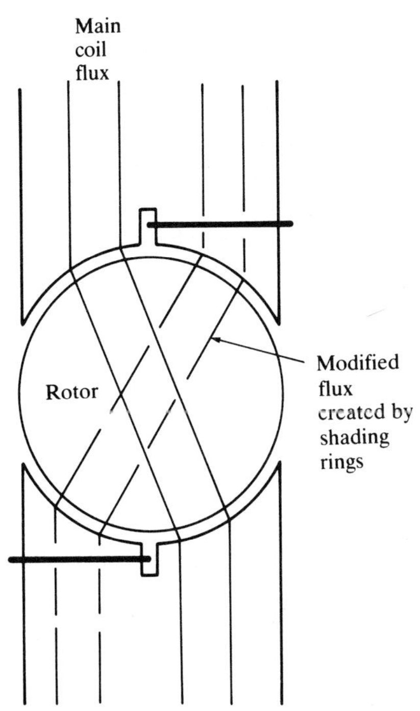

Figure 4.9

Two fluxes now link with the rotor as in the single-phase induction motor. The two fluxes are displaced physically in space and their maximum values do not occur simultaneously. Neither of these conditions is ideal, i.e. there is neither 90° physical displacement or 90° phase displacement which are the ideal conditions but some torque is produced and the rotor runs at near synchronous speed.

The two flux paths are illustrated in *Figure 4.9*. Shaded pole motors may incorporate more than one shading ring mounted on a continuous core as shown in *Figure 4.10*. The principle of action remains unchanged. Reducing the cross-sectional area of the steel next to the shading ring increases the reluctance at this point so diverting the flux into the rotor.

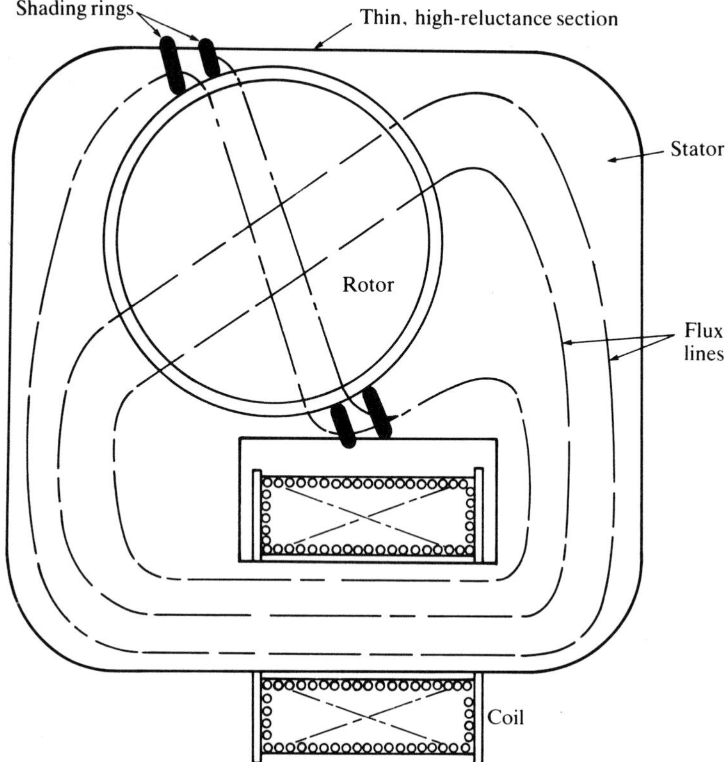

Figure 4.10

Shaded pole motors have ratings of up to a few tens of watts. They develop low torques and are not very efficient but with very small ratings this is not a major consideration. They are used to drive small devices such as cooling fans associated with high-power electrical and electronic equipment. Many are to be found in cheaper record players, which take advantage of their very simple construction and virtually constant speed at the low loading encountered. However, where very precise speed limits are imposed and a measure of speed control is required they are not ideal.

THE UNIVERSAL COMMUTATOR MOTOR

The name universal is applied to a series-connected motor which will run equally well when connected to direct or alternating supplies. When an alternating supply is used there are problems with commutation and the speed is slightly lower than on d.c. because the current is limited by the winding inductance. Again, because of inductance, at maximum torque the current tends to stabilise at a fairly-low maximum value even if the armature stalls making fuse protection against overload impossible. Only a thermal protective device will give adequate protection against overload. The general arrangement is shown in *Figure 4.11*, and characteristics in *Figure 4.12*.

The problems with commutation occur because the armature not only performs as in the direct-current motor but with alternating

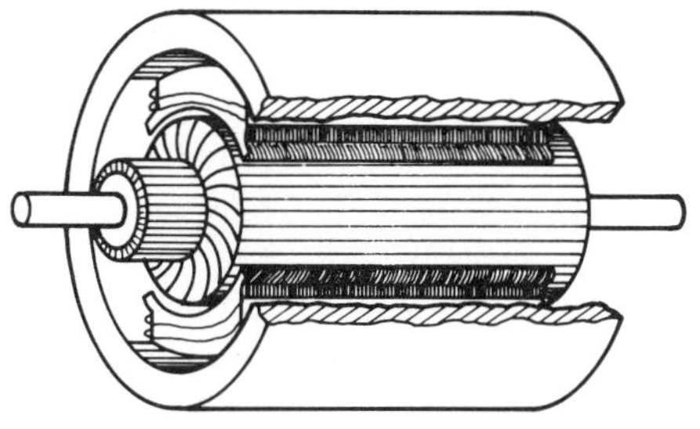

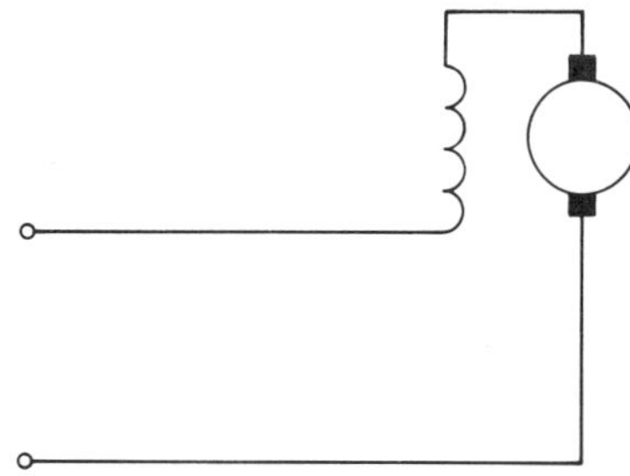

Figure 4.11

current flowing in the field coils, the armature is, in effect, a secondary of a transformer, the field coils being its primary. In the d.c. machine the brushes are placed on or close to the neutral axis so that coils undergoing commutation are outside the influence of the magnetic field in which position they have no e.m.f. induced in them. This gives virtually spark-free operation. With the same motor fed with alternating current, the coil on the neutral axis; coil A, A′ in *Figure 4.13*; has the maximum transformer-induced e.m.f. of any coil on the armature since all the flux links with (passes through) it. Generally the result of this is severe sparking at the brushes. Moving the brushes back so that the coil undergoing commutation is under the influence of the pole flux causes the e.m.f. due to rotation to overcome the transformer e.m.f. in part. Wherever the brushes are placed, there is always some degree of sparking and because of this a

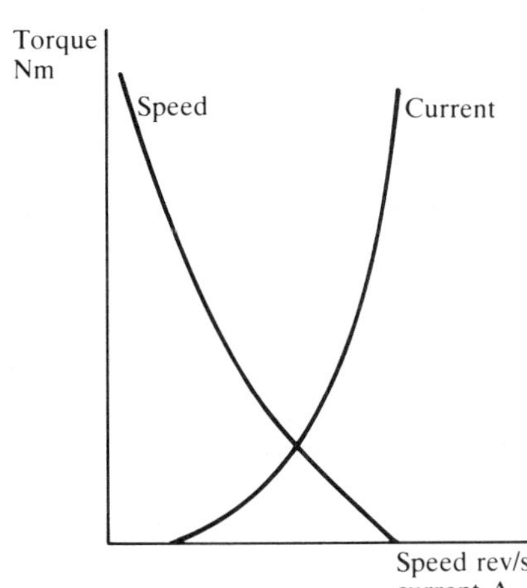

Figure 4.12

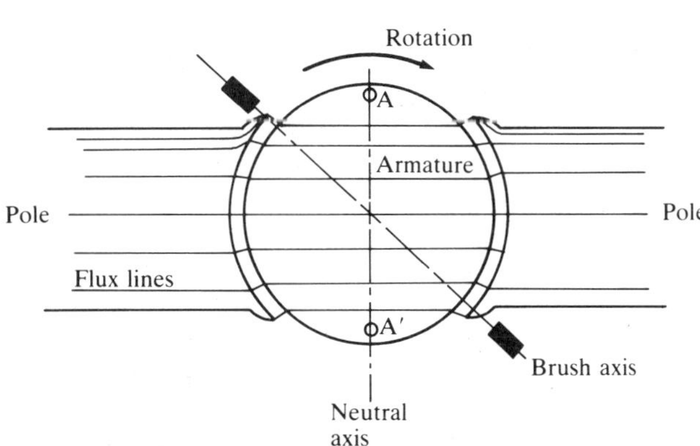

Figure 4.13

radio interference suppression system must always be fitted to this type of motor.

Universal motors run with typical light load speeds of 12 000 to 18 000 rev/min and have powers of a few hundred watts. The speed falls rapidly with increasing torque. They are most often found in equipments which are only required to run intermittently as, for example, in vacuum cleaners, where the fan is driven directly by the motor and in home workshop equipment such as drills, sanders and jigsaws which are driven through a gear train to achieve a more suitable lower speed.

THE STEPPER MOTOR

For some applications not only is it necessary to be able to control the speed of the drive accurately but the actual position of the motor rotor has to be known at any precise instant. As an example, consider a machine tool which is required to cut a series of teeth in a gear wheel. The gear blank could be turned or indexed from one cutting position to the next using an electric motor. A very basic arrangement is shown in *Figure 4.14*.

Using, for example, an induction motor, the contactor would be energised, the motor run up to speed moving the work probably through a reduction gear. When the work was in its new position, the contactor would be opened and a brake applied to the drive

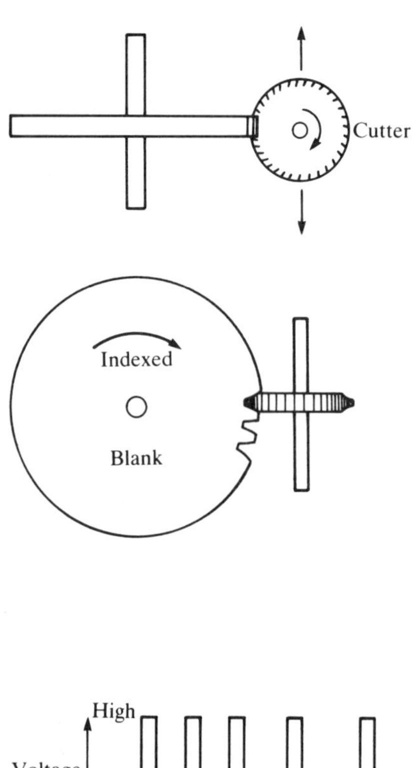

Figure 4.14

motor to bring it to rest. How many revolutions would the motor run on before stopping? This would depend on the mass of the work and motor rotor and the state of the braking system. Some form of feedback would be required, for example an operator who would have to make measurements and move the work back and forth a little until the precise position was obtained. A more sophisticated method would employ an electrical transducer to measure the position of the gear blank and feed back an error signal to the motor drive so making it self correcting.

A stepper motor moves its rotor in precisely known intervals, typically 1.8°, 2.5°, 3.75°, 7.5°, 15° or 30°. It is fed from a digital system as, for example, a microcomputer. In the example envisaged, if the interval between the teeth was say 15° then driving the work with a stepper motor would enable the work to be moved through precisely 15° by giving the motor the required number of pulses. There would be no need for any form of feedback, the position of the rotor and work being known exactly at any instant by counting the number of pulses given to the motor. Stepper motors may be made to revolve continuously by providing a continuous train of pulses. When the time comes to stop, provided that the motor has been able to develop sufficient torque to respond to every pulse, the exact number of revolutions made and the final position of the rotor will be precisely known.

Most manufacturers have adopted their own particular system so that there are many different types of stepper motor each with its own controller. It is only possible to examine the principles from which they have been developed.

TYPES OF STEPPER MOTOR

There are three basic types of stepper motor:

(i) The permanent magnet type.
(ii) The variable reluctance type.
(iii) The hybrid type which combines elements of types (i) and (ii).

The permanent magnet stepper motor

The arrangement of a four-pole permanent-magnet stepper motor is shown in *Figure 4.15*. The stator has eight poles and they are wound in pairs with coils which carry pulses of direct current. Coils on poles 1 and 1′ are connected in series as are those on 2 and 2′, 3 and 3′, and 4 and 4′. Poles 1 and 1′ are shown in *Figure 4.16*. When coil-end 1 is positive with respect to 1′ the current flow is as shown and two north poles are produced. Making 1′ positive with respect to 1 reverses the current flow and two south poles are produced.

The rotor is a permanent magnet with alternate north and south poles. The stator is not permanently energised. With no stator currents the permanent magnet rotor will lock itself into a position where its pole faces are directly facing a stator pole, a position of minimum magnetic reluctance. An externally-applied torque called the *detente torque* would be required to turn the rotor. Once in a set position it is difficult to displace the rotor by external means.

Now consider supplying the stator coils with currents to create the pole arrangement shown in *Figure 4.15(a)*. Look at poles 1 and 2, for example. They are both north and the rotor south pole will be

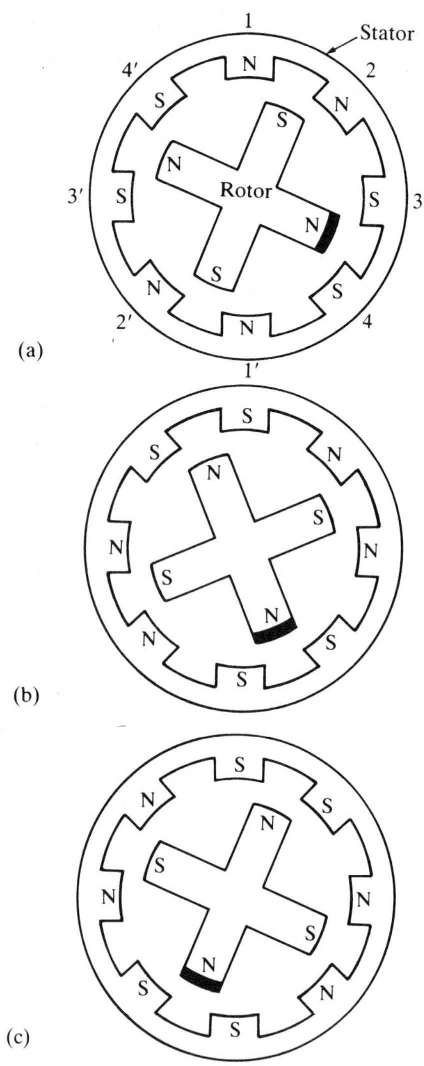

Figure 4.15

attracted towards both of them. It will settle in the mid position as drawn. This will be strongly held, great external effort would be required to upset this condition. All the other poles are creating the same effect. Now the currents are changed to produce the pole arrangement in *Figure 4.15(b)*. Pole 1 now has south polarity and this will repel the permanent-magnet south pole which was locked to it in *Figure 4.15(a)*. The rotor moves to its new position where once again it is stable. A final position is examined in *Figure 4.15(c)*. The new polarities on the stator causes the rotor to move to a further stable position. Each polarity change on the stator causes the rotor to move 45°.

For continuous rotation the sequence is continued and a table of the terminal conditions follows. Remember that when the coils 1, 2, 3 and 4 are at high positive potential, indicated by 1, north poles are produced. When 1′, 2′, 3′ and 4′ are at positive potentials, 1 south

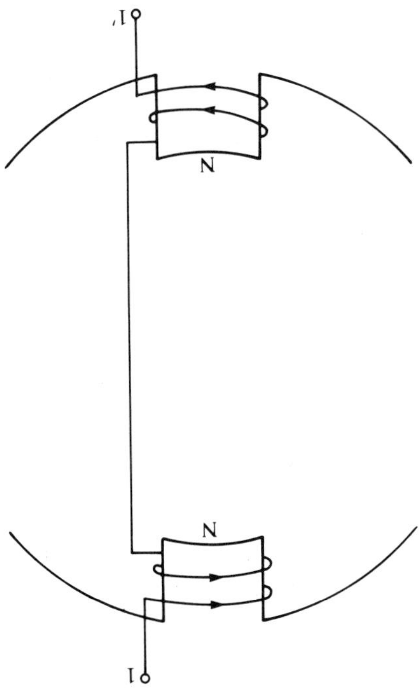

Figure 4.16

poles are produced. A 0 indicates that the connection is at zero potential or grounded.

Table 4.1 *Terminal conditions for the permanent magnet stepper motor*

Terminal number	*State: 1 = energised(+ve) 0 = grounded*									
Sequence:	*1*	*2*	*3*	*4*	*5*	*6*	*7*	*8*	*9*	*10*
1	1	0	0	1	1	0	0	1	1	0
2	1	1	0	0	1	1	0	0	1	1
3	0	1	1	0	0	1	1	0	0	1
4	0	0	1	1	0	0	1	1	0	0
1′	0	1	1	0	0	1	1	0	0	1
2′	0	0	1	1	0	0	1	1	0	0
3′	1	0	0	1	1	0	0	1	1	0
4′	1	1	0	0	1	1	0	0	1	1

Because each rotor pole is opposite one stator pole face when the stator is de-energised whilst when operating, it moves from mid-pole position to mid-pole position, the final position of the rotor is indeterminate by one half pole pitch. If the last pulse provided brought the rotor to the position in *Figure 4.15(c)*, with the stator de-energised the black-tipped north pole could move on to pole 2′ or slip back to 1′. Increasing the number of poles would decrease the increments of movement so reducing the error of resolution in the final position. The variable reluctance type lends itself more readily to the use of smaller increments, the permanent magnet type being more useful in making use of the large increments to obtain higher speed.

The variable-reluctance stepper motor

The variable-reluctance stepper motor has a rotor made from low-retentivity soft iron. The stator poles are wound as with the permanent-magnet motor but poles situated on a diameter will be of opposite polarity when current flows. Referring to *Figure 4.18*, with terminal 1 at a positive potential and terminal 1′ earthed the polarities will be shown. Making terminal 1′ positive and earthing terminal 1 the polarities are both reversed. Only one pair of coils is energised at a time. In *Figure 4.17(a)*, energising terminal 2 and earthing 2′ creates the poles shown and the rotor will pull into a position to give low reluctance. In this position the magnetic field will be at its strongest and considerable mechanical effort would need to be applied to the shaft to move it. Next in sequence, terminal 3 is made positive while terminal 3′ is earthed. The rotor poles will pull into a new position shown in *Figure 4.17(b)*. A final condition is shown in *Figure 4.17(c)*. Terminal 1′ is made positive while earthing terminal 1. The rotor moves on a further half-pole pitch.

Making the terminals positive in sequence around the stator while earthing all other terminals will give continuous rotation. There are twelve steps to a complete revolution. Using more poles increases the number of steps per revolution. Twelve stator poles and eight rotor poles gives twenty-four steps per revolution. This motor has no detent torque.

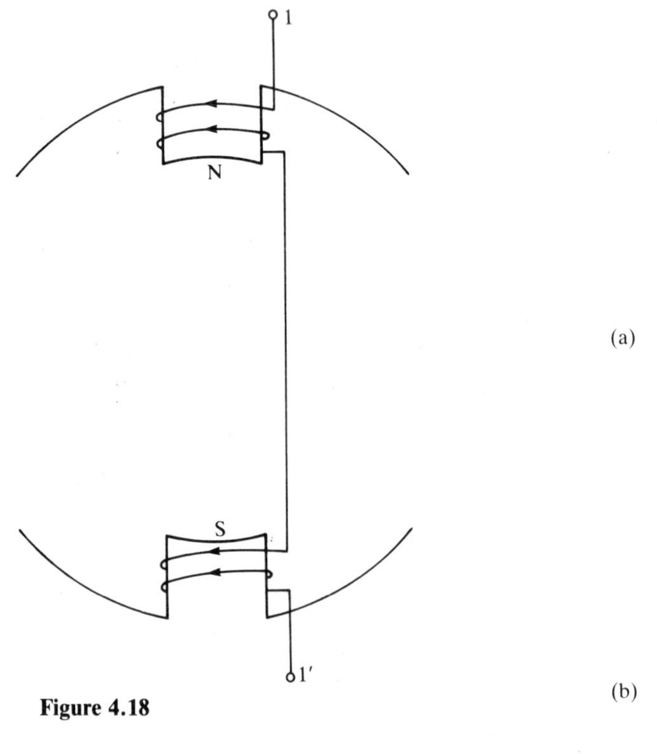

Figure 4.18

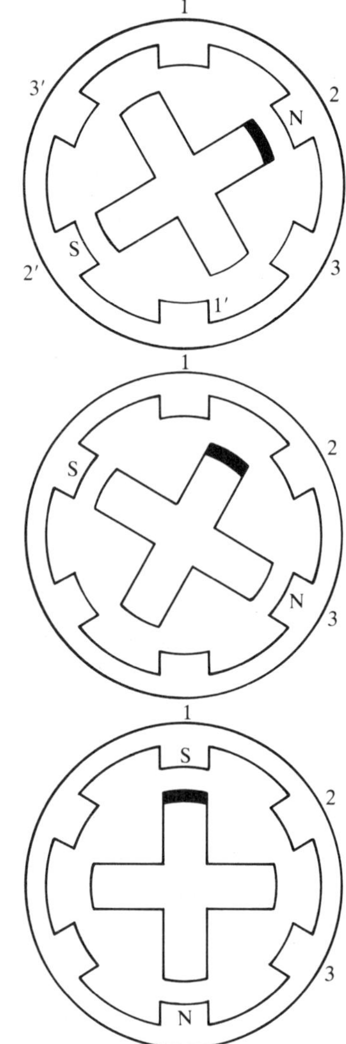

Figure 4.17

The hybrid-type stepper motor

This type makes use of a permanent-magnet rotor which sets itself up in the minimum reluctance position in response to a step input. The rotor is permanently magnetised from end to end with raised pole faces as shown in *Figure 4.19*.

Figure 4.20 shows the arrangement of the motor looking from the north-pole end of the rotor. The stator coils are arranged in two groups or phases. Phase 1 comprises coils 1, 2, 3 and 4 and these are connected in series. Phase 2 comprises coils 5, 6, 7 and 8, and these are also connected in series. Only one phase is energised at any one time. Three steps are considered.

Figure 4.20(a) shows phase 1 is energised producing the stator polarities shown. The rotor takes up its minimum reluctance position for poles 1 and 3, a north pole on the rotor being attracted by a south pole on the stator at the bottom of the motor as drawn and

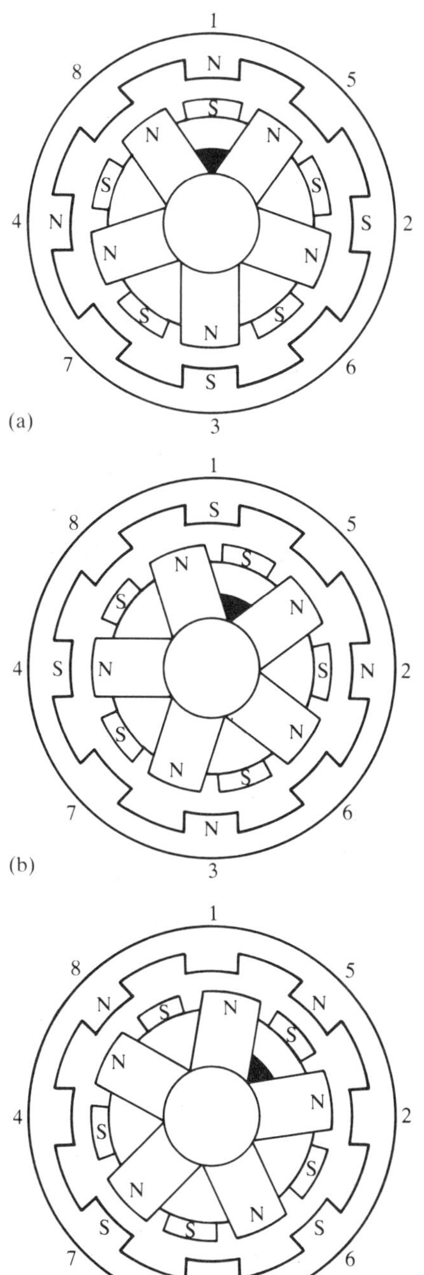

Figure 4.20

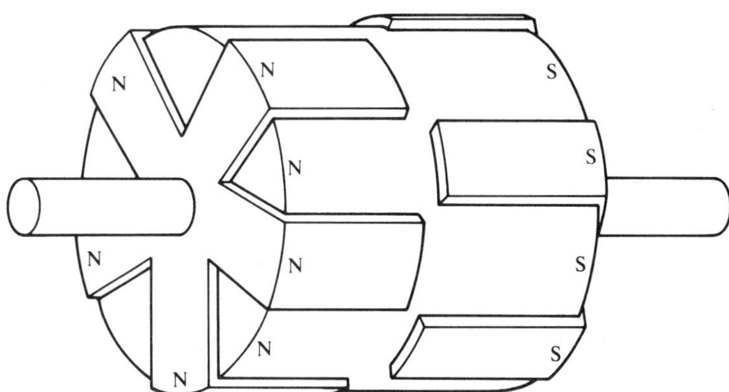

Figure 4.19

vice-versa at the top. Poles 2 and 4 are situated exactly midway between north and south poles on the rotor so attractive and repulsive forces balance; no torque is produced by this coupling.

Figure 4.20(b) shows the current in phase 1 is reversed, reversing the stator polarities. The rotor is pulled into a new position of minimum reluctance between stator poles 2 and 4. Poles 1 and 3 are now exactly midway between rotor north and south poles so there is no effective torque set up by this coupling.

Figure 4.20(c) shows phase 2 is energised producing the polarities shown. The new minimum reluctance position is between stator poles 5 and 7.

The next step is achieved by reversing the current in phase 2, which will give a minimum reluctance position across poles 6 and 8, the rotor moving a further half stator-pole pitch. Continuous rotation is maintained by repeating the current/phase sequence. Using more poles smaller steps may be achieved and steps down to 1.8° are possible.

Mounting three stepper motors on the same shaft with their rotor poles mutually displaced by one third of a pole pitch and energising them in sequence will result in much smaller steps per input pulse. As each motor is energised the rotor will advance only one third of the distance that a single motor would advance since the equilibrium position for the previous motor would be only one third of a pole pitch behind the new position.

Stepper motors are used extensively in robotics and in printers, plotters and computer disc drives all of which require precise positioning or speed.

RELUCTANCE MOTORS

We have already seen how in the stepper motors a toothed rotor will move to a position where the magnetic circuit has minimum reluctance. This principle may be applied to a number of other motors.

In the section on 'The shaded-pole motor' the effect of causing one section of pole face to carry magnetic flux out of phase with that in the rest of the pole face was discussed. A rotating magnetic field was created which caused cage rotor to develop a torque and so to

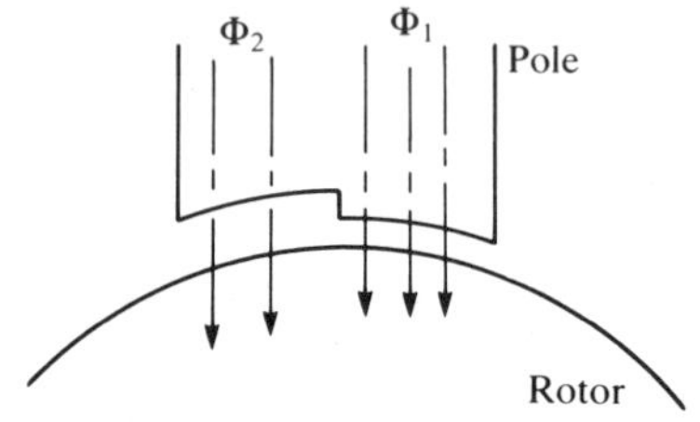

Figure 4.21

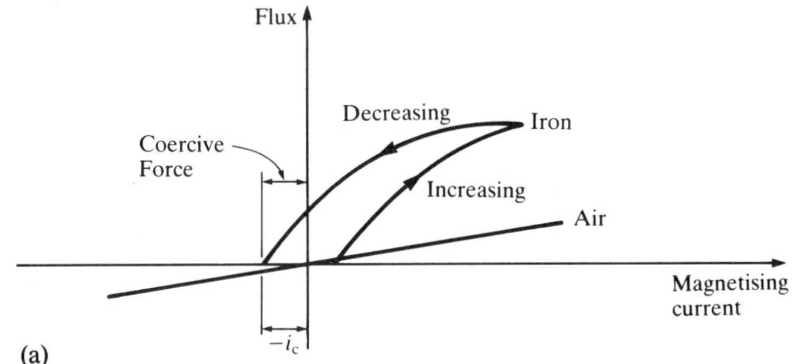

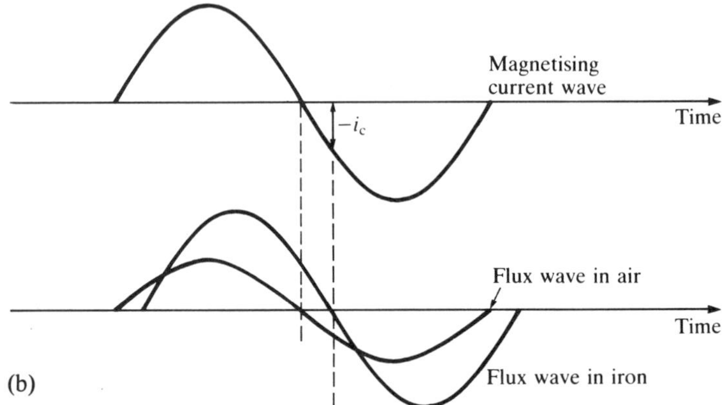

Figure 4.22

run at slightly subsynchronous speed. A similar effect may be produced by stepping the pole as shown in *Figure 4.21*. To explain the action it is necessary to look at the magnetisation characteristics for iron and air which are shown in *Figure 4.22(a)*. For soft iron, as the magnetising current increases from zero going positive, for example during a positive half cycle of an alternating current wave, the magnetic flux created rises. As the current is reduced the flux reduces but not at the same rate as it did when rising. When the magnetising current is zero there is still some remanent flux. It is not until the current has reached a slightly negative value that this coerces the flux down to zero. The coercive current is marked $-i_c$. With air this force is not required. At zero current the flux is zero. In *Figure 4.22(b)* it is seen that the flux wave passes through a zero when the current wave has reached a value $-i_c$ amperes. In air the current and flux waves pass through zero at the same time.

In *Figure 4.8*, replacing the pole with the shading ring with a stepped pole as in *Figure 4.21*, the two fluxes Φ_1 and Φ_2 will be out of phase since Φ_2 is produced in a substantially longer air gap than Φ_1. Clearly neither pole behaves exactly as described above since they both comprise air *and* iron but there is sufficient difference between the two reluctances to produce a small phase difference which causes the rotor to start. Once running rotation is maintained as in

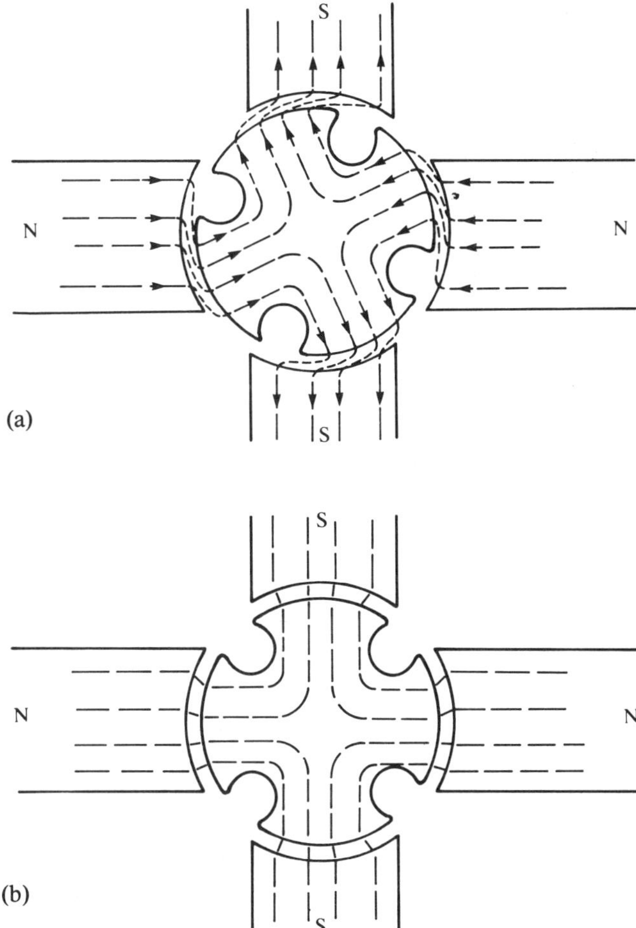

Figure 4.23

the single-phase induction motor, the rotor creating a flux of its own.

A salient pole rotor will always pull into a position of minimum reluctance as in *Figure 23(b)* when the stator poles are energised. A single- or three-phase induction motor may be made to run synchronously by removing part of the cylindrical rotor iron to form poles. The rotor needs to be of cage construction and to run up to speed using one of the methods discussed in the 'Single-Phase Induction Motor' section or in Chapter 3. Because of the tendency for flux lines to shorten, instead of the rotor always running slightly slower than the stator field producing a flux distribution as in *Figure 4.23(a)*, the rotor is pulled forward at the instant of peak flux shortening the flux lines when the salient pole centres (very nearly) on a stator pole.

The torque developed in this mode is between one quarter and one third of that produced as a normal induction motor. If torques of greater value than this are demanded the motor reverts to induction running. This is a cheap way of driving light loads at synchronous

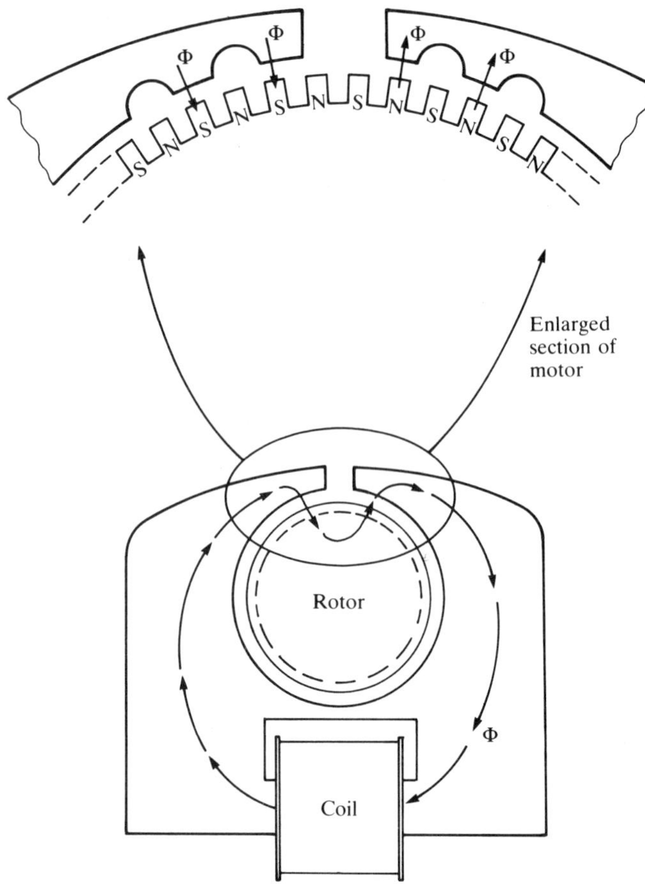

Figure 4.24

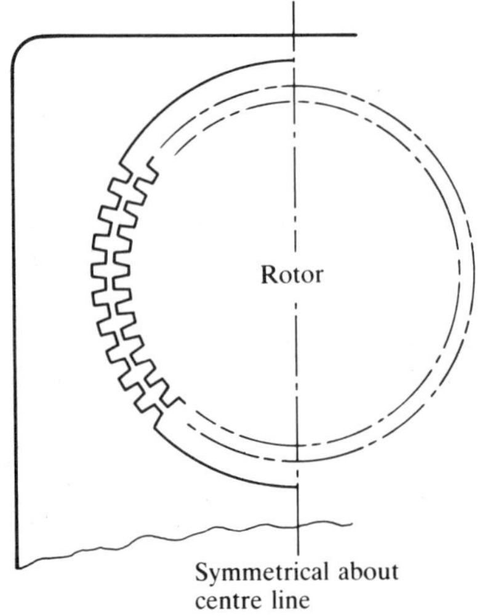

Figure 4.25

speed, there being no requirement for a wound rotor and the provision of excitation current.

Electric, mains-operated clocks operate on the reluctance principle. The rotor comprises a disc or discs which have teeth permanently magnetised with alternate polarities as shown in *Figure 4.24.*

The coil is supplied from an alternating supply. The magnetic flux set up in the core is concentrated in the narrowing ends shown in the enlarged detail in *Figure 4.24.* This effect has already been discussed when dealing with the shaded-pole motor. As drawn, during one particular half cycle of coil input, the flux enters on the left through two south poles and leaves again by two north poles on the right. Between the core and these north and south poles the air gaps are narrow, high reluctance being created over the intermediate poles by cutting out the two half circles of core metal. As the coil current reverses during the next half cycle, the flux direction reverses and the rotor is caused to move one pole pitch in either direction to allow flux to enter on the right through two south poles and leave on the left by two north poles. The rotor will continue to turn in the direction in which it sets off, one tooth per half cycle. In a clock, where rotation must be in a particular direction, there is a small ratchet attached to the rotor which allows about one half of a revolution of incorrect rotation when it comes up against a spring which absorbs the energy of rotation springing back so giving the rotor a kick in the right direction when rotation will continue.

Older, non-self starting clocks used a toothed rotor of soft iron. The general arrangement is similar to *Figure 4.24*. The rotor is spun in the correct direction using an external lever. The rotor teeth pull into line during each half cycle as illustrated in *Figure 4.23*. The core is toothed for about one quarter of its periphery on either side of the rotor as shown in part in *Figure 4.25*.

SMALL DIRECT-CURRENT MOTORS

One of the disadvantages of the single-phase induction motor is its low output and efficiency from a given frame size. In a situation where only a single-phase supply is available a considerable weight saving can be achieved by using a d.c. motor. The direct current will be derived from the alternating supply using either simple diodes or thyristors.

D.c. motors have additional advantages over the single-phase machine namely:

(i) They can deliver momentarily up to five times their normal torque without stalling provided that the power supply is adequate.

(ii) The speed can be controlled down to zero and reversed very simply.

(iii) They generally have a high torque/inertia ratio which means that they can respond very quickly to changing supply conditions.

(iv) According to connection they will have series or shunt characteristics (induction motors have shunt characteristics only.)

The mass of a d.c. machine can be reduced by substituting permanent magnet poles for wound poles in shunt machines. These will often be of ferrite material which is lighter than steel and extremely difficult to demagnetise. Such a motor is referred to as a *PM motor*.

Where extremely rapid acceleration and deceleration are required as, for example, in a servo-system, it is essential to have an armature with as near zero inertia as possible. This is achieved by creating an armature and commutator from heavy duty, double sided printed circuit board. All the armature conductors and commutator segments have very small mass and are plated directly on to the board. The diameter is kept small while increasing the length of the armature to maintain the length of working conductor. This type is called a *PC motor*.

PROBLEMS

1 Explain why it is that if a single-phase induction motor rotor commences to rotate in a particular direction, the rotor will accelerate up to near synchronous speed.

2 Describe the construction of a split-phase, single-phase

induction motor. Explain how sufficient phase displacement is obtained between the two winding currents to cause starting.

3 Describe three ways in which capacitors may be used in association with a single-phase induction motor.

4 What is the function of the centrifugal switch mounted on the shaft of some single-phase induction motors?

5 Draw a diagram showing a method of starting a single-phase induction motor using a starting relay.

6 What is the function of the shading ring in a shaded pole single-phase motor?

7 Why is the performance of a series universal motor generally less satisfactory when operated on an a.c. supply as compared with that on a d.c. supply?

8 What is the fundamental difference between the mode of operation of a stepper motor as compared with any other type of motor?

9 Describe the principle of operation of the reluctance type stepper motor.

10 How can a cage rotor induction motor be made to run at synchronous speed?

11 What are the advantages to be gained by using PM and PC motors as opposed to (a) single-phase induction motors and (b) conventional iron-yoked d.c. machines?

12 What type(s) of small motor could be selected where high starting torque is a prime requirement?

13 What type(s) of small motor could be selected where inherently constant speed is required over a fairly wide range of load torques?

14 What type(s) of small motor would be required to operate in conjunction with a digital control system in which precise positioning of a work piece is required?

15 Suggest suitable types of small motors for the following applications: (i) a desk-top fan; (ii) a food mixer; (iii) to drive the washing drum in a washing machine; (iv) to drive the drum in a spin dryer; (v) a hand-held drill/sander; (vi) a vacuum cleaner. (*Note:* there is not always a clear-cut case for a particular type of motor. When answering justify your choice by summing up the motor characteristics, possible cost and whether speed variation has been considered.)

5 Motor selection

Aims: At the end of this chapter you should be able to:

Select a drive motor for a particular application after considering the required starting conditions, the speed stability of the drive, the operating environment and the required rating and duty cycle.

Almost invariably a three-phase alternating supply of electricity is available and this will be assumed as the drive requirements are examined. Where only a single-phase supply is available then the choice of drive and power are strictly limited (see Chapter 4).

First the required characteristic of the drive must be examined under the headings:

1 Is a high starting torque required?
2 Are there limitations as to starting current inrush?
3 Is the speed of the drive to be substantially constant, precisely constant or variable over a wide range?
4 In what environment is the drive to be operated? Is it dusty, wet or possibly explosive?
5 What is the required rating and duty cycle? Does the machine operate in a high or low ambient temperature?

1 STARTING TORQUE

Where a high starting torque is required this may be obtained using:

(a) A multiple-cage induction motor.
(b) A wound-rotor induction motor with added resistance in the rotor circuit during starting.
(c) A wound rotor machine with slip power recovery (see Figure 7.36). There are other forms of this drive employing the rectified output from the rotor to drive an auxiliary d.c. motor on the same shaft to provide extra torque at low speeds or using a special frequency changing rotor with a commutator instead of the electronic equivalent.
(d) A d.c. shunt or series motor. This will involve the use of rectifiers fed from the three-phase supply.

2 STARTING CURRENT LIMITATION

Starting current inrush may be limited using:

(a) A wound rotor induction motor with added rotor resistance.
(b) A wound rotor induction motor with slip power recovery.
(c) A star/delta or auto-transformer starter. (Note that this method cannot be used where a high starting torque is required.)
(d) A d.c. machine with resistance or electronic (possibly thyristor) starting.

(e) Voltage and frequency reduction on a squirrel cage induction motor where the drive is to have closely controlled speed (see Figure 7.35).

3 SPEED CONSIDERATIONS

(a) Where a substantially constant speed is required a motor with shunt characteristics is required. The squirrel cage induction motor is the first choice since it is very robust and cheap compared with all other types. The stator may have a two winding or changing pole combination arrangement to provide two or three basic speeds each with the same characteristic. The shunt-wound d.c. motor is also suitable but would only be used if some other consideration indicated that the use of d.c. was desirable.

(b) Where a single precise speed is required the use of a synchronous machine is indicated. This may require the provision of a frequency changer (see Chapter 2, section 'Synchronous machines').

(c) Where variable speed is required there are several possibilities:
   (i) A wound rotor induction motor with added rotor resistance. This is very inefficient however and should only be used for limited speed changes for short duration.
   (ii) Wound rotor induction motor with slip-power recovery system (see 1(c) above).
   (iii) Use of variable voltage, variable frequency arrangement (see 2(e) above).
   (iv) The stepper motor (see Chapter 4).

4 ENVIRONMENT

Having decided on the type of motor required attention must be given to the problem of providing sufficient cooling medium to carry away the heat from the windings but at the same time not allowing that medium to carry into the motor anything which will harm it or, in particular, block up the cooling ducts. Particularly harmful are oil vapour, carbon and cast iron dust. Where machines are hosed down or are located where they may be inundated with water, such as on a ship's deck, moisture ingress must be prevented or suitable insulation employed which is unaffected by water.

There have been a number of British Standards over the years – 2083:1954; 2960:1958; 3979:1966; 2613:1957 and 1970. The most modern standards for metric motors are BS 4999 and 5000:1972, with some later amendments. There are motors presently working which have been manufactured to all these standards.

To ensure that solid material and water do not enter the motor protection is afforded to one of the following classifications:

0 This is an unprotected motor, the windings are open to the surroundings.

1 A motor protected by some form of mesh screen to prevent solid material greater in size than 50 mm from entering.

2, 3, 4, 5 Indicate motors protected against successively smaller particles, 5 indicating protected against the ingress of dust.

A further number is added to indicate the degree of protection against water ingress.

0 Again this indicates no protection.
1 Protected against water dripping from above.
2 Protected against water falling from above up to an angle of 15° from the vertical.
3, 4, 5, 6, 7, 8 Indicate motors protected against successively greater risk of water penetration, 8 being for totally submersible motors.

Probably the most commonly found machine is the totally-enclosed, fan-cooled motor (TEFC). The motor winding is totally enclosed in the motor housing which is usually ribbed on the outside. A fan is mounted on the shaft external to the housing and is protected by a shield. This fan blows air over the casing removing heat from the motor. In larger sizes there is also a fan inside the casing blowing air over the windings transferring heat to the casing. The most common classification for this motor is 44 which means that it is protected against ingress of particles down to 1 mm and against water splashing on it from any direction.

Where motors are required to operate in explosive situations the requirement is that the motor must be of flame-proof construction. This means that it must be enclosed in such a manner that any explosion which may occur within the motor must be contained within the motor and the flame shall not be transmitted to the surrounding atmosphere. Construction of motors with such a specification is possible up to a few hundred kilowatts but often it is easier to prevent the explosive gases from entering the motor and so avoid the possibility of an explosion. To this end pipe ventilated motors are used drawing air from an uncontaminated area pumping it into the motor so keeping its internal pressure above that of the surrounding medium and then discharging the air into the contaminated zone so diluting the contamination. Alternatively, the air may be carried away again by duct.

5 RATING AND DUTY CYCLE

Each type of insulation has a maximum safe working temperature and this must be associated with the rating of the motor. The machine rating is the output of the motor which can be sustained without overheating when the life expectancy should be perhaps twenty years. If the operating temperature is increased beyond the recommended value the life of the motor is greatly reduced. An increase of, say, 5% in temperature can reduce life by 30%.

The rating is affected by the ambient temperature. In order that a device can dissipate heat it needs to be hotter than its surroundings. If the ambient temperature is low, heat can readily be got rid of and the motor can work harder developing more power, and more losses, quite safely before it reaches its recommended working temperature. If the motor operates in a hot situation, say, in a boiler house, then its ability to dissipate its losses is greatly reduced and it may be necessary to restrict its output to prevent the top temperature being exceeded.

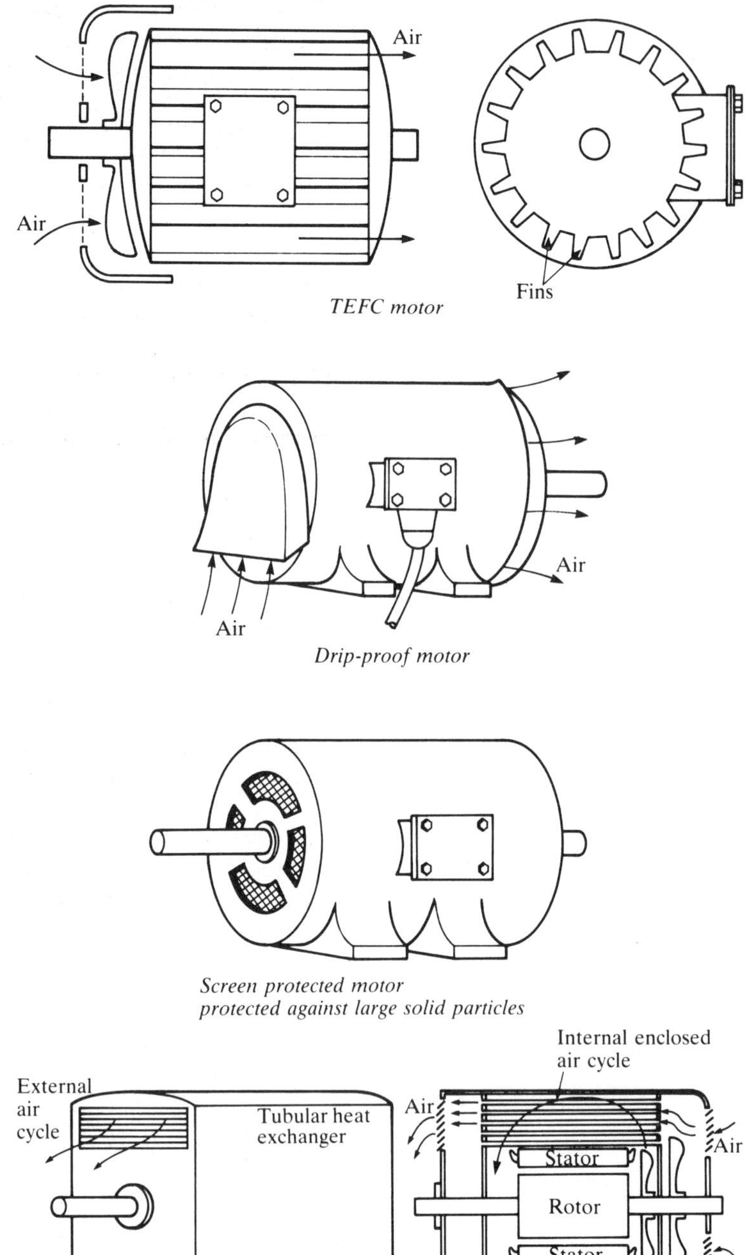

TEFC motor

Drip-proof motor

Screen protected motor protected against large solid particles

Motor with secondary cooling system protection against most solid material and splashing water

Figure 5.1

The maximum temperature of the various classes of insulation are as follows:

Class A: paper and paper products, silk, cotton, wire enamels based on natural oils: Top temperature 105°C.

Class E: wire enamels based on polyurethane, epoxy resins and polyester. Top temperature 120°C.
Class B: top temperature 130°C.
Class F: top temperature 155°C. Both of these classes comprise mica, glass fibre, asbestos and epoxy resins in various combinations.
Class H: as classes B and F with the addition of silicone materials. Top temperature 180°C.

Motors have name plate ratings classified:
CRPO (continuous rating with permitted overload) It can perform its name plate rating continuously with a specified degree of overloading for a period.
CMR (continuous maximum rating) The motor can operate at its name plate rating permanently. A small overload can cause overheating and failure. Most modern motors work extremely closely to their top temperatures when performing their rated duty and even a very small overload will result in failure. Where an older CRPO motor is being replaced with a modern equivalent great care has to be taken to ascertain that the overload capability of the older motor has not been used inadvertently. If this is the case, the modern machine will need to have a higher rating reflecting this use.
STR (short time rating) Motors with 1 hour, $\frac{1}{2}$ hour or even 10 minute ratings are available to perform specific duties. The motor performs this duty and in so doing most of the heat produced is stored in the frame raising its temperature to the top safe limit. The frame is too small to dissipate the total losses. After this, the motor has to remain off load for long enough for its temperature to drop to that of its surroundings. This enables considerable cost and weight savings to be made since the motor selected is extremely small compared with its continuously rated equivalent.

A selection of motor types is shown in *Figure 5.1*.

PROBLEMS

1 What type of motor is available which will (a) combine a high starting torque with near constant speed over a range of loadings and (b) combine a high starting torque with the provision of a wide range of speeds when loaded?
2 What type of a.c. motor starter might be employed (a) where starting current inrush must be limited and the motor is started off load and (b) where the starting current inrush must be avoided while providing a high starting torque?
3 What types of motor are available for driving a load at a precisely known speed?
4 What types of drives are available for providing a wide range of speeds at high efficiency?
5 What special features would you expect to see specified when motors are being purchased to operate in the following situations:
   (i) In a workshop housing a wood planer.
   (ii) In a boiler house basement which is regularly hosed down.

(iii) In a sewage pump house where the presence of methane gas can be expected.

(iv) To drive a centre lathe used for turning cast-iron components.

(v) To position the work precisely on the bed of a milling machine.

6 A motor which was purchased to operate in an ambient temperature of 20°C is to be relocated at the top of a boiler house. State with reasons what the possible effect on the motor rating might be.

7 The alternating current generator fitted to aircraft can only be used at its full rated power when the aircraft is flying. When on the ground auxiliary generators are used. What factors influence the rating of the aircraft generators?

8 What is meant by the term *short time rating*? Describe one duty or load cycle for which a motor with this type of rating would be suitable.

6 Circuit protection

Aims: At the end of this chapter you should be able to:

Discuss the significance of fault level on an electricity supply system.
Describe the requirements for earthing, the methods of achieving them and the application of protective multiple earthing.
Describe the construction and the modes of operation of fuses.
Describe circuit breaker and relay protection.
Discuss the various types of circuit breakers and relays available.

FAULT LEVEL

When considering circuit protection, the fault level at the point to be protected must be taken into account. The fault level is the number of volt-amperes which would flow into a short circuit if one occurred at the particular point. On a 415 V, three-phase street main this could be around 2000 kVA which represents a current of nearly 3000 A. The fault level is limited by the impedance of all the apparatus between the point of the fault and the supply generator. Hopefully, when such a current flowed a protective device such as a fuse would operate so cutting off the supply. The value of current which could flow if nothing was done to limit it is called the *prospective current*.

At a similar voltage within a factory where the distance from the supply transformer may be less and the transformer itself larger, the fault level could rise to 18 000 RVA which represents a current of approximately 25 000 A. The nearer the fault is to the supply generators, the larger is the fault level. A fault on the 400 kV system can give fault levels in excess of 30 000 MVA (1 MVA = 1000 kVA).

EARTHING

Both the IEE Regulations and the Electricity Supply Regulations require that one point in a transformer-fed system shall be earthed. The secondaries of all transmission and distribution transformers are star connected and their star points earthed. Such earthing provides a return path for fault current so that in the event a live line touches the earthed metal screen around a piece of apparatus or an earth fault occurs on a distribution cable or overhead line, sufficient current can flow from the fault back through the earth to the transformer star point to operate the protective device and make the circuit or transformer dead.

Transformers operating at up to 440 V line have their star points connected directly to ground, while those operating at higher voltages have current-limiting resistances connected in the earth connection to limit fault current to a safe value. The resistance may take the form of heavy gauge wire or a cylindrical water tank with a central electrode. The correct resistance is obtained by adding a weak solution of washing soda to demineralised water.

PROTECTIVE MULTIPLE EARTHING

This system involves earthing the neutral wire on a distribution network at a number of points instead of just at the supply transformer. In addition, consumers have their earth and neutral terminals connected together on their premises and these in turn are bonded to the gas and water systems to prevent the potential of these rising above that of earth. The increased use of plastic main water pipe means that the water service can no longer be regarded as a safe earth in many areas. In the case of the gas service, any rise in potential could cause sparking and an explosion.

The advantages claimed for this system are:

(i) Four-core cable need not be used. Three-core cable with armouring or metallic sheathing which becomes the neutral/earth conductor is cheaper and there is a weight saving.

(ii) If the neutral/earth conductor becomes discontinuous at any point, say, at a joint in a cable, current can continue to flow between the disconnected sections through the ground because of the regular earth points and the safety and operation of the system is unimpaired.

FUSE PROTECTION

There are two types of fuse in general use:

1 The semi-enclosed, rewirable fuse.
2 The high rupturing capacity fuse, or cartridge fuse (HRC).

Marked on each cartridge fuse and quoted for each size of fuse wire is a current rating. The current rating is that value of current which the fuse can carry indefinitely without melting or deteriorating.

The rated minimum fusing current is the least value of current which will actually cause the fuse element to melt.

$$\text{Fusing factor} = \frac{\text{Rated minimum fusing current}}{\text{Current rating}}$$

This factor may lie between approximately 1.2 and 2.0.

With a fusing factor of 1.5, a fuse rated at 10 A will require a current of $1.5 \times 10 = 15$ A to operate.

OPERATION OF FUSES

When current flows in a fuse element heat is produced. If that current is less than the current rating of the fuse then the body of the fuse is able to dissipate the heat to the surroundings, usually into the air. When the rate of producing heat is equal to the rate of dissipating it, then the temperature remains constant at a value lower than that necessary to melt the fuse element.

When a current slightly greater than the minimum fusing current flows heat is produced in the element faster than it can be dissipated and after a period of time the element melts and the circuit is interrupted. In the event a short circuit or possibly an earth fault then the prospective current will be extremely large and heat is generated in the element at such a high rate that there is no time for any of it to be dissipated. The element melts extremely rapidly, circuit clearance times being very short. When operating in this manner the fuse is said to have 'inverse time characteristics'. This means that the larger the current is the shorter is the time taken to clear the circuit.

THE SEMI-ENCLOSED REWIRABLE FUSE

These comprise a ceramic fuse base with an asbestos or similar liner into which the fuse carrier is slotted. The fuse carrier has male contacts of brass and pushes into spring-loaded female contacts of brass or berylium copper in the base. The fuse element is tinned-copper wire, the diameters for particular current being specified in the IEE Regulations. They are the subject of BS 3036 (see *Figure 6.1*).

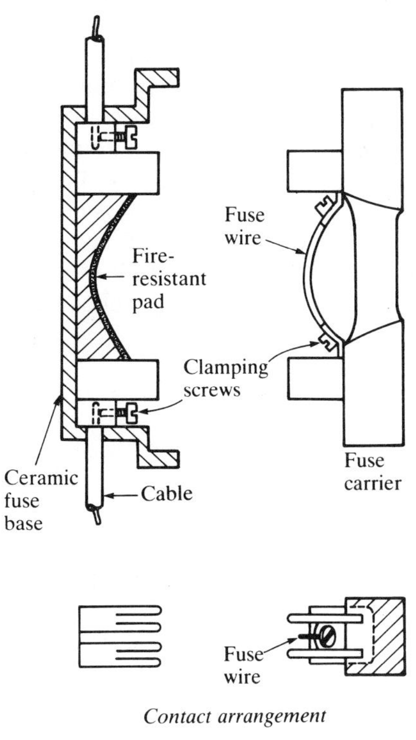

Contact arrangement

Semi-enclosed rewirable fuse

Figure 6.1

They are manufactured with ratings up to about 100 A and are suitable for use in alternating-current circuits operating at up to 250 V. In clearing, the fuse element melts and so interrupts the circuit current. The copper of the element partly vapourises and partly spreads itself over the surface of the carrier. It operates perfectly satisfactorily with overloads and fairly small fault currents. However, with very high prospective currents this melting takes place explosively and current may continue to flow in the metallic vapour present. The danger here is that the fault would have to be cleared by a much larger protective device further back in the network, possibly at the main circuit breaker. Should this happen a large part of the network would be shut down and many consumers left without a supply of energy. Rewirable fuses are also open to abuse in that they can be rewired using almost any conductor, hair pins and nails, for example. The IEE Regulations recommend that wherever possible a cartridge-type (HRC) fuse be used. At the fault level found in domestic situations a semi-enclosed rewirable fuse is generally quite adequate.

THE HIGH RUPTURING CAPACITY FUSE (HRC)

The HRC fuse comprises a cylindrical ceramic body to the ends of which are attached brass or copper end caps. The fusible element is generally of silver since this is the best electrical conductor known. Three forms of the element are shown in *Figure 6.2*. On one of them a small bead of soft solder has been deposited. The body is tightly packed with very fine quartz grains which keeps the element in place at all times including while melting and gives controlled heat conduction away from the element. With currents just large enough to cause melting, the element with the solder bead melts first at this point while the other type melts at one or more of the narrow sections. The presence of the solder bead gives a lower fusing factor that is possible by most if not all other methods.

Where very large currents are involved the heat produced explosively melts the silver which chemically combines with the filling forming a compound the resistance of which increases rapidly as it

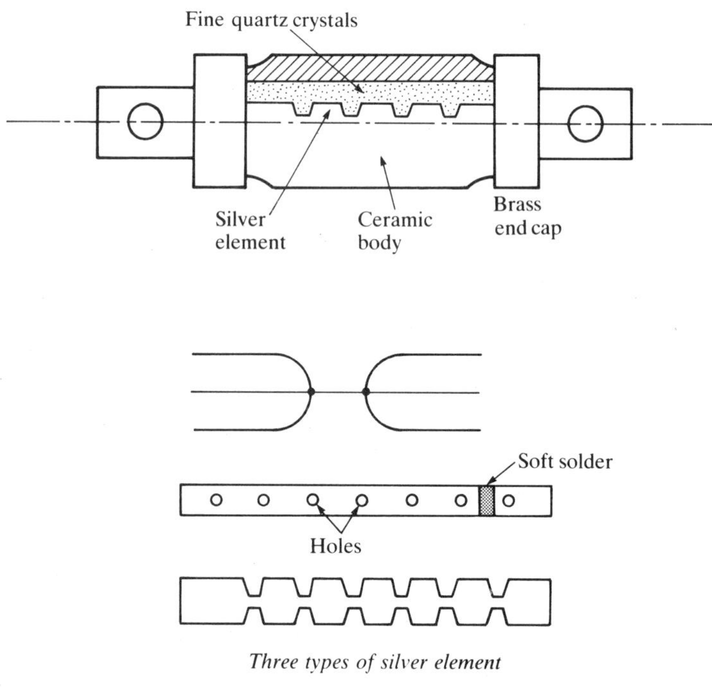

Three types of silver element

The HRC fuse

Figure 6.2

cools. BS 88 covers fuses for working up to 1000 V a.c. with ratings of several hundred amperes. They may be used to protect circuits with extremely high prospective currents, tests having been carried out on some types using values of over 100 kA. Cartridge fuses for domestic premises generally only up to 100 A rating are covered by BS 1361.

The small cartridge fuses found in domestic ring-main plugs have ratings between 3 A and 13 A and can interrupt up to 6000 A. They comprise a ceramic tube, quartz filled with a single wire element and employ the solder bead principle to give rapid clearance at low values of overcurrent.

Small cartridge fuse links for telecommunication and light electrical apparatus are rated from about 50 mA to 5 A at 250 V. They are covered by BS 2950. Other miniature fuses appear in BS 4265.

FUSE CHARACTERISTICS

Should a much larger current than normal full load be allowed to flow in a circuit, the cable may suffer damage in two ways. First, the excess current will generate a large amount of heat. Second, currents

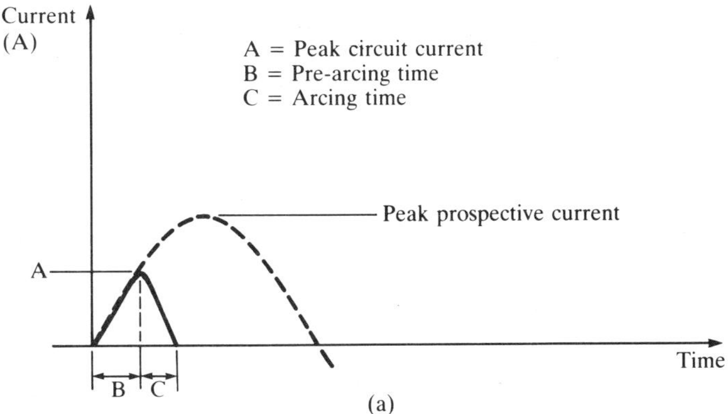

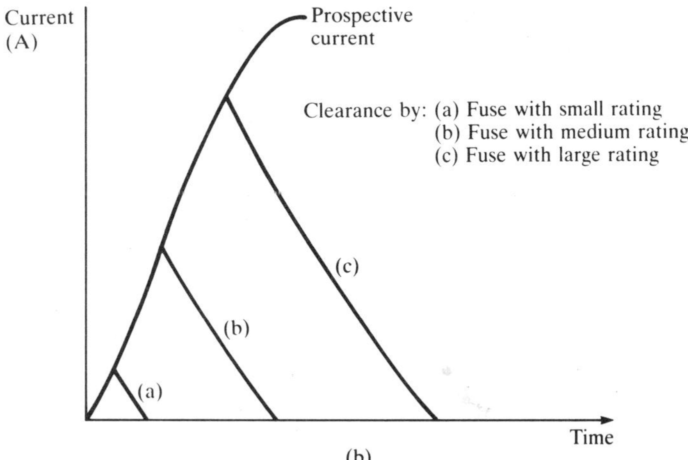

Figure 6.3

flowing in adjacent conductors set up mechanical forces. These forces may be large enough to disrupt the cable.

For these reasons, the fuse must be capable of interrupting extremely large prospective currents before they ever reach their first maximum value. The fuse must begin to melt during the first quarter cycle of current and so prevent the full prospective value being realised. *Figure 6.3(a)* shows the prospective current in a circuit as a dotted line. This is the current which would flow in the circuit if the fuse were not present and nothing was done to limit the fault current. After a short time the energy dissipated in the fuse element by the large and rapidly increasing current is sufficient to start it melting. The time taken up to this instant is called the *pre-arcing time*. Once the element begins to melt, the resistance of the fuse rapidly increases and the circuit current decreases. During this time there is an arc within the fuse and this period is called the *arcing time*. The pre-arcing time plus the arcing time is the *total clearance time*. Typical clearance curves are shown in *Figure 6.3(b)*.

Since power in a circuit = I^2R watts

$$\text{Energy} = \text{watt seconds} = I^2Rt \text{ joules}$$

The fuse manufacturer could tell us the actual energy requirement, I^2Rt J, to melt the fuse but it is just as useful to quote a value of I^2t only since this is the same for both fuse and circuit, whatever current flows in the fuse must also be flowing in the circuit since they are in series. The value quoted assumes that there is no time for the element to pass heat the surrounding air, i.e. the value quoted is for short-circuit fault conditions.

Fuse manufacturers quote values of I^2t input (i) to cause arcing to commence and (ii) to totally clear the fuse and provided that the I^2t requirement to clear the fuse is less than that necessary to damage the associated circuit then all is well.

This is particularly important in high-power electronics employing devices such as thyristors. These can carry extremely high currents but are physically very small. The amount of energy required to destroy them is quite small and a special range of very fast HRC fuses has been developed to protect such devices.

As an example, consider two 20 A fuses: (i) a high speed type having I^2t value of 250 A²s and (ii) a motor protection fuse with I^2t = 3000 A²s. In each case the circuit being protected develops a short-circuit fault with resistance 0.05 Ω.

Fuse (i) will allow $I^2t \times 0.05 = 250 \times 0.05 = 12.5$ joules into the circuit, while fuse (ii) will allow $3000 \times 0.05 = 150$ joules to pass.

Which fuse is selected will depend upon knowing the energy level which will damage the circuit. If it is a cable, 150 joules is unlikely to harm it. If the fuse is connected directly to a solid semi-conductor device it may well be that it will be necessary to limit the energy input to 12.5 joules to prevent damage.

In, for example, a domestic installation, the main fuse at the supply point may be rated at 60 A, while the fuse feeding the cooker might be rated at 30 A. Should a short-circuit fault occur on the cooker it is desirable that the 30 A fuse should clear without affecting the main 60 A fuse. In order to ensure that this occurs, the total

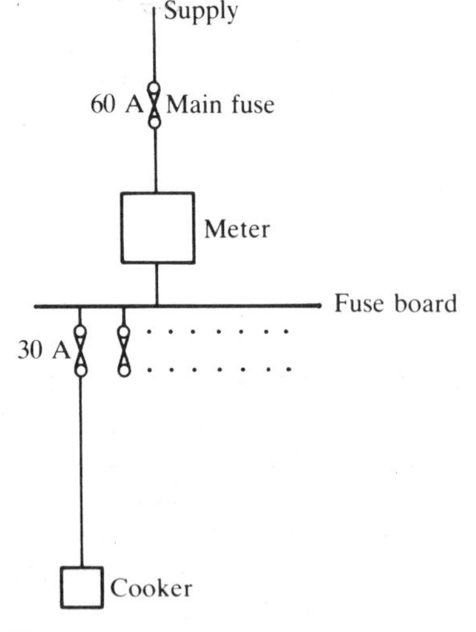

Figure 6.4

I^2t which clears the 30 A fuse must be less than the pre-arcing I^2t of the 60 A fuse so that when the 30 A fuse has completely cleared, the 60 A fuse has not started to melt.

CIRCUIT BREAKER AND RELAY PROTECTION

So far we have considered circuit protection by fuses. These are available up to 11 kV but suffer one disadvantage in that when they have cleared a fault they have to be replaced. Especially at the higher voltages this is extremely costly. An alternative to the fuse is the circuit breaker which having operated may be reclosed once the reason for its operation has been ascertained. Circuit breakers need to have an auxiliary device called a relay to cause them to open in the event of, say, an overcurrent or earth leakage. First we will define what is meant by the terms *circuit breaker*, *isolator* and *contactor*.

Circuit breaker

A circuit breaker is a mechanical device which is capable of making and breaking an electrical circuit under *all* conditions. This means that it can be used to energise a circuit which has a short-circuit fault on it without causing distress to the device as it opens to interrupt the resultant very large current. Circuit breakers are available for circuits with fault levels ranging from a few MVA at 230 V when they are known as *miniature circuit breakers*, up to 35 000 MVA at 400 kV three-phase.

Isolator

An isolator is a mechanical device which is capable of making a circuit under all conditions but only being opened when the circuit is carrying very little or no current. As the name suggests, an isolator is used to isolate a circuit from the supply when work is being carried out. The isolator is capable of being locked in the open position for safety purposes. Isolators on transmission and distribution systems are interlocked with an associated circuit breaker so that they cannot be opened with the circuit breaker in the closed position.

Switch

This is a device capable of making and breaking a circuit under normal conditions. It may be manually operated, as in the case of a light switch, or electrically operated when it is termed a *contactor* (see *Figure 6.13*). A switch always needs to be backed up with a circuit breaker or fuse. In the event of a short-circuit fault the back-up device clears the circuit since the switch is incapable of clearing excess currents.

TYPES OF CIRCUIT BREAKER

Bulk oil

The oldest of all forms of power circuit breaker is that containing oil. It comprises essentially a tank of oil in which the fixed and moving contacts are situated. The centre operating spindle is lifted up against a strong spring either by a solenoid energised from a battery in the larger sizes or manually using an external handle in the smaller ratings. In all but the smallest sizes it is recommended that remote electrical operation be adopted to avoid the possibility of injury should a circuit breaker be closed on to a fault and an

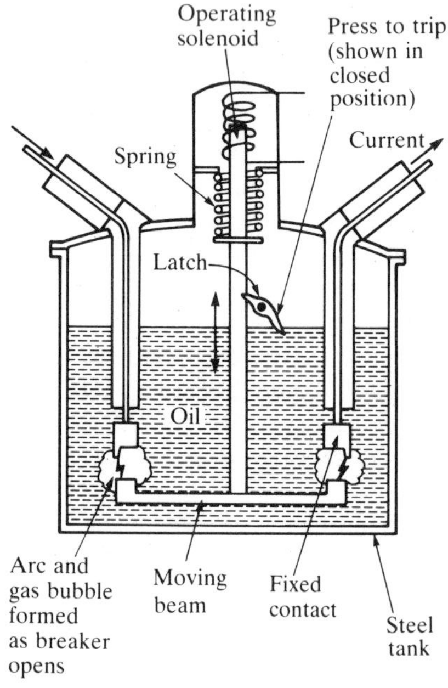

Figure 6.5

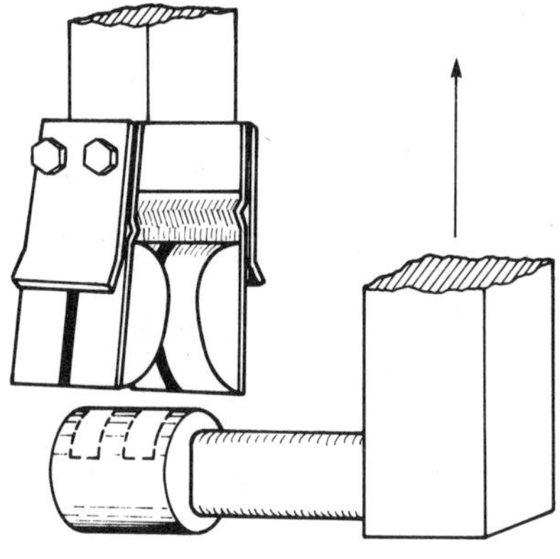

Wedge and fiinger type contact

Figure 6.6

explosion ensue. Having lifted the spindle it is latched mechanically into position. To trip (open) the circuit breaker the mechanical latch is struck either by hand or by another small solenoid energised via a tripping relay. The spring forces the spindle downwards separating the electrical contacts at high velocity. Buffers limit the travel at the bottom. All circuit breakers must be capable of opening without external power hence the spring and latch mechanism.

There are several types of these breakers for each manufacturer. They are basically *plain break type* or *self-generated pressure type*.

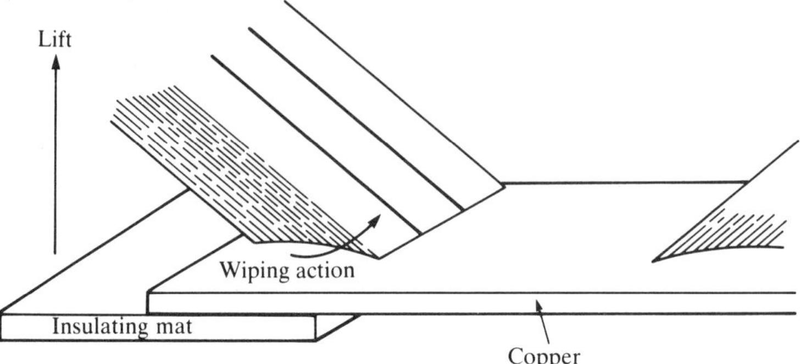

Laminated contacts

Figure 6.7

Plain break type

Figure 6.5 illustrates the general configuration while *Figures 6.6* and *6.7* show two types of contact. As the circuit is interrupted an arc is formed between the fixed and moving contacts. This arc is extinguished by the speed of the contact separation and by the mass of cooling oil rushing in on the arc. This type has fairly small rupturing capacity perhaps up to 150 MVA at which level its performance is somewhat unpredictable because there are no arc control devices. The arc can spread between the contacts in an uncontrolled manner. Manually and electrically operated types are in use at 415 V with breaking capacities of 25 and 35 MVA.

Self-generated pressure type

The basic arrangement is as in the plain break type except that some form of enclosure is used to make the arc build up pressure within the oil which can be used to force that oil at high velocity across the arc thus extinguishing it. *Figure 6.8* shows the general arrangement of a cross-jet arc control pot in which the arc is closely controlled making possible much larger breaking capacities typically 750 MVA at 33 kV and 2500 MVA at 132 kV. A development of this type is the minimum oil breaker which contains only a few litres of oil as opposed to several hundred litres in the bulk oil type. The principle of operation is, however, identical.

In *Figure 6.8(a)* the moving finger contact has just pulled down from the spring-loaded fixed contacts forming an arc. The arc burns a small quantity of oil creating a gas bubble. Since there is no escape route for the gas it builds up considerable pressure. In *Figure 6.8(b)*

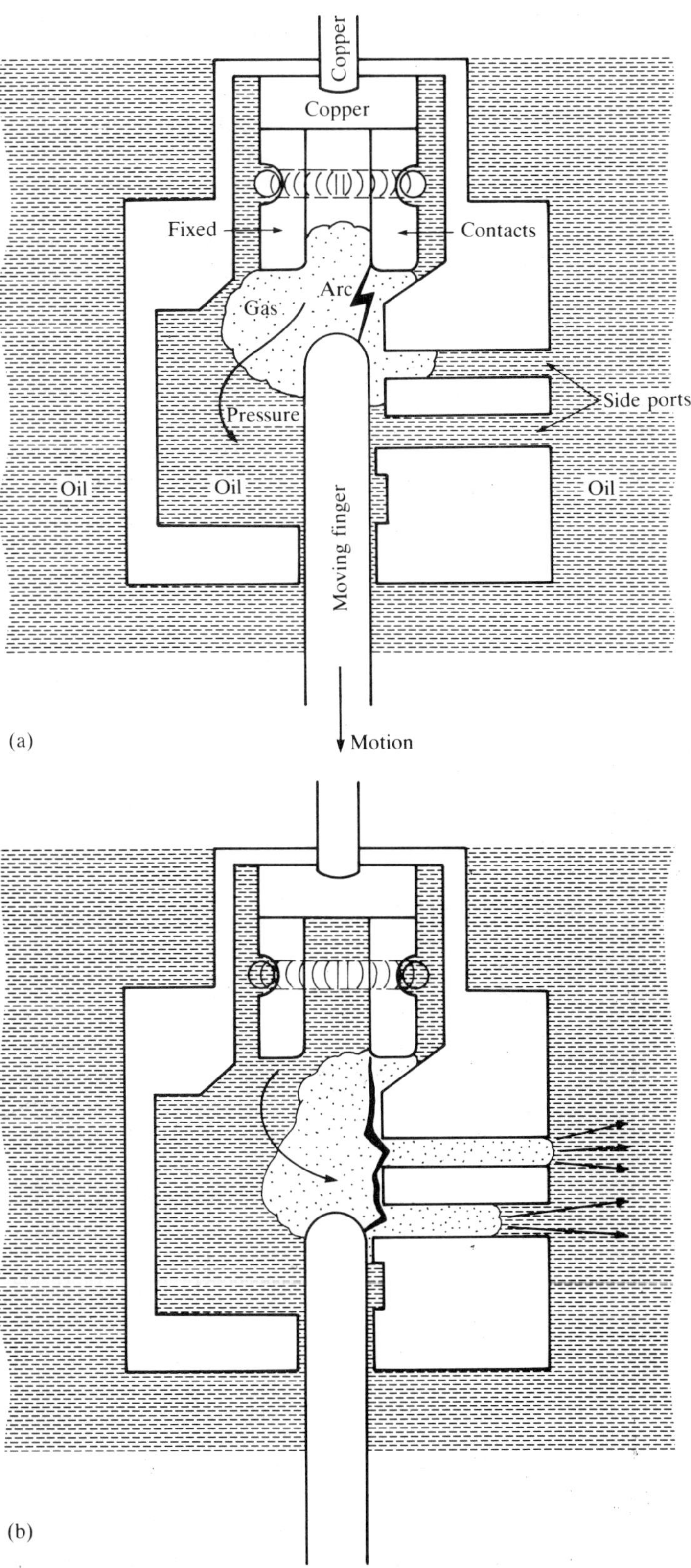
Copper
Copper
Fixed
Contacts
Arc
Gas
Pressure
Side ports
Oil
Oil
Oil
Moving finger
(a)
Motion
(b)

Figure 6.8

the moving finger has pulled down until its tip is near the bottom opening to the pot. The arc is now long and thin and the two outlet ports on the right-hand side have been uncovered. The high-pressure gas bubble forces oil and gas at high velocity out through the ports carrying the dying arc with them. The pressure of gas is determined by the current being interrupted. When clearing a very small current, the arc is small and the amount of gas produced also small. A fairly gentle movement of oil and gas through the first port will clear the arc. When opening under fault conditions the arc is large producing large amounts of gas and a violent discharge through the side ports.

Air natural

The air natural type circuit breaker employs air as insulant and arc extinguishing medium. The general arrangement is shown in *Figure 6.9*. The contacts are situated under an arc chute into which the arc is drawn by heat convection as the circuit breaker opens, extending

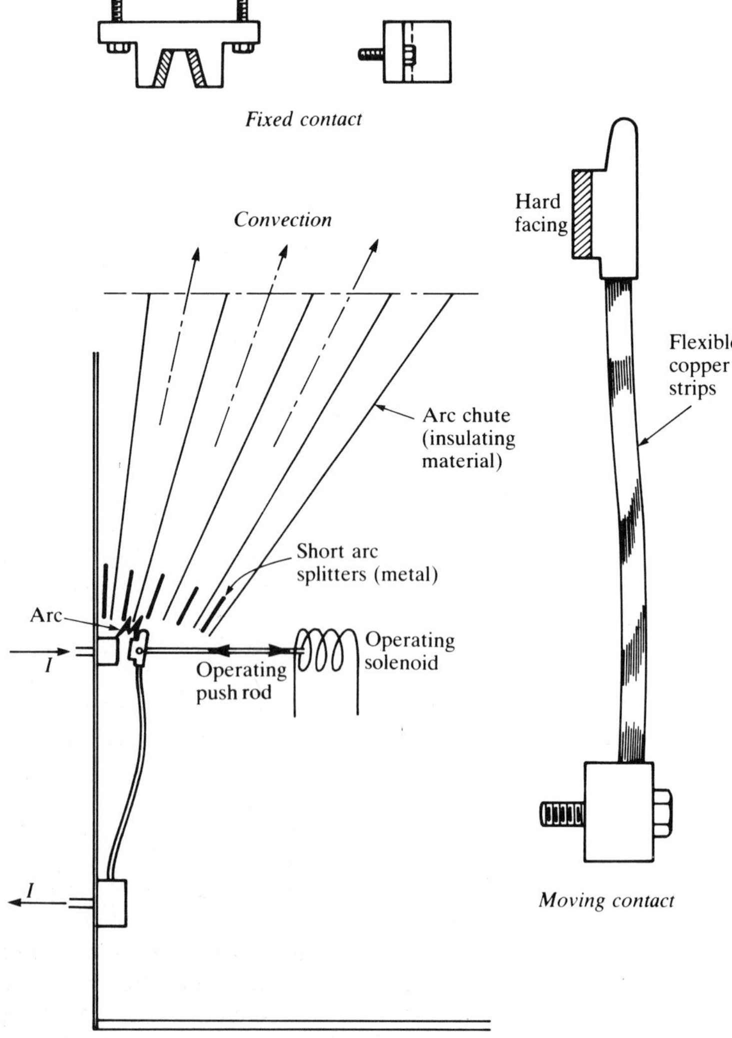

Figure 6.9

the length of the arc while causing it to come into contact with cold metal arc splitters which extinguishes it. Typical ratings are: 25 MVA at 415 V; 35 MVA at 3.3 kV and up to 750 MVA at 11 kV.

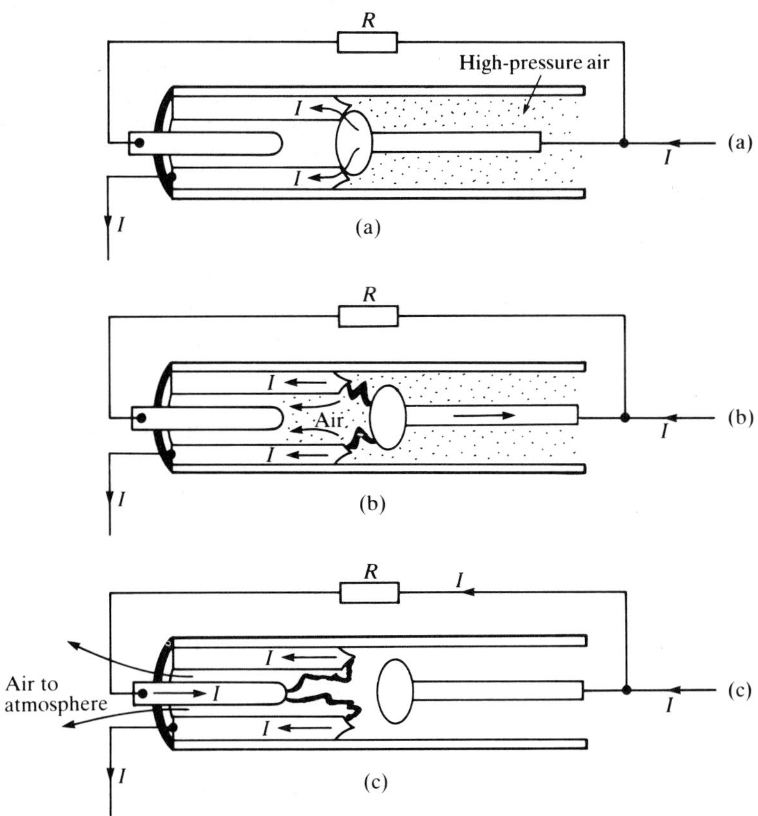

Figure 6.10

Air blast The air-blast breaker uses air at a pressure of about 14 atmospheres to rapidly cool and blow out the arc formed as the contacts separate. The basic difference in operation between this type and the previous two types is that the moving contact does not remain in the open position. It pulls back drawing the arc which is blown out and five or six cycles later is forced back into the closed position at high speed. All air blast breakers are equipped with a series isolator which has to open during the short period that the main current breaking contacts are operating. Interlocks are provided which allow the isolator to be closed to energise the circuit but not to open until the circuit breaker has cleared the circuit. A further interlock is provided which will not allow the circuit to be energised unless there is enough air in the storage reservoir to open the circuit breaker. Should the air pressure fall while the breaker is closed and the circuit energised an alarm is given so that remedial action can be taken.

In *Figure 6.10(a)* the circuit breaker is shown in its closed position. Current enters on the right, passes down the central spindle to the contact mushroom, on to the fixed contact and leaves the breaker at bottom left as drawn. The contacts are mounted in what is called a *blast pipe* and to the right is a reservoir containing a large quantity of high-pressure air.

In *Figure 6.10(b)* the moving contact has drawn back creating an arc. Current continues to flow on its original route through the arc. The high-pressure air rushes through the blast pipe expanding and cooling as it does so. The arc is blown to the left.

Figure 6.10(c) shows the arc is blown on to a central finger or arcing contact and the current has now been diverted through the external resistance. The path is now from the right, through the external resistance, on to the arcing finger, through the arc and into the circuit. The effect of the resistance is to immediately reduce the current in magnitude and the high-velocity, cold air blows out the arc. The moving contact immediately returns to position (a).

In a 400 kV breaker with rupturing capacity 35 000 MVA there may be eight such interrupters in series per phase.

Sulphur hexafluoride

Sulphur hexafluoride gas is a particularly good arc quenching medium in that it rapidly absorbs free electrons created in an arc. This means that as the current flowing in an arc passes through a zero, electrons which are present and which would allow the arc to restrike as the alternating voltage begins to increase in magnitude once again are absorbed, turning the arc path into an insulating region. The arc duration time is much shorter in sulphur hexafluoride than it would be in air.

The construction of the sulphur hexafluoride circuit breaker is very similar to that of the air blast breaker except that the gas cannot be allowed to escape into the atmosphere. It is therefore held at high pressure (14 atmospheres) and when the breaker operates it expands into a larger, low-pressure receiver (3 atmospheres) from which it can be taken and pumped back up to high pressure once more.

The following advantages accrue from the use of this gas:

(i) A reduced number of series breaks are required for a given voltage and rating. The breaker is much less bulky than its air blast equivalent.
(ii) Due to the quicker clearance burning of contacts is less than in the air breakers.
(iii) Since the gas blast is not released into the atmosphere the operation of the breaker is much quieter than with air blast which can often be heard a very long way away.

VACUUM

The ideal situation in which to interrupt a current might seem to be in a perfect vacuum and the possibility was investigated in the early 1920s. At the time, however, the problems in producing metals which did not contain dissolved gases seemed insurmountable. When contacts made from metals interrupt an arc in vacuum the dissolved gases are liberated thus contaminating the vacuum. Also without the scouring action of high velocity air or oil the contacts tended to weld together and any liberated metal vapour settled on the insulating surfaces.

By careful attention to the geometry of the interior (see *Figure 6.11*) the problems have been overcome and they are presently used

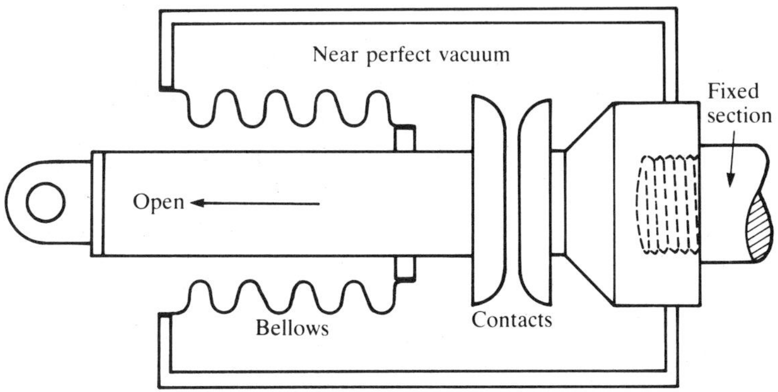

Figure 6.11

over the range of voltages up to 11 kV employing single devices and on up to 132 kV using several devices in series as was the case with the air blast breaker.

The vacuum breaker offers a number of advantages which are (i) they are totally enclosed and sealed so that replacement of an element involves only unscrewing the old one and adding the new, (ii) there is no fire risk as with the oil breakers and (iii) they are almost silent in operation and emit no gases when operating.

TYPES OF RELAY

Thermal

The essential feature of a thermal relay is one or more bimetallic strips made from brass and steel alloy. Brass expands more than steel when heated so under the influence of a temperature increase the strip will distort with the steel on the inside of the bend as shown in *Figure 6.12*. The strip is heated by using a heating coil carrying all or part of the current flowing into a circuit or by passing the current directly through the strip itself.

The movement of the strip can be made to open a pair of tripping contacts associated with a contactor so switching off the power supply to the operating coil as shown in *Figure 6.13*. The contactor

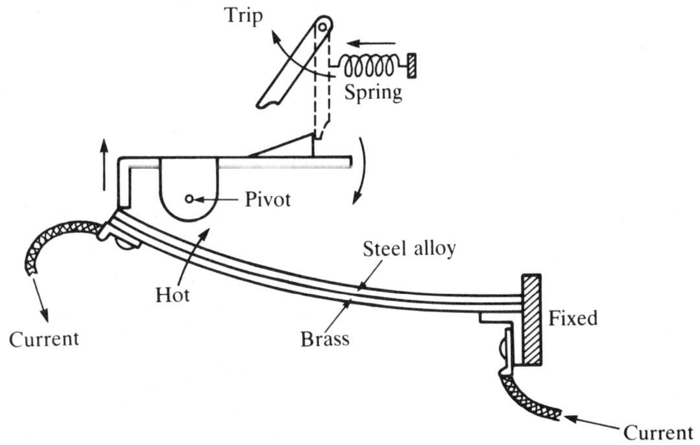

Figure 6.12

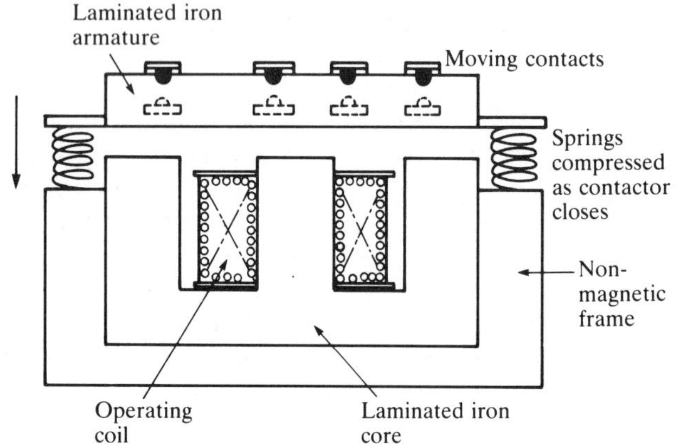

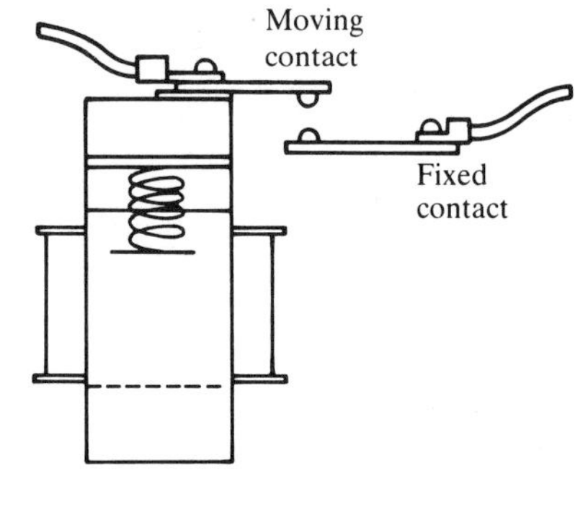

Physical arrangement

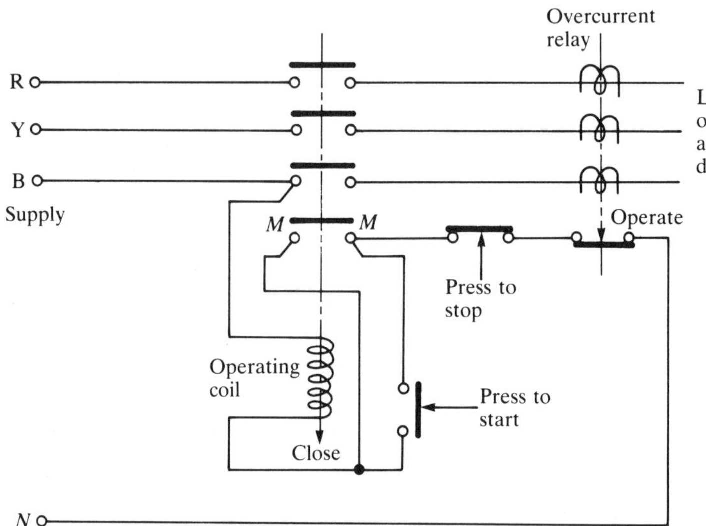

Contacts MM closed when contactor operates allowing start button to be released

Electrical connections

Figure 6.13

is closed by pressing the start button which energises the operating coil closing four pairs of contacts, one in each line of the supply and one pair called the maintaining contacts which maintain the supply to the operating coil when the start button is released. The contactor will open under three circumstances: (i) the stop button is pressed, (ii) the overcurrent relay operates or (iii) the supply voltage drops substantially when the spring opens the contacts.

Alternatively, the movement of the bimetal may be made to close a pair of contacts so energising a small coil which will knock out the latch on a circuit breaker (see *Figure 6.6*). Some adjustment is possible by moving the starting position of the strip so that more or less distortion is necessary to cause tripping.

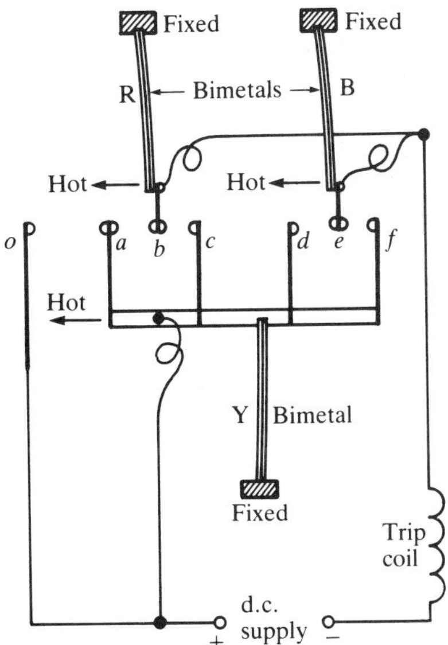

Figure 6.15

There are various patented ways to enhance the action of this type of device basically by either winding the bimetal strip into a coil as shown in *Figure 6.14(a)* or into a helix as in *Figure 6.14(b)*. When protecting a three-phase circuit, the simplest arrangement causes an overcurrent in any one phase to trip the contactor or circuit breaker. Other arrangements are capable of comparing the movement of each bimetal and if they differ by more than a small amount showing that although all or any of the phases might not be overloaded, an out of balance loading is present, and the relay operates. This is illustrated in *Figure 6.15*. If, for example, the blue phase is carrying more current than the yellow, the blue bimetal will heat up more rapidly than the yellow and contacts *d* and *e* will touch. This will energise the trip coil. Any one phase carrying more or less current than any other will cause a pair of contacts to close with the same effect. If all three currents are identical and become too large the whole contact system moves to the left until contacts *a* and *o* cause the trip coil to be energised.

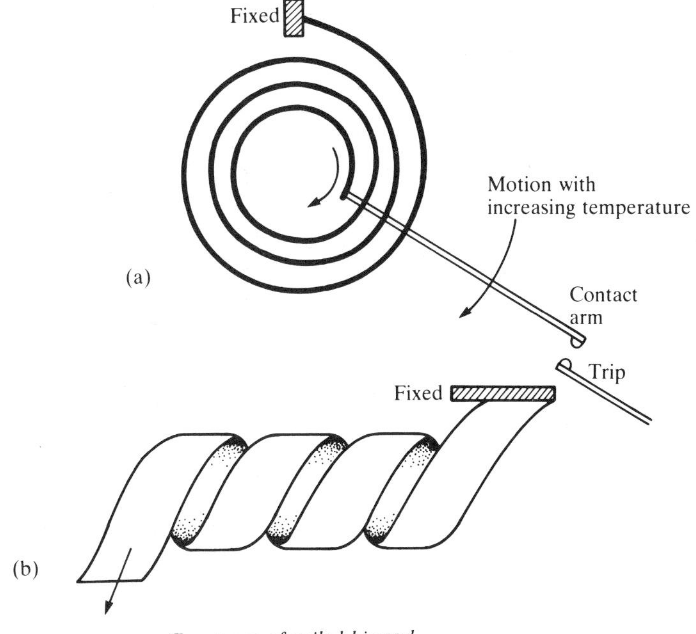

Two types of coiled bimetal

Figure 6.14

Magnetic-hydraulic

Current flowing in the coil of the relay shown in *Figure 6.16* attracts the iron plunger upwards against the force of gravity. When a predetermined value of current is reached, tripping occurs by lifting the cross beam which is connected to electrical contacts as in the thermal type. The movement of the beam opens the associated contactor or circuit breaker (see *Figures 6.6* and *6.13*). The current at which the relay operates is adjusted by raising or lowering the dashpot so altering the relative positions of the plunger and coil. For the first few millimetres of travel the piston moves slowly as it is pulled through

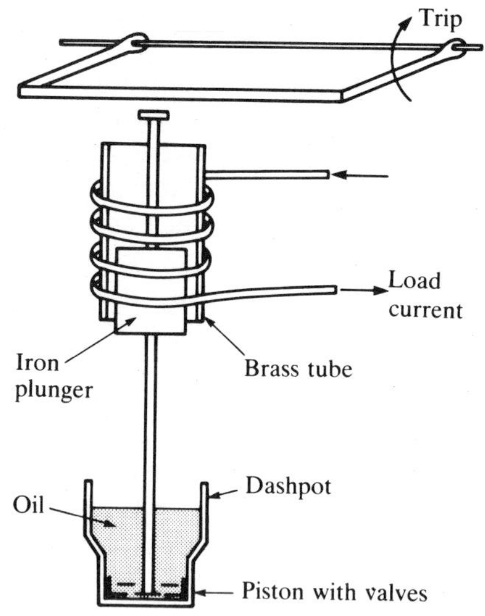

Figure 6.16

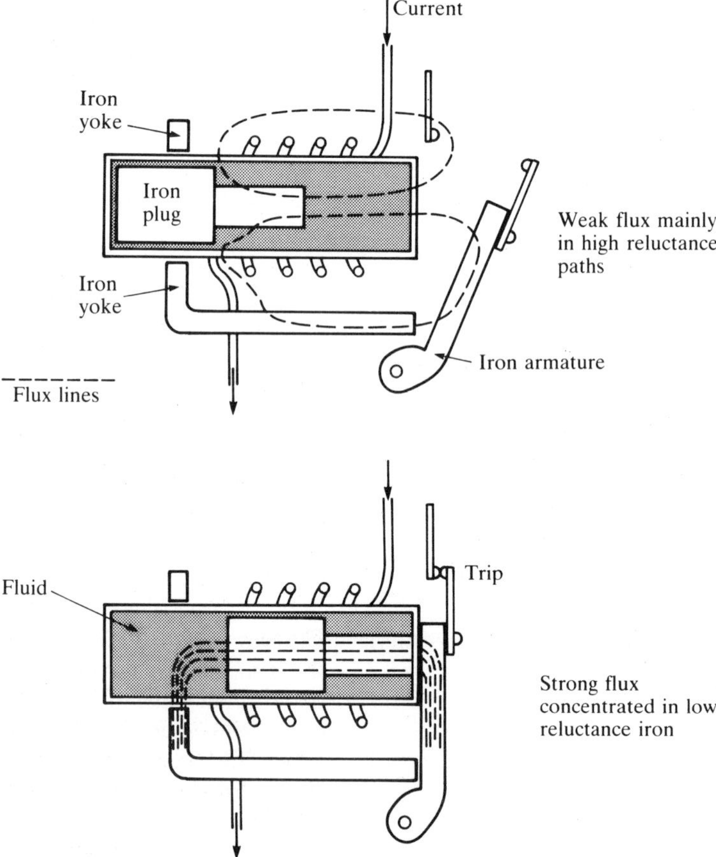

Figure 6.17

the oil, the valves being automatically closed by the action. As the piston moves into the wide section of the dashpot the speed increases and the trip bar is knocked upwards. The dashpot prevents instantaneous operation during very short periods of overcurrent. The valves automatically open as the plunger falls allowing the relay to reset automatically.

A more refined version of this relay is shown in *Figure 6.17*. The coil is wound round a sealed dashpot containing silicone fluid. A fine spring holds the steel plunger at the left-hand end. When an overcurrent occurs the plunger is attracted into the coil being pulled through the fluid at a fairly slow rate so preventing instantaneous operation. The magnetic flux is set up mainly in the low-permeability fluid and will be small so that the force of attraction on the external armature will be small. As the plunger nears the right-hand end the flux is set up mainly in high-permeability materials, the plunger and the external steel frame. The magnetic field becomes strong enough to attract the external armature and the circuit-breaker is opened.

Electronic

Thermal and magnetic relays suffer from the defect that they cannot adequately protect a motor from being damaged by excess temperature. The relay is actuated by excess current or an out-of-balance current, the latter case indicating that a fault has probably already occurred. Having tripped on overcurrent the motor may be at the limit of its temperature range. However, as soon as the relay element has reset the motor can be restarted when it may draw excess current for as long a time as it takes for the relay to trip once again. This could well be too long a period for the health of the motor resulting in a failure of the insulation.

One way of overcoming the problem is to fit thermistors in the motor winding itself. Thermistors are very small devices, about the size of a match head, which have virtually constant resistance over a specified range of temperature but at a specific known temperature their resistance either increases by a considerable amount, when the thermistor is said to have a positive characteristic, or decreases by a large amount, when the device is said to have a negative characteristic.

Figure 6.18 shows two positive characteristic thermistors fitted inside a motor. Their critical temperature for resistance change is chosen to match the upper temperature limit of the motor insulation. They carry half-wave rectified current derived from a transformer and a diode. The coil *R* is energised with this current and the relay is held with contacts *b* closed. The motor may be started by pressing the start button (see also *Figure 6.13*). If at any time the motor temperature reaches the critical value, the thermistor resistances rise reducing considerably the current in coil *R*. The relay is released and the contacts *a* close (shown dotted in *Figure 6.18*). An indicator lamp comes on while current to the motor contactor operating coil is lost and the motor stops. It can only be restarted when the thermistors cool down.

For stalled conditions even the thermistor may provide inadequate protection in that the rotor and actual copper of the stator winding will heat up extremely rapidly giving no time for heat transfer to the

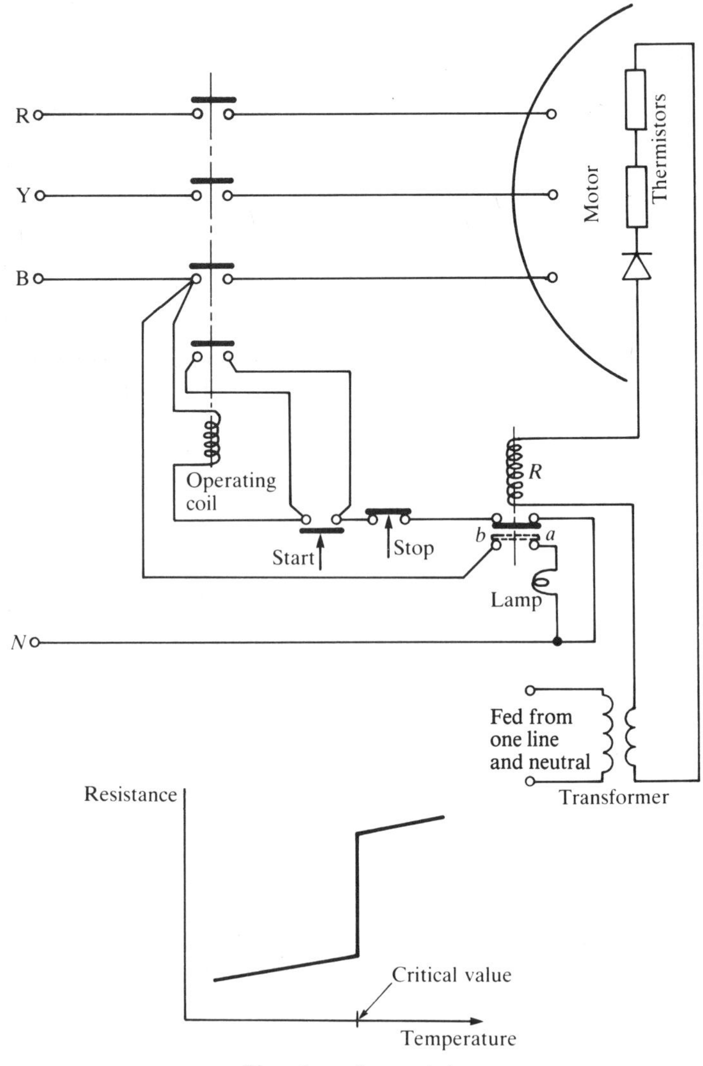

Thermistor characteristic

Figure 6.18

stator and into the thermistors which will under respond. Electronic motor controllers are available which use external electronic simulation to monitor all conditions within the motor. They have separate elements which consider the rate of heat production in the windings by monitoring the input current, and of transfer of the heat from the windings into the iron by being programmed with the thermal resistance of the winding insulation. Thus very large currents for short duration produce a different response to some overcurrent for a longer time which would allow heat transfer to the iron. An early warning of overcurrent may be given followed by tripping if the condition persists. These devices will trip in the event of a one-phase failure, an earth fault or if the motor stalls.

Induction The output from a current transformer is fed to coil 1 on the laminated E core shown in *Figure 6.19*. This current sets up an alternat-

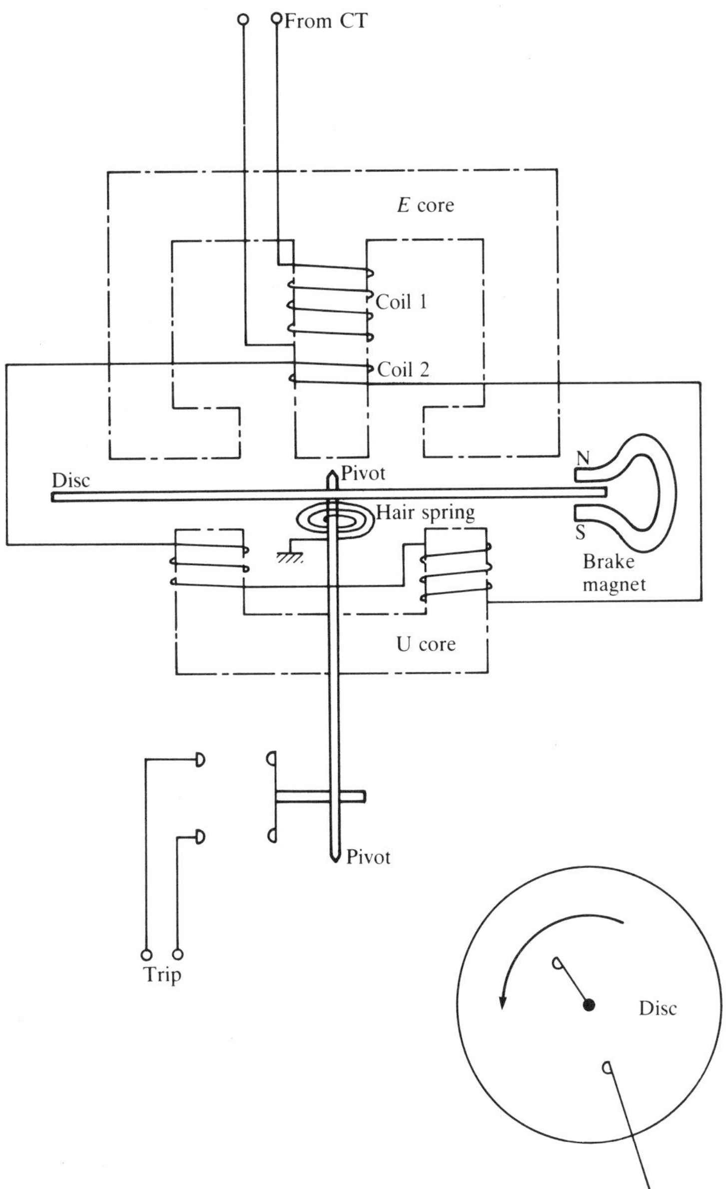

Figure 6.19

ing magnetic flux in the core, across the gap in which a circular copper or aluminium disc is situated, and into the bottom U core which is also of laminated construction.

Coils 1 and 2 make up a transformer and the alternating flux set up by the current in coil 1 induces a voltage in coil 2 which is 90° out of phase with the flux (see Chapter 1). This voltage drives a current through the two coils on the U core setting up a flux which crosses the gap into the E core. There are now two magnetic fluxes linking with the disc, both alternating and differing in phase. Under these conditions a torque is set up in the disc which would cause it to rotate if it were free to do so. The device is, in fact, a small two-phase induction motor. The disc is restrained by hair springs and at a predetermined value of current the torque produced in the disc overcomes that of the springs and the disc turns so closing a tripping circuit. The time taken to trip at a particular value of current is adjusted by altering the starting position of the disc so that it has a different distance to travel. The disc can be made to start turning at a selected value of current by altering the number of turns on coil 1.

This relay is used in association with a circuit breaker to protect large motors and sections of transmission and distribution systems.

OPERATING CHARACTERISTICS OF FUSES AND RELAYS

Figure 6.20 shows typical characteristics of HRC fuses, induction relays and thermal and magnetic relays. There are many different types designed for specific purposes so that it is only possible to make general comments.

Assuming that the fuse rating and full load currents are the same and that the induction relay disc makes its full travel, it may be seen from the curves that for currents greater than 2.5 times full load the fuse will clear a fault faster than any of the relays. For currents below this value the induction relay is faster.

There is a similar crossover point between the induction relay and the other relays in the region of ten times full load current. The induction relay is unable to operate much faster above this value of

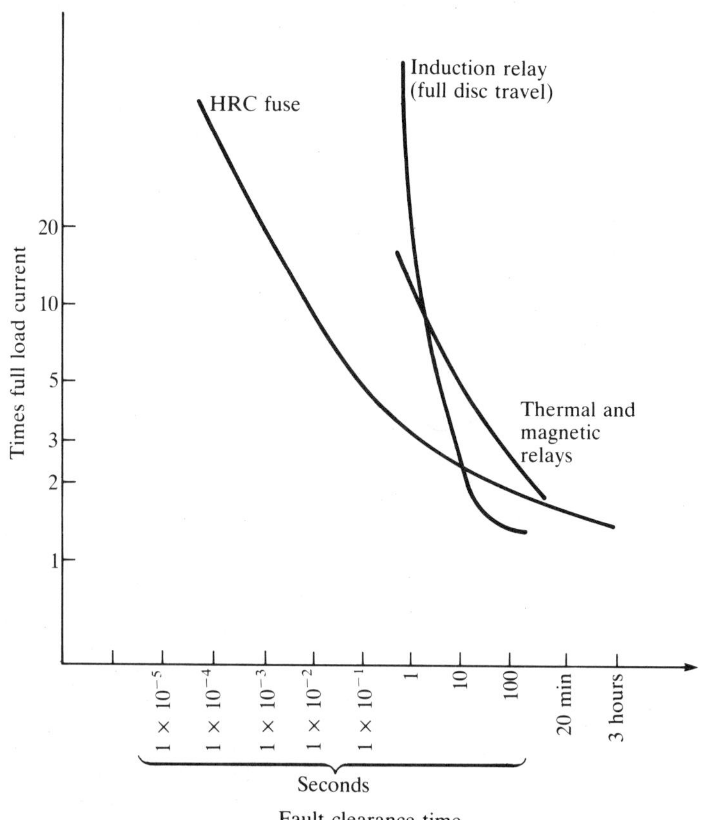

Figure 6.20

current due to saturation effects in the relay and the current transformer so that the characteristic is nearly vertical above ten times full-load current.

It follows that where protection is required against short circuit faults the fastest possible clearance time is essential to limit damage due to heating and from the mechanical stresses involved and this is achievable using the HRC fuse. From the characteristic in *Figure 6.20,* a current which in prospect could reach 100 times the full load value will be interrupted in less than 0.001 s.

For overcurrent protection a device which will carry some overcurrent for a period without deterioration and which can be reset is desirable. The relays associated with contactors are best suited to this function. Thermal and magnetic relays are cheaper than induction types and are used extensively for small- and medium-sized motor protection. In this field the thermistor and more recently the electronic analogue device are rapidly gaining ground. It is not possible to compare speeds for these types because they operate on a different principle and must be recommended on operational grounds rather than pure speed. With all these relays a series fuse protects the system against short-circuit faults. The fuse acts as back-up protection to relay and contactor. If an overload occurs and the relay fails to operate then the fuse will clear the circuit.

The induction relay tends to be used in association with a circuit breaker for feeder protection and large motors.

One further consideration when considering fuse or relay protection is that in a three-phase system it is possible for one fuse to clear leaving the other two phases live. Any associated motor will then operate in the single-phase mode across two lines which is undesirable. A relay operating for any reason will open its contactor or circuit breaker totally clearing the circuit.

EARTH LEAKAGE PROTECTION

In a single-phase system the current flowing along the live wire is equal in magnitude to that returning along the neutral wire unless the circuit has an earth fault. In a three-phase system the sum of the three line currents in a healthy circuit is zero. The fuse depends on faults being severe enough to cause very large currents to flow so clearing the fuse. If the earth leakage was through the human body due to contact with a live wire, the current would most likely not be large enough to clear the fuse but the shock could well be fatal. An earth leakage detection system much more sensitive than the fuse is clearly desirable.

THE CURRENT BALANCE (OR RESIDUAL CURRENT) EARTH LEAKAGE BREAKER

Figure 6.21 shows a current balance schematic for a single-phase supply. The live and neutral wires pass once or twice round the soft-iron core in opposite directions. When the currents in live and neutral wires have the same values the net magnetomotive force in the ring is zero and there is no magnetic flux in the ring to link with the detector coil. When the two currents differ, as they will do if an earth fault is present on the load, then there will be a resultant magnetisation of the ring. By transformer action a voltage will be induced in the detector coil which will give rise to a current in the

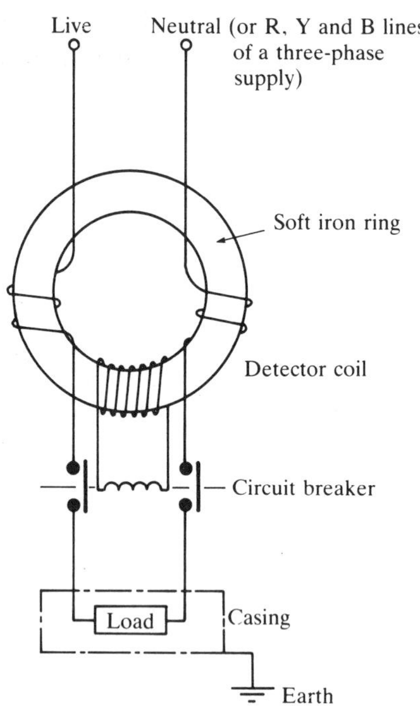

Figure 6.21

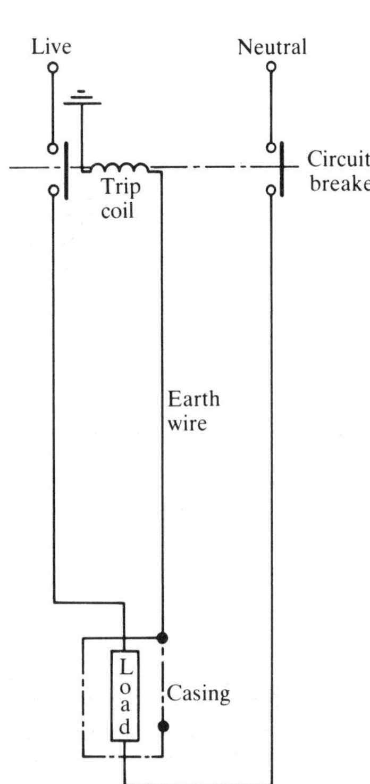

Figure 6.22

trip coil and the circuit breaker will open. An out-of-balance of only a few milliamperes is sufficient to cause operation. For three-phase operation, the three line wires link with the core. While the sum of the currents is zero all is well. Should an earth fault occur, the resultant current and flux will no longer be zero and the circuit breaker will open.

Voltage operated relay and circuit breaker

If a fault develops on the load such that the potential of the casing rises above that of earth, a current flows in the earth wire through the trip coil and the circuit breaker opens. Less than 40 V is required for operation at which level human safety should be assured.

Neutral current detection

Power supply transformers and generators are protected in a number of ways against overcurrents, out of balance currents and earth leakage. One of the ways of protection in the event of an earth fault is to detect the current returning from such a fault as it flows in the neutral connection using a current transformer.

In *Figure 6.23* an earth fault on one line from a high-voltage generator is envisaged. Its star point is earthed through a current-limiting resistance. Even a fairly small neutral current will cause the output from the current transformer to rise to a detectable value. When this occurs the circuit breaker is opened so de-energising the circuit. The operation of this device is much faster than that of an overcurrent device fitted in the supply line. Overcurrent devices are none the less required because should all three lines be faulted simultaneously, in theory at least, there would be the same value of current in each line resulting in no neutral current. The circuit breaker would need to be opened in response to excessive current rather than earth leakage.

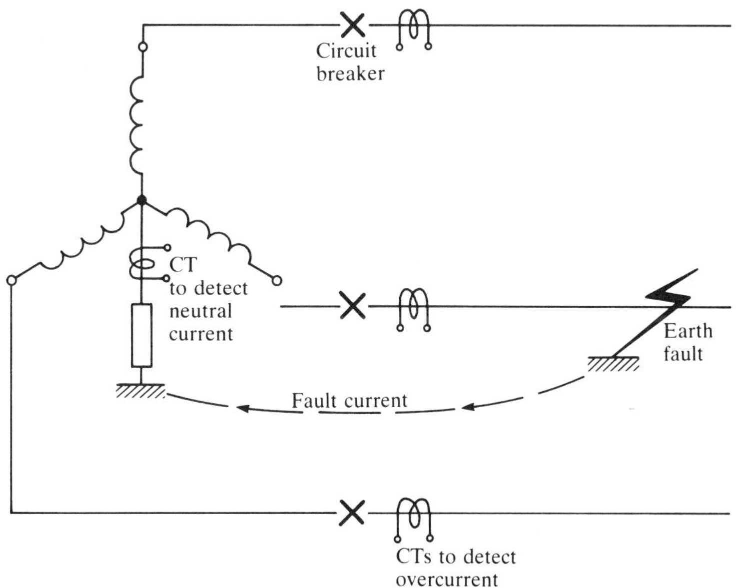

Figure 6.23

PROBLEMS

1 What is meant by the term *fault level*? What is its significance when considering the type of circuit protection to be used.
2 The star point of a distribution transformer is usually connected to earth, either directly or through a resistor. Describe two ways in which this earthed point is instrumental in de-energising a circuit should an earth fault occur.
3 Name, and briefly describe the construction of, two types of fuse employed in power circuits.
4 What are the advantages claimed for protective-multiple earthing as compared with single-point earthing?
5 What are the advantages and disadvantages of using a fuse to protect a circuit against an overcurrent as compared with using a relay and circuit breaker?
6 Why is an HRC fuse used in preference to a semi-enclosed type where the fault levels are high?
7 Draw a diagram to illustrate the terms: (i) pre-arcing time and (ii) arcing time, as associated with a fuse. Why would it be undesirable to reduce the arcing time to an extremely short duration? (*Hint:* think about the effect of circuit inductance.)
8 Define the terms: (i) circuit breaker, (ii) isolator and (iii) switch.
9 A particular type of switch which is electrically operated is called a contactor. What design features of a contactor and

circuit breaker will generally cause a contactor to automatically open should the power supply voltage dip whereas a circuit breaker will remain closed?

10 Name, and briefly describe the construction of, four types of circuit breaker.

11 What are the benefits of using a cross jet arc control device in a bulk-oil circuit breaker as compared with using plain-break contacts?

12 What is the difference between an air circuit breaker and an air-blast circuit breaker?

13 Why is it that an air-blast circuit breaker must be equipped with a series isolator?

14 What method is used in an air-blast circuit breaker to reduce the current level before finally blowing out the arc? (This method may be applied to bulk-oil circuit breakers though not illustrated in the text).

15 What benefits are claimed for the sulphur hexafluoride circuit breaker when compared with the air-blast circuit breaker?

16 What benefits are claimed for the vacuum circuit breaker when compared with all others of a similar rating?

17 What is a *thermal relay*? What method is used to give it good sensitivity?

18 As well as protecting against overcurrent the thermal relay may be adapted to protect against single-line faults. How is this achieved?

19 In a relay, what function is served by the *maintaining contacts*?

20 What feature in the magnetic-hydraulic type relay protects against operation by very short-term overloads?

21 What benefits are there to using thermistor type motor protection as compared with a thermal or magnetic relay mounted externally to the motor?

22 What are the benefits of using a residual current relay (balanced current relay) as compared to a fuse when the safety of personnel is to be considered?

23 Briefly describe the construction and operation of an induction-type relay. Why can this relay not operate as quickly as a fuse when dealing with a short-circuit fault?

24 All the relays dealt with in the chapter have what is called *inverse-time characteristics*. What is meant by this term?

7 Servomechanisms

Aims: At the end of this chapter you should be able to:

Explain the function of a servomechanism.
Discuss the requirement for and the action of various transducers.
Explain the action of the electrical amplifiers associated with servo systems; the cross-field machine and the magnetic amplifier.
Describe the action of the thyristor as an element in a servo system.

The word *servo* comes from the same root as *servant* and a servomechanism is one which controls a process automatically. One of the earliest servomechanisms was James Watt's centrifugal governor for steam engines. A pair of spring-loaded weights were mounted on the engine-driven shaft and were thrown outwards against a restraining spring by the rotational force. The weights controlled the steam valve. Any variation from the design speed of rotation would cause the weights to move thereby either closing or opening the steam valve. Such a system is known as a *closed-loop system* because there is an input to the system (steam through a control valve) causing an output (rotation of the shaft), the value of which is compared with the required value (set by altering the spring tension on the weights) and any error is fed back to the input (mechanical link between the governor weights and the steam valve) causing a remedial change to take place.

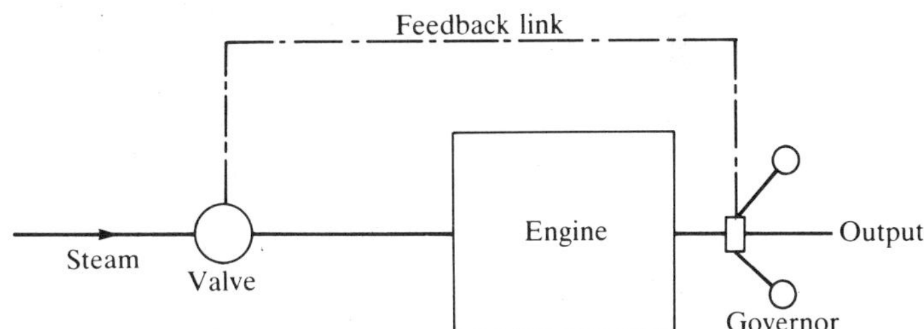

Figure 7.1

The basic arrangement is shown in *Figure 7.1*. The mechanism could be made much more sensitive by having some form of amplification in the feedback loop. In *Figure 7.1*, the governor parts and the steam-valve spindle are linked mechanically and so the movements are related by the length of various levers. If amplification of the governor motion could be achieved by employing an external power source, for a very small movement of the governor weights which would not be restricted by the mechanical forces imposed on it by the steam valve, the valve could be made to have a far greater response giving a considerable change in input power. The danger with this is that with a very large change in steam input the response could be too great and the speed change would overshoot. Consider the speed to be slightly too high, the governor moves to reduce the steam input, the steam valve overreacts so shutting too far, the speed drops and the governor needs to take action to re-open the valve. The final speed could be very variable, first too fast, rapidly changing to too slow, perhaps never stabilizing at the correct speed.

One method of overcoming this problem is to include damping on the steam valve. Mechanically this could be considered as having an auxiliary shaft connected to the steam valve spindle. The auxiliary shaft could drive a piston in an oil-filled cylinder which would impede motion but would have no effect when the whole system was in equilibrium, i.e. not changing. Such a system is fitted to road vehicles in the form of dampers to limit the effect of road irregularities. Without them the vehicle response to hitting a bump might well be similar to the underdamped curve in *Figure 7.2* which shows the responses of a mechanism including amplification and damping.

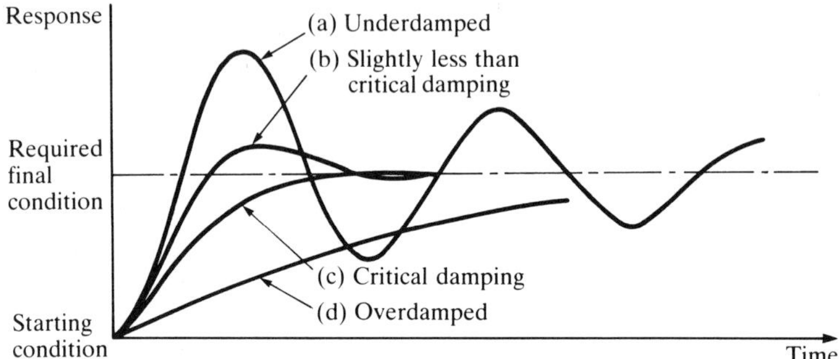

Figure 7.2

It is envisaged that the mechanism is at a datum condition which requires a large change to bring it to the required state. A substantial change is considered to make the response large enough to illustrate. The input is suddenly applied. With little or no damping the response would be as seen in *Figure 7.2(a)*. There will be a rapid change in output condition, possibly the speed or position of a shaft, and the required position will be overshot. Successive corrections will cause an oscillatory condition. With a damped mechanism there will be one particular amount of damping which will cause the final condition to be approached without any overshoot. This degree of damping is known as *critical damping* (*Figure 7.2(c)*). With slightly less than the critical value there will be some degree of overshoot. With far too much damping the final condition is approached very slowly (*Figure 7.2(d)*) taking a considerable time to reach the required value. Slight under damping gives the fastest time to the required final condition.

A complete schematic servo system is shown in *Figure 7.3*. Starting on the left there is a mechanism for setting the required output condition, speed, position or any required process state. This will typically involve setting a potentiometer to give a particular voltage input. The set reference is compared with the signal which is coming back from the output transducer which is sending back a signal dictated by the final condition as it is at the moment. If there is any difference between the returning output signal and that set on the reference then an error is indicated; the output is not exactly what is required.

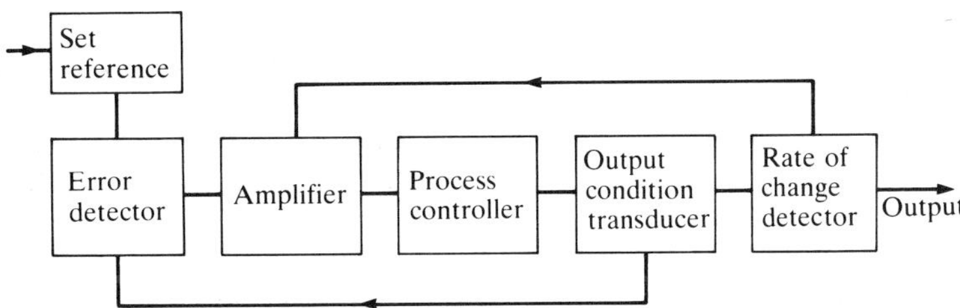

Figure 7.3

The difference between the two signals, the error signal, is fed into the next stage which is a large power amplifier. According to the system involved this might be an electrical amplifier or a hydraulic or pneumatic amplifier in which small changes in a fluid pressure is caused to create very large output pressure or flow changes. The output from the amplifier feeds the process controller. In the steam engine above this was the steam valve. In other systems it might be an electric motor, a valve supplying fuel to an engine or an electronic controller of a heating or cooling system. As previously stated, the actual performance of the process is measured by the output condition transducer.

Finally, at the end of the control chain is a damping device. This may be a damper containing oil as envisaged above. As an alternative to this, damping may be created artificially. A device for measuring the rate of change of the output is added to the control line and its output is fed back to the main amplifier. When the rate of change of output is high the signal from the device is high. This is used to reduce the response of the main amplifier so reducing the risk of an overshoot. When the output approaches the ideal, the rate of change of output is small, the damping effect virtually disappears and the full amplifier gain is used to correct the remaining error. The overall response of the system depends on the ratio of the output from the damping circuit to the gain of the amplifier and may be changed over the range of responses shown in *Figure 7.2*.

TRANSDUCERS

The output condition is sensed using a transducer which is a device which gives an electrical output signal in response to a mechanical input. Some examples are:

1 *Strain gauges*. The resistance of a wire or piece of semiconductor material changes when it is bent or stretched. The measuring element will become one arm of a resistance Wheatstone bridge. As the specimen is distorted the bridge becomes unbalanced and the current in the detector arm is used to create the error signal. The servosystem would be activated to correct whatever was causing the stretching.

2 *Position indicators:* (a) Variable inductance. As a body moves it may be caused to move an iron core with respect to a coil thus changing its inductance. The inductance change will be detected in a bridge circuit as in (i).

(b) Variable capacitance. One conductor moving with respect to another, without touching each other, will cause a change in capacitance between them. The change in capacitance can be detected in a bridge circuit and used as in (a) above.

(c) Variable resistance. Movement of body can be caused to move the wiper arm of a potentiometer so producing a changing potential difference between the wiper and one end of the potentiometer.

3 *Speed.* A small generator with a permanent magnet field and connected to a shaft the speed of which is to be controlled, gives an output voltage which is proportional to the speed of the shaft.

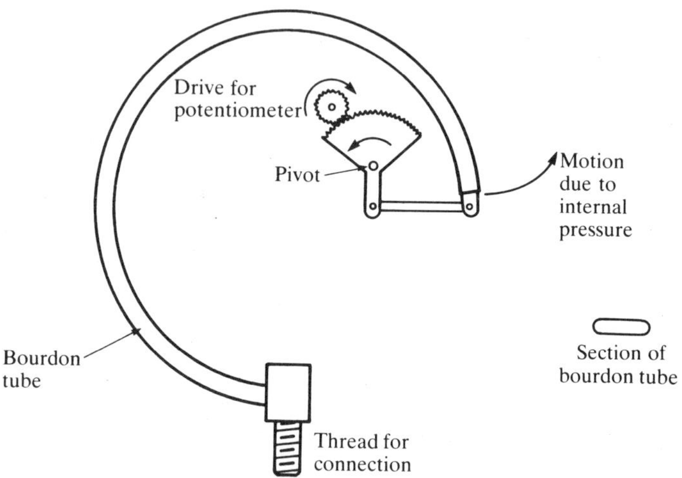

Figure 7.4

4 *Pressure.* (a) The Bourdon tube. An oval cross-section tube is closed at one end and formed into a coil as in *Figure 7.4*. Applying fluid pressure to the inside of the tube causes it to unwind slightly. The movement of the closed end can be used to move the wiper of a potentiometer so giving a change in potential difference as in 2(c) above.

(b) Piezo type. Applying pressure directly to a Piezoelectric sensor results in an output voltage directly proportional to pressure.

5 *Temperature.* There are many types of temperature transducer available among which are (a) the mercury pressure type. Expanding mercury is used to pressurise a Bourdon tube so giving an output proportional to temperature as in (4)(a) above.

(b) Resistance type. A metallic element will change its resistance with changes in temperature. The element will form one arm of a resistance Wheatstone bridge as in 1 above.

ELECTRICAL AMPLIFIERS

Cross-field machines

Cross-field machines are, in effect, rotating transformers for direct current applications. They are ideally suited for operation in servosystems responding to a small change in control current by giving a large change in either output current or output voltage. All generators are in fact amplifiers since their output current is much larger than their field current. Their response time is much too slow for use in servosystems, however. It might take several seconds for the output to fully respond to a change in the field control rheostat. In order that the machine may be used as an element in a control system it is necessary to have high gain and a very short response time.

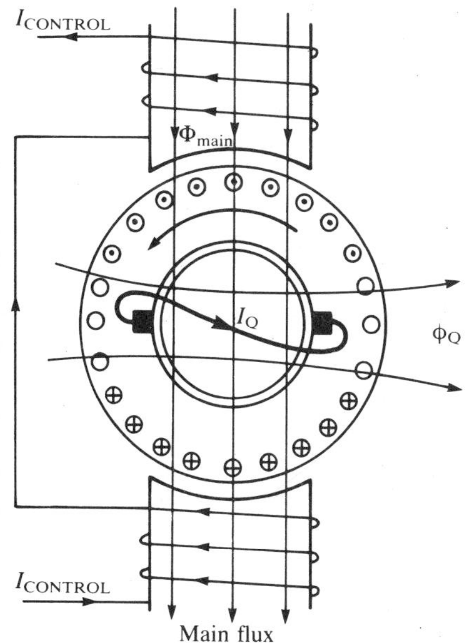

Figure 7.5

The cross-field machine consists of a conventional two-pole d.c. generator with two extra brushes at right angles to the main brushes. It will generally be driven by an induction motor connected to a three-phase system.

In the normal d.c. generator, the brushes which supply the load current are situated on commutator segments connected to coils outside the main magnetic field. In the cross-field machine these brushes are short circuited and for an anti-clockwise armature rotation the direction of the coil currents together with the magnetic flux produced by these currents is shown in *Figure 7.5*. Because the flux is at right angles to the main-pole flux it is called quadrature flux, ϕ_Q. This flux will be much larger than the main flux since the current in the short circuit will be large. To deduce the polarity and direction of ϕ_Q, use the right-hand grip or screw rule on the armature currents. The main flux Φ_{main} is created by the control current, the value of which will determine the output from the machine.

Now consider the effect separately for the moment of adding two more brushes directly under the poles which will supply load current. The armature conductors are being driven through ϕ_Q. The

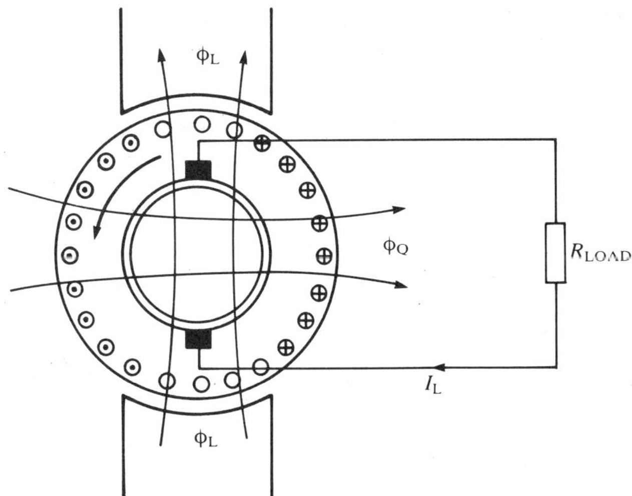

Figure 7.6

potential difference between these two brushes, and hence the magnitude of the load current and cross flux Φ_1, is proportional to Φ_Q. The quantities are shown in *Figure 7.6.* Again, to determine the polarity and direction of Φ_L use the right-hand grip or screw rule on the new armature currents.

Φ_L is in direct opposition to the main flux. The resultant flux Φ_R in the vertical direction as drawn has a magnitude:

$$\phi_R = (\Phi_{main} - \phi_L)$$

Combining the two effects in *Figure 7.7* it is seen that I_Q is in fact due to the armature conductors cutting the resultant flux Φ_R and therefore that the magnitude of I_Q and Φ_Q is a function of Φ_R.

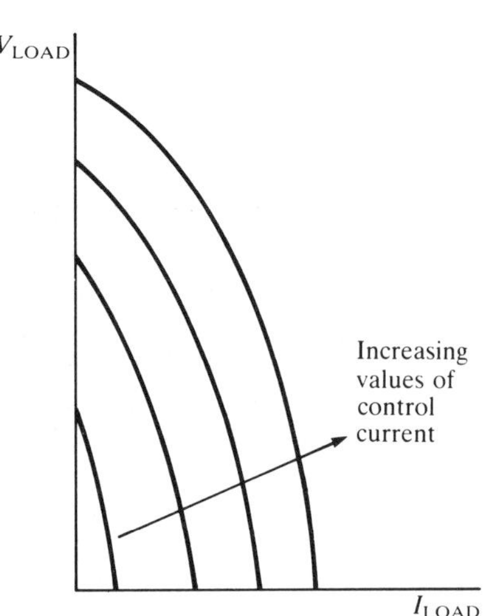

Figure 7.8

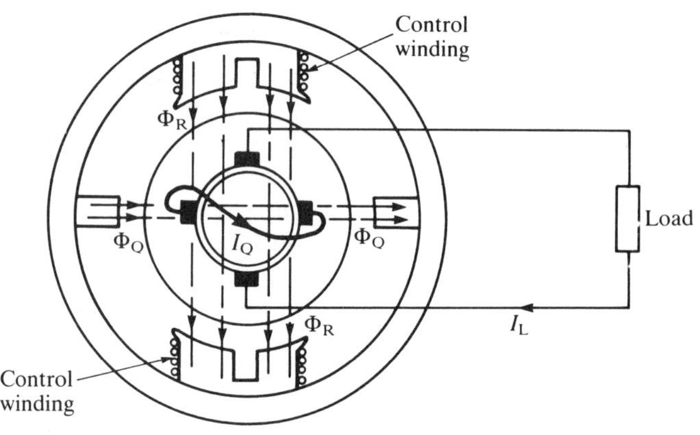

Figure 7.7

The characteristics of the device are shown in *Figure 7.8.* The load current I_L will tend to be constant for a particular value of control current. For very small values of I_L, Φ_L will be small so that the resultant flux Φ_R will be relatively large. I_Q and Φ_Q will be large so that the load voltage will be large. For large load currents Φ_L will be large, Φ_R will be small so that I_Q and Φ_Q will be small. The load voltage is proportional to Φ_Q so that this will also be small. Increasing the control current shifts the characteristic, giving greater load currents.

The device is a current amplifier capable of delivering very large currents when excited by small control currents. It is particularly useful where a d.c. motor is being accelerated since this device delivers virtually constant current over a wide range of voltage giving constant acceleration and torque. It is also used for excitation of synchronous generators which requires large direct currents with the capability of rapid change.

The characteristics may be changed to suit particular applications by adding compensating windings to the main and quadrature axes.

MAGNETIC AMPLIFIERS

Figure 7.9 shows an iron-cored coil being fed from an alternating supply. The phase relationship between the applied voltage and the coil current is shown in *Figure 7.10.* The current lags on the applied voltage by very nearly 90° since the circuit resistance is very small compared with the inductive reactance. The current produces a magnetic flux Φ in the core.

The magnitude of the flux will depend on the number of turns N on the coil and with the instantaneous value of the current i amperes; zero current, zero flux; maximum current, maximum flux. The flux wave will therefore be in phase with the current wave. Applied voltage, current and flux waves are shown in *Figure 7.11*.

The relationship between the exciting amperes ($N \times i$) and flux Φ can be deduced from the hysteresis loop for the material.

$$\text{Flux density } B \text{ tesla} = \frac{\text{Flux } \Phi}{\text{Area}} \quad \therefore \text{flux } \Phi = B \times \text{Area}$$

$$H = \frac{\text{amperes}}{\text{length (m)}}\frac{N \times i}{l} \quad \therefore i = \frac{Hl}{N}$$

For a material like cold-rolled grain orientated steel which saturates quite suddenly, the hysteresis loop is shown slightly idealised in *Figure 7.12*. A typical saturation flux density of 1.6 tesla is indicated.

The original axes are those for B and H. Multiplying the values: vertically by the cross-sectional area of the core, A m^2 and horizontally by l/N the scales become ϕ and i as indicated in brackets.

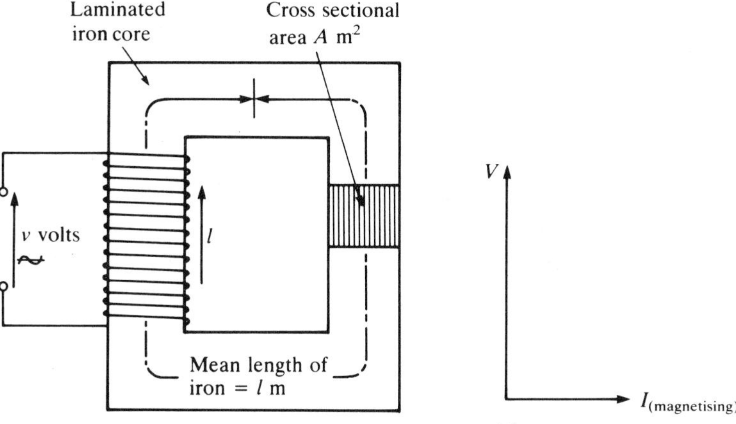

Figure 7.9

Figure 7.10

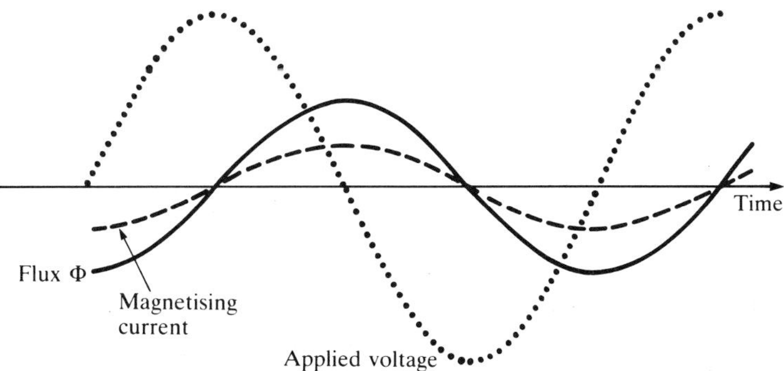

Figure 7.11

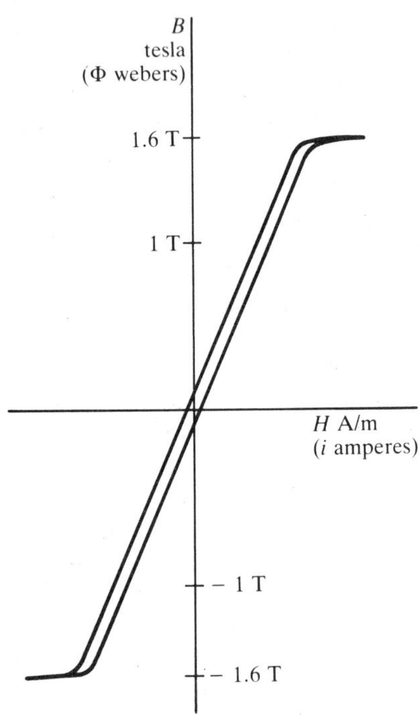

Figure 7.12

From Faraday we have the formula:

$$e = \frac{N \mathrm{d}\Phi}{\mathrm{d}t} \text{ volts}$$

and using Lenz's law we know that the direction of the induced e.m.f. in a coil is such as to oppose the applied voltage. In *Figure 7.9*, the applied voltage v volts is opposed by induced e.m.f. e volts. The net driving voltage in the circuit is $(v - e)$ volts. It is this resultant voltage which drives the current in *Figure 7.11*. The net driving voltage is very small and needs only to overcome the resistance of the circuit.

$$(v - e) = iR \therefore v - \frac{N \mathrm{d}\Phi}{\mathrm{d}t} = iR$$

As an example, let $N = 500$ turns and the cross-sectional area of the core be 0.001 m². For saturation flux density 1.6 tesla this means a maximum flux of $1.6 \times 0.001 = 1.6 \times 10^{-3}$ webers.

Let the frequency of the supply be 50 Hz.

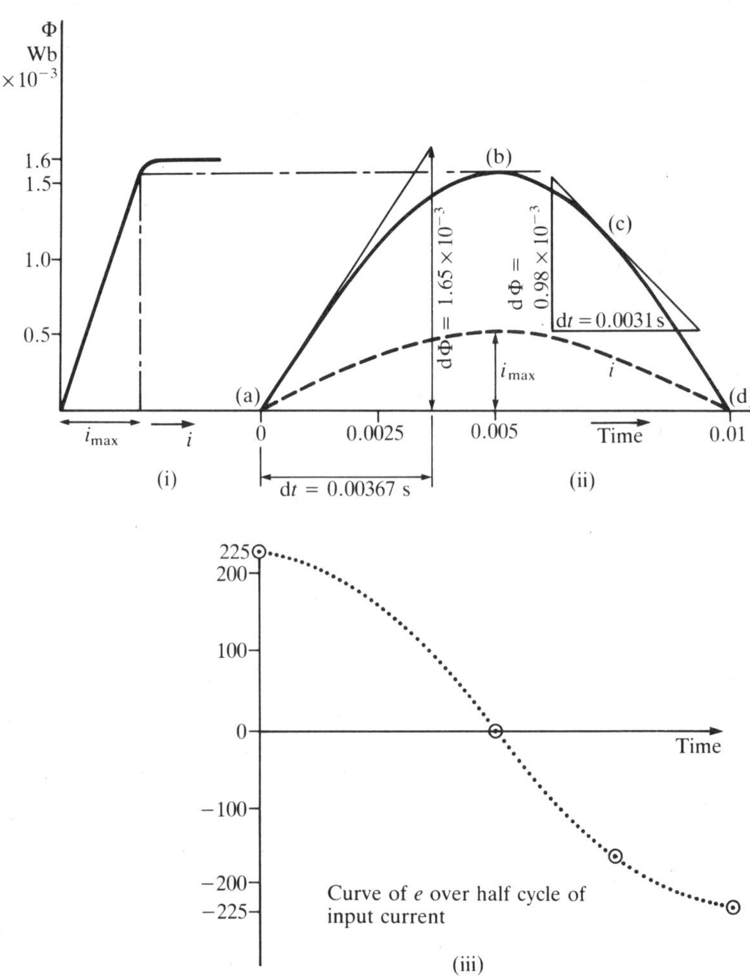

Figure 7.13

In *Figure 7.13(ii)* a current is shown as in *Figure 7.11*. This current is producing a magnetic flux with maximum value just less than 1.6×10^{-3} webers, i.e. just less than the saturation value shown in *Figure 7.13(i)*. At point (a) in *Figure 7.13(ii)* a tangent is drawn and a triangle constructed.

The value of $\dfrac{\mathrm{d}\,\Phi}{\mathrm{d}t}$ scales at $\dfrac{1.65 \times 10^{-3}}{0.00367} = 0.4496$

The back e.m.f. $= N\dfrac{\mathrm{d}\,\Phi}{\mathrm{d}t} = 500 \times 0.4496 = 224.79$ volts

At point (b) in *Figure 7.13(ii)* the value of $\mathrm{d}\,\Phi/\mathrm{d}t$ is zero. It has risen to its maximum value and is about to start falling. The back e.m.f. at this point must therefore be zero. At point (c) $\mathrm{d}\,\Phi = -0.98 \times 10^{-3}$ webers and the corresponding value of $\mathrm{d}t = 0.0031$ seconds. $\mathrm{d}\,\Phi/\mathrm{d}t = -0.317$ and the back e.m.f. $= 500 \times -0.317 = -158$ volts. At point (d) the slope $\mathrm{d}\,\Phi/\mathrm{d}t$ has exactly the same value as at (a) but is negative. The e.m.f. at (d) is therefore -224.79 volts. Further points can be tested over the flux wave and it is found that the values arrived at, when plotted, give a wave which coincides with that for v, the applied voltage, in *Figure 7.11*. Indeed, at all times the induced voltage e is slightly less than v, the difference being used to drive current resistance as mentioned before.

Now consider the effect of increasing the magnitude of the applied voltage so increasing the value of the magnetising current i amperes.

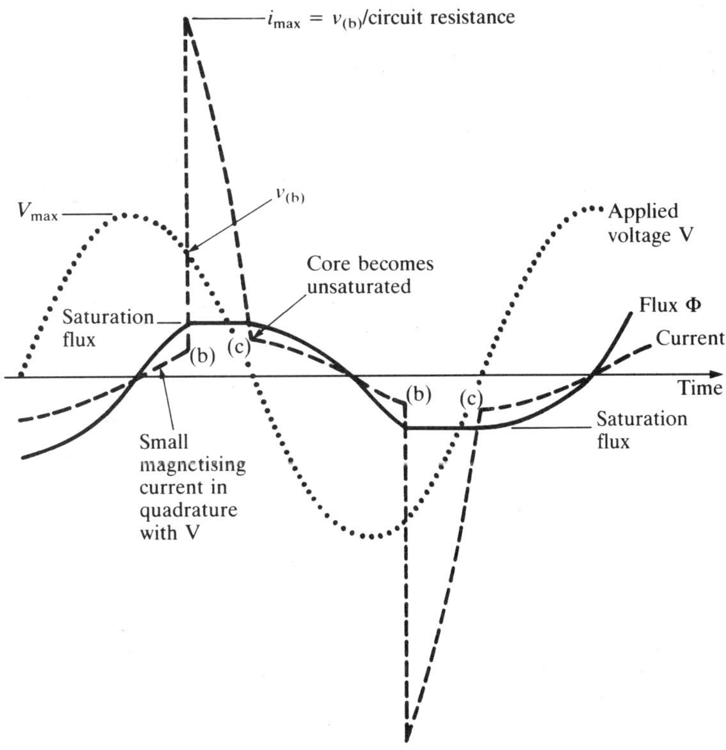

Figure 7.14

Increasing the value of the current increases the magnitude of the magnetic flux.

Consider the current in *Figure 7.14*. As it rises from the origin to point (b) the flux rises at a faster rate than in *Figure 7.13* so giving a greater value to $d\Phi/dt$ and hence a greater back e.m.f. This back e.m.f. opposes the greater applied voltage and all goes as previously until point (b) is reached. At (b) the saturation flux has been reached and no further increase in flux is possible. However large the current would be between points (b) and (c) the flux remains constant. While the flux is constant $d\Phi/dt$ is zero and the back e.m.f. is zero.

Now since $v - e = iR$ and $e = 0$, $v - 0 = iR$ and $i = v/R$

In the example chosen (*Figures 7.9* and *7.10*) we have considered the resistance to be very small so that the value of current will be extremely high. It would be necessary to add external resistance to the circuit to prevent disruptive values of current flowing. During the period (b) to (c) in *Figure 7.14*, the only thing limiting the size of current is the resistance. In a resistance the current in phase with the supply voltage so that the current wave has the same shape as v, the applied voltage, during this period. The current rises instantaneously from point (b) to a high value and then falls with sinusoidal form (it follows the voltage wave) until the current is small enough not to saturate the core when the original current wave is resumed as in *Figure 7.11*. The waveforms are repeated in the negative half cycle.

Instead of increasing the voltage level the same result would be achieved by reducing the area of the core and hence the value of saturation flux.

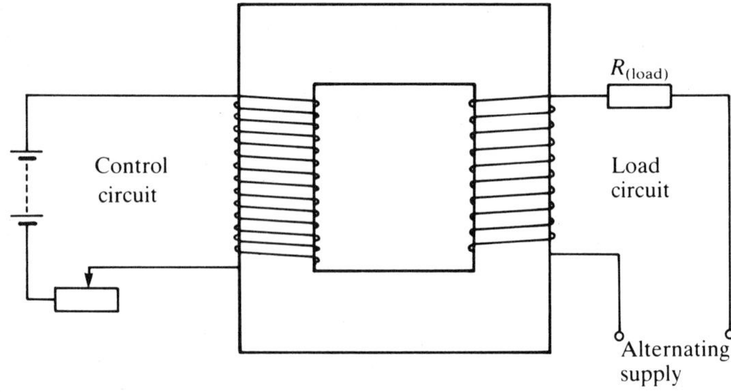

Figure 7.15

In *Figure 7.15* the iron core, as in Figure 9, now carries two windings: one fed from a direct voltage and in which the current may be varied; the other is fed from an alternating supply. The requirement is to be able to vary the average current and hence the power in the load resistance R. The design is such that with no current flowing in the control circuit the impedance of the coil on the load side remains high, that is to say, the core does not saturate and the back e.m.f. is maintained as in *Figure 7.13*. The current in the load is the small magnetising current for the core.

What will be the effect of a direct current flowing in the control winding? The core will be partly saturated with a steady flux in one direction before any alternating current flows. For the case where the direct control current flows in the same direction as alternating current during a positive half cycle, part way through the positive half cycle the core will saturate under the influence of both currents and the back e.m.f. will fall to zero. The current is only limited by the load resistance which means that the full alternating supply voltage appears across the load terminals for the period of core saturation. During the negative half cycle of the alternating supply the core will never saturate because the direct control current and the alternating current are flowing in opposite directions keeping the core flux low.

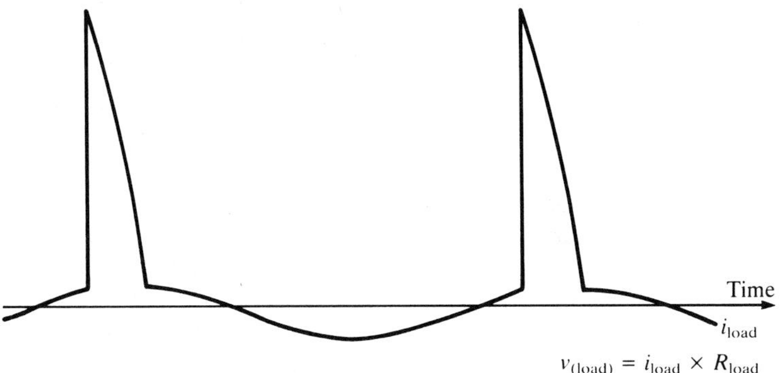

Figure 7.16

The waveform of the load current and the voltage which appears across *R* are shown in *Figure 7.16*.

Variation in load current is thus achieved by varying the value of current in the control winding. With zero control current only magnetising current flows in the load resistance so that it dissipates very little power. By passing increasing values of current in the control winding saturation can be caused to occur at different times during the cycle. Point (b) in *Figure 7.14* is moved to the left, i.e. the full supply voltage is impressed on the load resistance earlier in time so that the large load current flows for a longer period producing more power. It should be noted that during the periods when the core is not saturated the changing flux set up by the load winding is linking with the control winding and is inducing an e.m.f. in it in the same manner as in the single-phase transformer. This e.m.f. drives an alternating current in the control circuit with consequent power losses.

This is the basic principle of operation of the magnetic amplifier. However in this simple arrangement substantial load current flows only during one half cycle and it is necessary to adapt the design for full wave operation and to improve the ratio of power output to control power.

THE THREE-LIMB ARRANGEMENT

In *Figure 7.17* the control winding is on the centre limb. Direct current in this winding will set up a magnetic flux in a particular direction. As illustrated here, upward in the centre limb, one half of

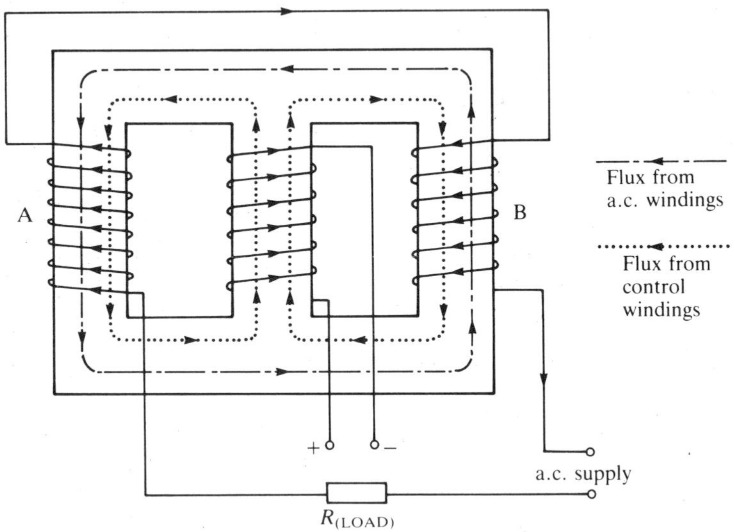

Figure 7.17

the flux downward in each of the two outer limbs. The outer limbs carry the load winding split into two halves. These two coils may be in series as illustrated or in parallel. The currents in the two coils must flow in opposite directions. *Figure 7.17* shows current directions during the positive half cycle of alternating input. The alternating magnetic flux from the right-hand coil passes downwards through the centre limb and that from the left-hand coil passes upward through the centre limb. While neither limb is saturated this means effectively that there is no alternating flux in the centre limb since these two fluxes cancel. The resultant flux path is round the outside of the core as shown in *Figure 7.17*. In this situation neither of the outer limbs is saturated and there is no induced alternating e.m.f. in the control winding.

When alternating and direct currents are flowing simultaneously the flux in the outer limbs is the sum of the two individual fluxes. In one limb the flux will be large leading to early saturation (Limb A in *Figure 7.17* during positive half cycles) and in Limb B the resultant flux is low. A diagramatic arrangement of *Figure 7.17* is shown in *Figure 7.18*. Consider the control circuit to have a low impedance to alternating current. This would be the case, for example, if the direct control current were derived from a power supply being fed from an a.c. source and employing a rectifier and large smoothing capacitor.

In *Figure 7.18(a)* the limb on which coil A is wound saturates, the flux in that limb is constant, the induced e.m.f. falls to zero so that the coil offers no impedance to alternating current. The circuit is now as shown in *Figure 7.18(b)* coil A being effectively a zero impedance link. What is left is a single-phase transformer. The secondary of that transformer is the control circuit which has a very low impedance. It acts as a short-circuited secondary to the load circuit's primary. The input impedance of a transformer with a short-circuited secondary is very low (see the section on Short-circuit test, in Chapter 1) so that during saturation the circuit effectively

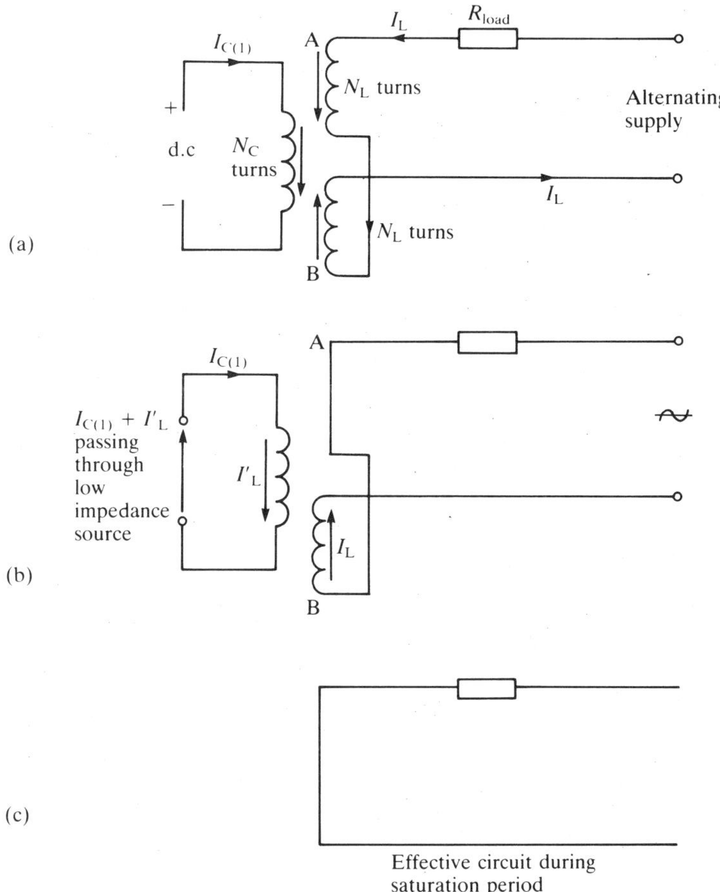

Figure 7.18

becomes as shown in *Figure 7.18(c)*. The full voltage is impressed upon the load resistance. The load current I_L flowing in N_L turns gives rise to a balancing current $I_L{}'$ in the control winding of N_c turns. The control winding carries the direct control current together with the load balancing current $I_L{}'$. Since it takes very little control current $I_{c(1)}$ to saturate the core, $I_L{}'$ is generally very much larger than $I_{c(1)}$. We will call the sum of the currents in the control winding I_c:

$$I_c = I_{c(1)} + I_L{}'$$

To a close approximation the size and form of the control current will be that of $I_L{}'$.

The transformer equivalence holds good in that:

$$I_c N_c = I_L N_L \text{ or } \frac{I_c}{I_L} = \frac{N_L}{N_c}$$

During the negative half cycle the process is repeated exactly, limb B being driven into saturation and a further spike of balancing current is reflected into the control circuit, the same way up as formerly since the load windings are reverse connected. (Winding B is upside

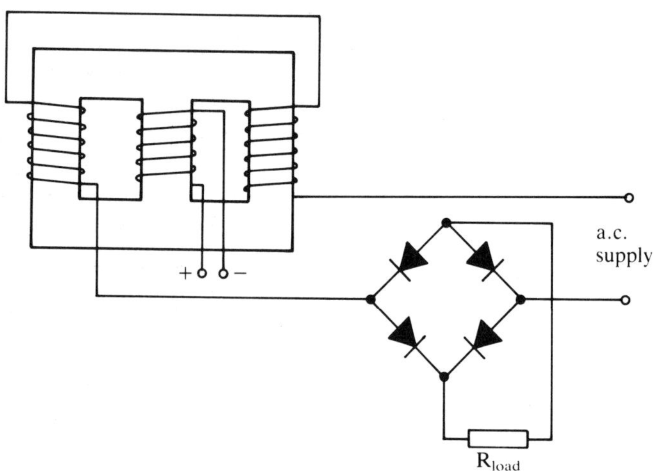

Figure 7.19

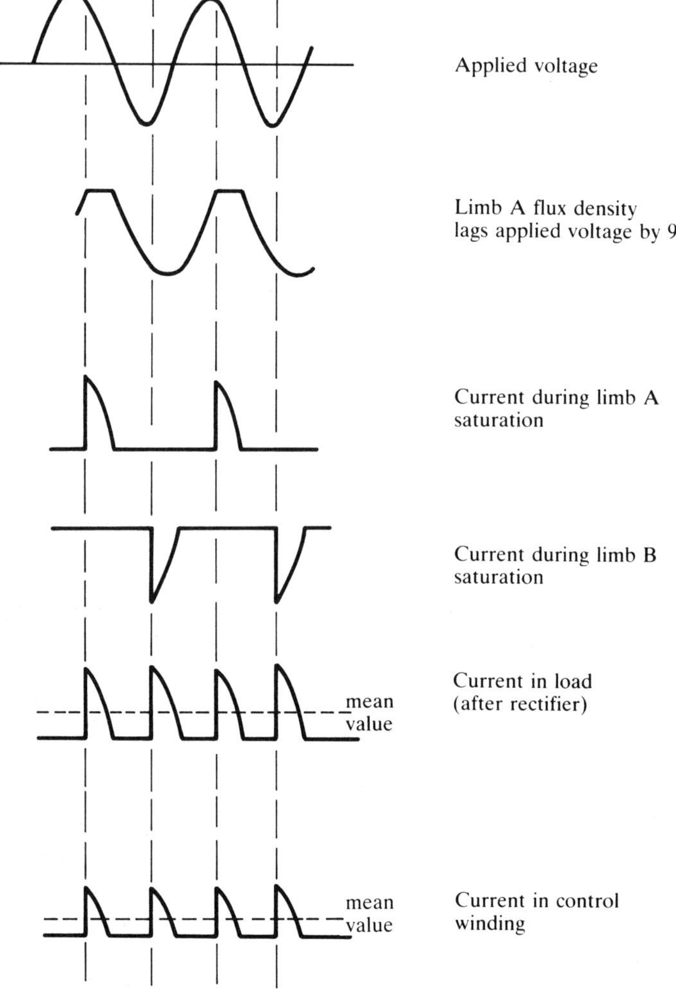

Figure 7.20

down as drawn in *Figure 7.18*.) Reversing the polarity of the control voltage means that limb B will saturate first but all the waveforms will be unchanged. Control polarity is thus not significant. A direct-current amplifier may be created by rectifying the alternating current flowing in the load circuit before passing it to the load. We then have a direct current in the control winding determining the size of a direct current in the load. This is illustrated in *Figure 7.19*. The relevant waveforms are shown in *Figure 7.20*.

In *Figure 7.20* observe the mean levels of load current and of control winding current. Since the same value of load current will be obtained whichever polarity of control voltage is used, the characteristic is a symmetrical one as shown in *Figure 7.21*. With zero current in the control winding and so zero ampere turns there will be a very small current in the load being the magnetising current for the core. Increasing the control current causes the load current to increase in direct proportion. The characteristic is therefore a linear one on either side of zero control ampere turns. If the load resistance is very high linearity is lost since the magnetising characteristic of the core becomes more significant than the load in determining the value of the current.

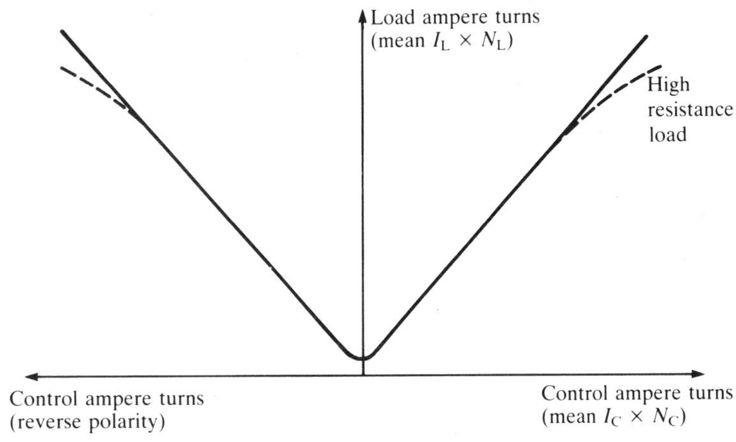

Figure 7.21

POWER GAIN

$$\text{Power gain} = \frac{\text{Power supplied to the load}}{\text{Power dissipated in control circuit}}$$

$$= \frac{I_L^2 R_L}{I_c^2 R_c}$$

and since $I_c N_c \simeq I_L N_L \quad I_c \simeq I_L N_L / N_c$

$$\text{Power gain} = \frac{I_L^2 R_L}{(I_L N_L / N_c)^2 R_c}$$

$$= \frac{I_L^2 N_c^2 R_L}{I_L^2 N_L^2 R_c}$$

$$= \frac{N_c^2 R_L}{N_L^2 R_c}$$

In order to keep the control circuit impedance low N_c is limited so that R_c will be small. Associating this with a fairly high load resistance makes the term R_L/R_c quite high. However the number of turns on the load winding is high so that the term $(N_c/N_L)^2$ tends to be very small. The power gain is, in practice, strictly limited. Gains of little more than unity and up to ten being reasonable. It is necessary to improve the gain of the amplifier by the use of feedback.

THE REGENERATIVE FEEDBACK AMPLIFIER

Figure 7.22 shows the arrangement of a regenerative-feedback amplifier. As in *Figure 7.19* the load is fed via a bridge rectifier. In addition, the load current passes through another rectifier feeding the rectified load current through a feedback winding of N_F turns. This is wound on the centre limb of the core together with the control winding. The load current therefore reinforces the effect of the control current giving much greater gain.

With no feedback $I_cN_c = I_LN_L$

Introducing feedback turns N_F carrying I_L amperes gives an additional m.m.f. of I_LN_F ampere turns on the control limb of the core.

$$\therefore I_cN_c + I_LN_F = I_LN_L \text{ or transposing, } I_cN_c = I_LN_L - I_LN_F = I_L[N_L - N_F]$$

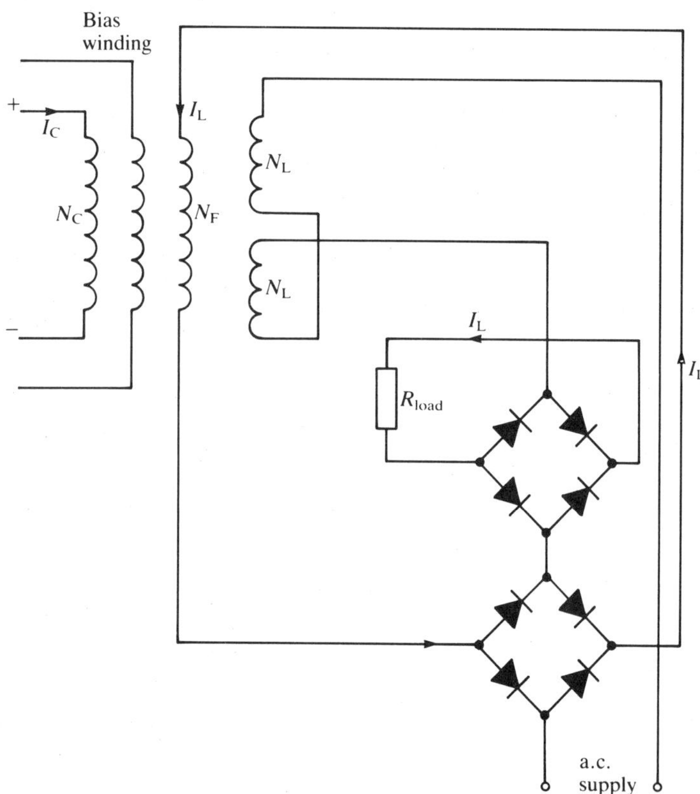

Figure 7.22

$$\text{Current gain} = \frac{I_L}{I_c} \qquad = \frac{N_c}{[N_L - N_F]}$$

$$\text{Power gain with feedback} = \frac{I_L{}^2R_L}{I_c{}^2R_c} = (\text{Current gain})^2 \times R_L/R_c$$

$$= \left\{\frac{N_c}{N_L - N_F}\right\}^2 \times \frac{R_L}{R_c}$$

The feedback winding will have less turns than the load winding. Should $N_L = N_F$ in the power gain expression $(N_L - N_F) = 0$ and hence gain $= \infty$ and the device would be unstable.

The effect on the characteristic is shown in *Figure 7.23*. We will consider the case where N_F = 80% of N_L. We are using 80% feedback.

Point (a) on the new characteristic is obtained as follows:
On the original characteristic $I_cN_c = I_LN_L = 70$ ampere turns. The term I_LN_F will therefore be 80% of I_LN_L.
We have $I_cN_c = I_LN_L - I_LN_F$
so that the new value of I_cN_c = 70 ampere turns – 80% of 70 ampere turns
= 70 – 56
= 14 ampere turns.
For load ampere turns of 70, the new control ampere turns are 14.

One further point will be considered on the reverse control ampere turns side. On the original curve to obtain load ampere turns of +50, the control ampere turns were –50. On the new curve at point (b), the new control ampere turns are –50 – (80% of +50) = –90 ampere turns.

The complete curve may be constructed in this manner. Observe that with the control ampere turns in a positive sense it requires very small control winding input to obtain large load outputs.

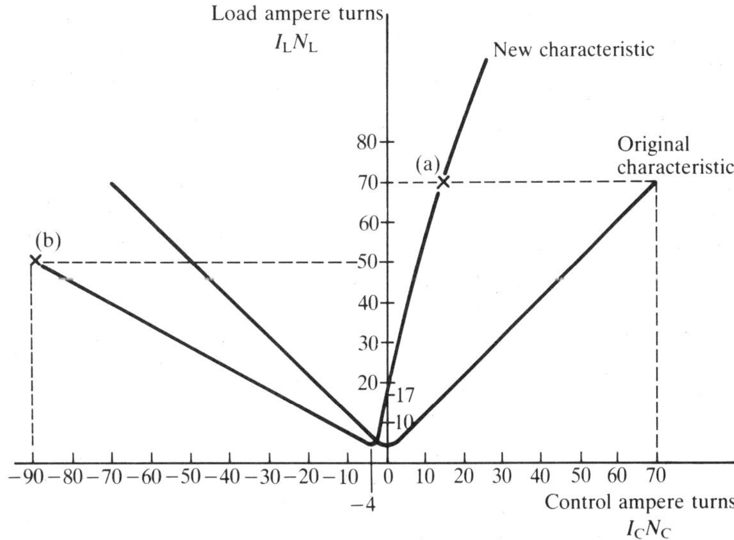

Figure 7.23

BIAS On the new characteristic shown in *Figure 7.23* it will be observed that with zero control ampere turns, the load ampere turns have a value of 17. This means that with no control current there is a fairly large load current. If this is undesirable a further winding may be added to the centre limb of the reactor. This is called a bias winding. It may carry a standing current to cause the load current to be a minimum when the control current is zero. For the case considered, the bias current would need to introduce a negative m.m.f. of approximately 4 ampere turns to fulfil this objective. For some purposes it may be desirable to have a standing load current when the control stands at zero in which case the bias can be set at the appropriate value. The additional bias winding is shown in *Figure 7.22*.

FREQUENCY RESPONSE We have examined the action of the magnetic amplifier in amplifying direct current. A small value of direct current flowing in the control winding results in a larger (average) direct current flowing in the load. The load carries two pulses of current per cycle of alternating voltage supplied to the load winding. This device is not an amplifier which one could use to produce large outputs of exactly the same waveform as the input as is required, for example, in an audio amplifier where the very small alternating voltages read from a tape or disc need to be magnified without distortion and fed to a loudspeaker. For this application the transistor amplifier would most probably be employed.

The magnetic amplifier is used for the control of electrical energy. Unlike the transistor amplifier it has considerable inductance. Circuits with resistance and inductance cannot respond immediately to the input, a time delay is always in evidence. Suppose a sudden input E volts is applied to the control winding. The control current cannot establish itself to its full value immediately but rises to that value exponentially according to the formula:

$$i_c = E/R_c\{1 - \exp(-R_c t/L_c)\}$$

Where R_c = resistance of the control circuit
L_c = inductance of the control circuit
t = time in seconds after the step voltage E volts is applied

The output current establishes itself at the same rate. It follows that many changes in rapid succession at the input cannot be accommodated, only a few changes per second being possible. The ratio $R_c : L_c$ is the main factor in determining the speed of response of the magnetic amplifier.

There will also be a delay in output response. Once saturated the output current is controlled by the load resistance and cannot change in response to a control change until the core has reverted to the unsaturated state and the voltage wave has progressed into the next half cycle to a point at which the core can saturate again. The interval between successive saturations is in the region of one half of a cycle of the input. It follows that delays in output response could be minimised by operating at a high frequency and some systems operate at 400 Hz.

THE THYRISTOR

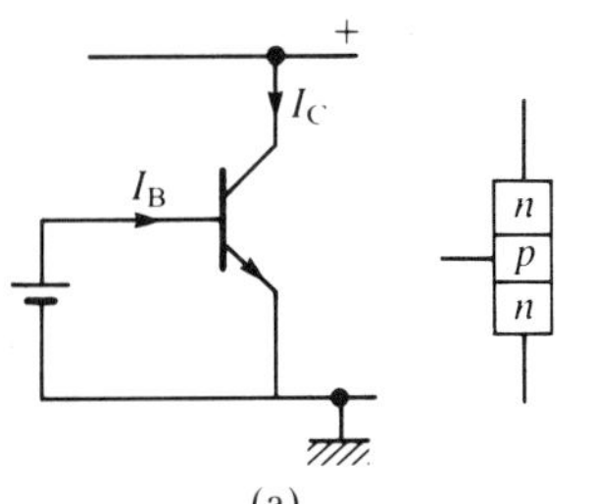

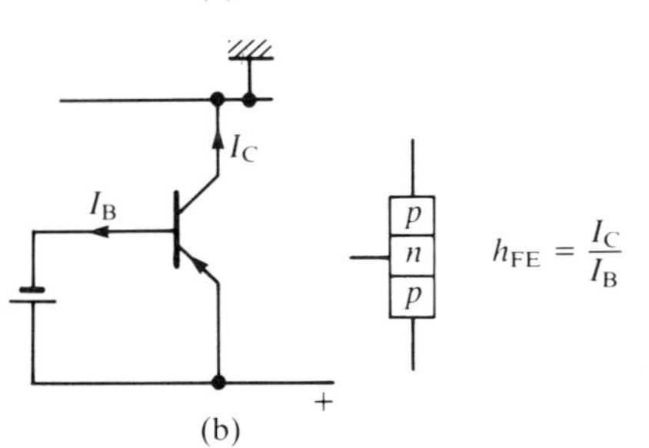

Figure 7.24

The thyristor is a solid state switch and its action is best examined in terms of the two transistor analogy. An *n-p-n* bipolar junction transistor requires a current to be supplied to its base when its collector is at a postive potential with respect to its emitter in order to obtain current amplification. For static direct current conditions this is quoted:

$$\text{Current gain} = \beta \text{ (or } h_{FE}) = \frac{I_c}{I_B}$$

The conditions are shown in *Figure 7.24(a)*. For a *p-n-p* transistor the same relationship between I_c and I_B exists but the direction of the base current needs to be reversed as does the polarity of the collector to emitter voltage. This is shown in *Figure 7.24(b)*.

In *Figure 7.25* T_1 is an *n-p-n* transistor and T_2 is a *p-n-p* transistor. T_1 base is called the *gate*. T_2 emitter is connected to the positive terminal of a direct supply while T_1 emitter is connected to the negative of the supply. Using an external power source connected between T_1 gate and emitter a small current I_G is injected into the gate connection. Provided that T_1 collector is positive, current amplification can take place. This is achieved by connecting it to T_2 base (the connection shown dotted). Current will now flow from the supply positive, leave T_2 base, and flow from collector to emitter in T_1. However, drawing current from T_2 base would turn on T_2 provided that a path for current from its collector is provided. Making a connection from T_2 collector back to the gate provides such a path.

The initial gate current I_G is amplified by T_1 and $h_{FE}I_G$ is drawn from T_2 base. T_2 collector current becomes $h_{FE}(h_{FE}I_G)$ and this is fed back to become the new T_1 base current. T_1 turns on further so affecting T_2 and in a few nanoseconds the arrangement becomes virtually a short circuit, the current flowing from the supply positive to negative being limited only by external circuit resistance. The device is a switch actuated by a small current input at the gate terminal, in some respects like a contactor being closed by a small coil current but this analogy must not be carried any further since once conducting, removing the gate input has no effect on the device.

Drawing the two transistors in a different way, showing the layers from which they are made, the electrical connections are added in *Figure 7.27(a)*. Now imagine that T_2 is rotated so as to shorten the external connections the arrangement in *Figure 7.27(b)* is achieved. The practical device has only four layers, a typical power thyristor being shown in *Figure 7.28*.

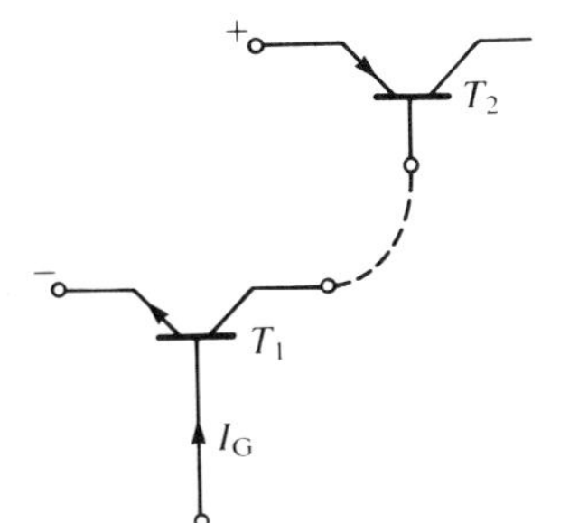

Figure 7.25

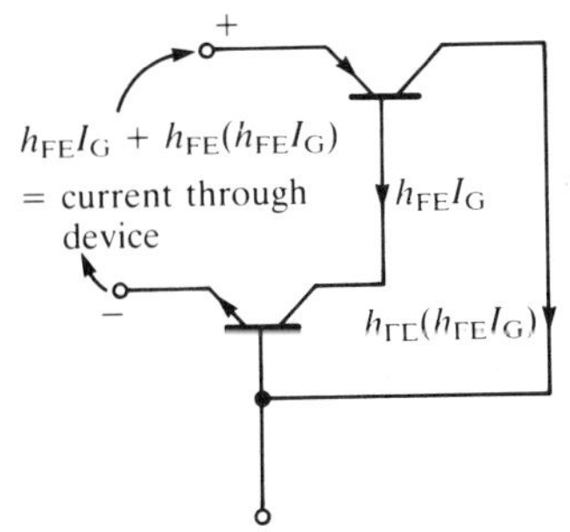

Figure 7.26

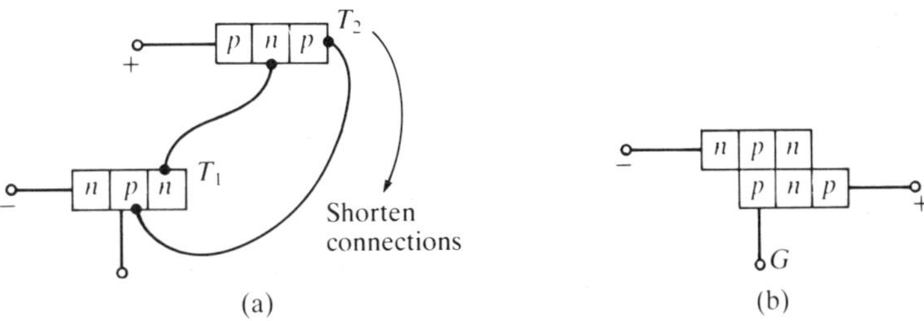

Figure 7.27

The thyristor chip is enclosed in a protective capsule and the larger ratings are provided with a threaded copper base which can be screwed into a heat sink to keep it cool.

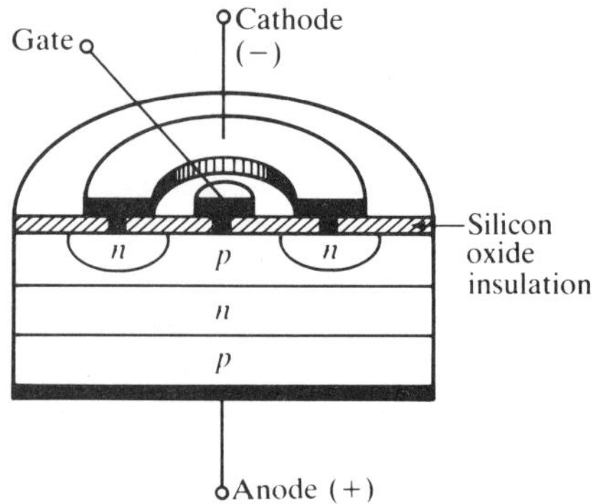

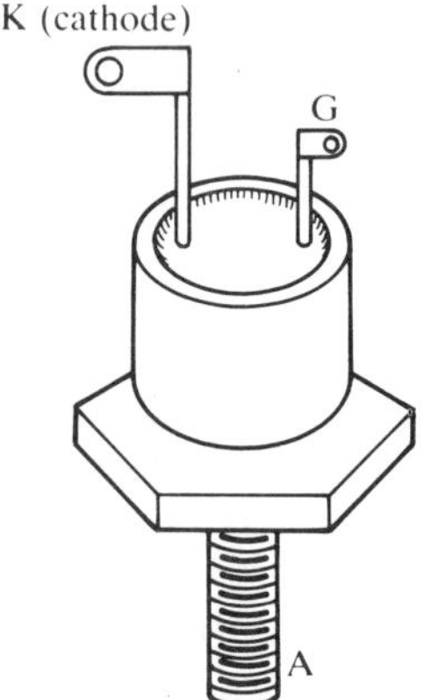

Figure 7.28

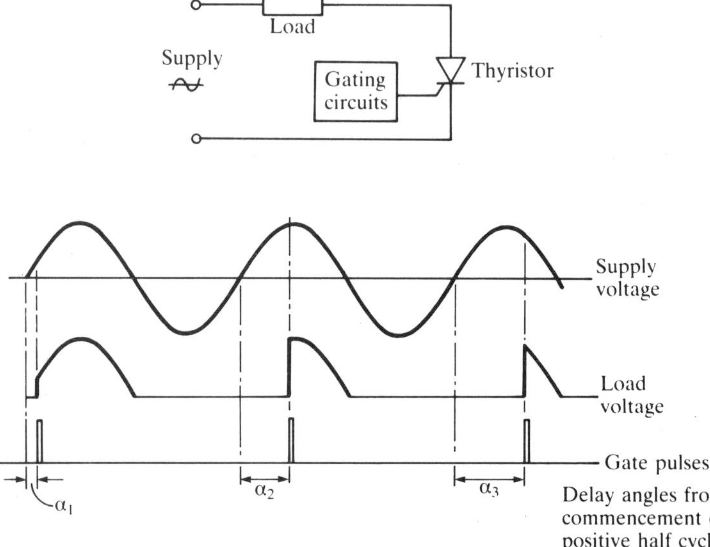

Figure 7.29

THE SINGLE-PHASE CONTROLLED RECTIFIER

In *Figure 7.29* a single thyristor is controlling the power being delivered from an alternating supply to a resistive load. The current to the gate is provided in the form of short pulses the time of arrival of which can be varied by electronic circuitry in the gating circuits. As soon as a current pulse arrives at the gate the thyristor turns on. The thyristor is effectively a switch so that when it is on, its resistance is near zero and the supply voltage appears across the load as when a switch is closed controlling, say, a lamp. Switch on may be achieved at any desired instant during a positive-going half cycle. The load voltage and power will have maximum values when the pulse is supplied at the beginning of the half cycle and may be progressively reduced by delaying the provision of the pulse. Typical load voltage waveforms for three delay angles α_1, α_2 and α_3 are shown in *Figure 7.29.*

Full-wave controlled rectification may be achieved using a bridge rectifier employing two thyristors and two diodes as shown in *Figure 7.30.*

THE THREE-PHASE CONTROLLED RECTIFIER

Where a three-phase supply is available the three-phase bridge circuit is used. The simplest form of this circuit is shown in *Figure 7.31*. It is formed using three thyristors and three diodes. The associated voltage waveforms are shown in *Figure 7.32.* To achieve the maximum possible load power the thyristors are triggered in sequence at natural changeover or commutation points A, D and E. Current flows between the two transformer terminals across which the maximum potential difference occurs at a particular instant. Firing Th 2 at instant A allows current to flow in the transformer yellow phase, to pass through the thyristor, the load, and back through D 3 to the blue phase of the transformer which is, at that instant, at its most negative potential. The potential difference across the load is scaled (a) and redrawn on the load voltage chart.

At B the load current takes the same path but both yellow and blue voltages have changed in magnitude. The load voltage now scales (b) and this value is added to the load-voltage chart. The load voltage is scaled again at time instant C (value (c)) and added below. At instant C Th 2 is still conducting but the return load current transfers to D 1 since at this point the red phase voltage becomes most negative. Load voltages (d) and (e) are scaled and added to the load voltage chart.

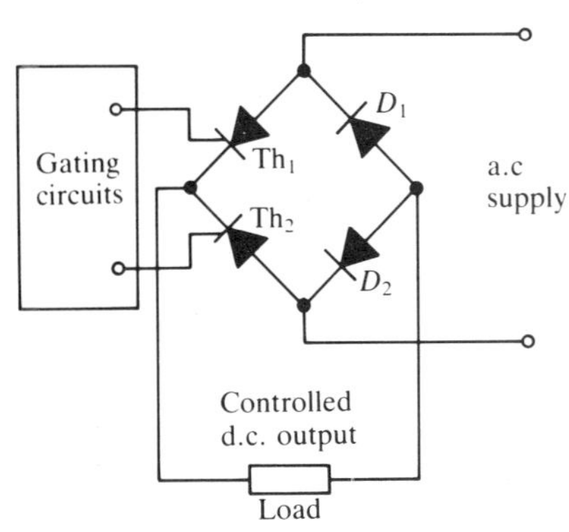

Figure 7.30

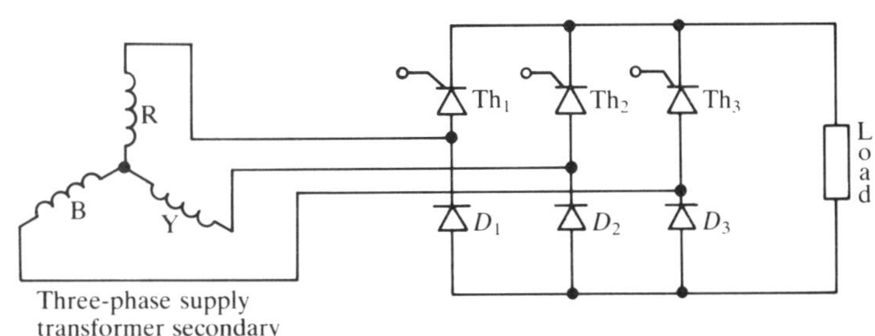

Figure 7.31

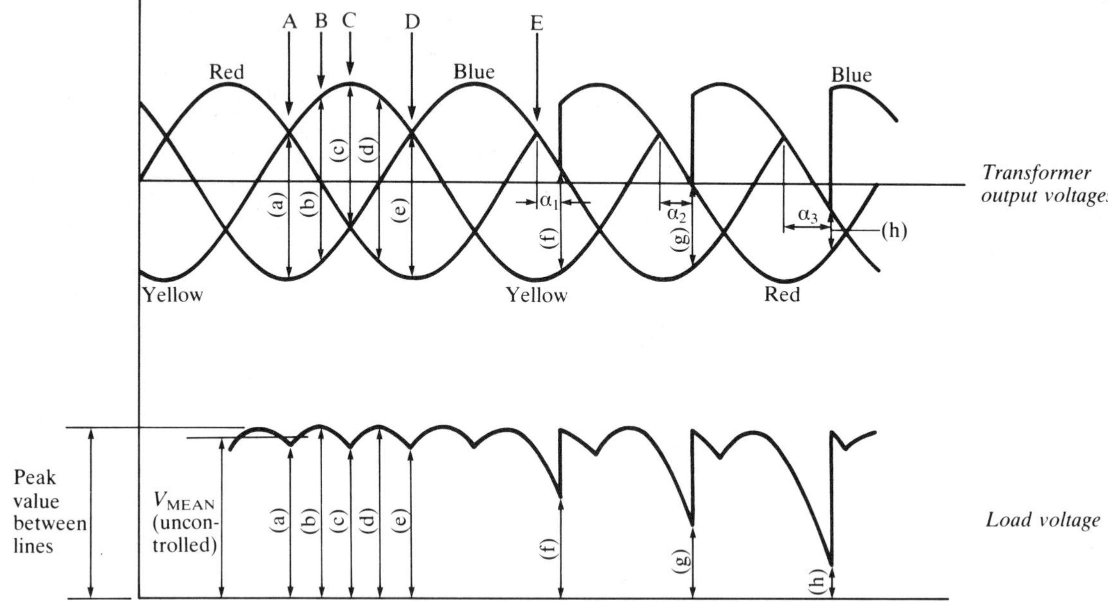

Figure 7.32

At instant D Th 3 is fired the return current still being through D 1. The load voltage waveform is seen to have some ripple with a mean value not very different from the peak value between lines.

Now let us consider the effect of delaying the firing of the thyristors. Instead of firing Th 1 at E, it is delayed by an angle α_1. The scaled load voltage just before thyristor 1 becomes conducting is (f). For other delay angles α_2 and α_3 the load voltages fall to (g) and (h). The mean load voltage and hence power are being reduced. Thus control of load power is obtained by varying the delay angle as in the single-phase case. More control is possible by replacing the three diodes with further thyristors.

THE BASIC THYRISTOR CHOPPER

Figure 7.33 shows a simple circuit of a chopper which enables the power being supplied to a load from a d.c. supply to be varied without the use of series resistors. It may also be adapted to 'chop up' a direct current into pulses to create alternating current after filtering out the square edges of the waveform. Such a process is known as *inversion*.

Consider both thyristors to be off. Th 1 receives a trigger pulse and current flows in the load, Th 1 and one half of the centre-tapped inductor. The sudden increase in current gives rise to induced voltages in both halves of the inductor since all of the turns are linked with the changing flux. The direction of the induced e.m.f. together with the resulting charge on the capacitor are shown in *Figure 7.33*.

If now Th 2 is triggered, the cathode of Th 1 is connected directly to the positively-charged plate of the capacitor and is thereby switched off. (The requirement for switching off a thyristor is to remove or momentarily reverse the anode/cathode potential so eliminating the forward current.)

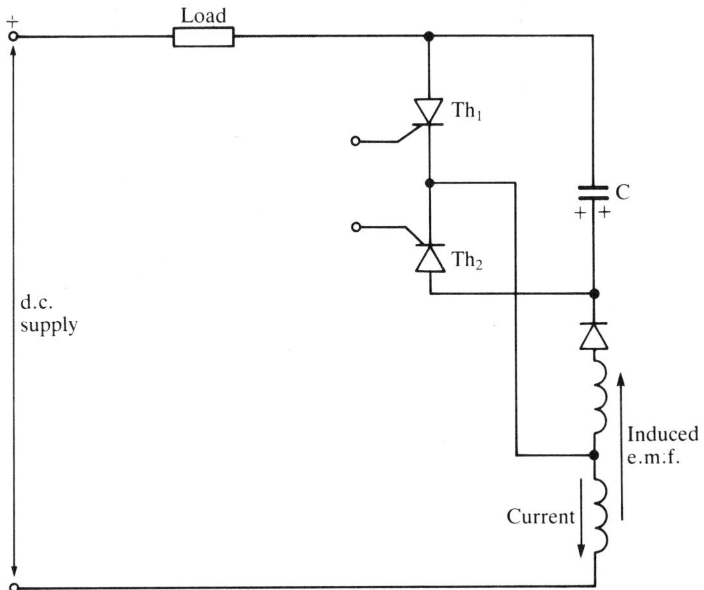

Figure 7.33

Load current ceases and can be re-established by triggering Th 1 again. The trigger pulses are generated by an oscillator and power in the load is controlled by varying the 'on' time, i.e. the interval between triggering Th 1 and Th 2 and by altering the frequency at which the switching is carried out. The frequency of switching will determine the frequency of the output when the chopper is being used to invert.

THE THYRISTOR AS AN ELEMENT IN A CONTROL SYSTEM

Control of induction motors

The torque developed by an induction motor is proportional to the square of the stator voltage (see Chapter 3, 'Starting methods for cage machines'). Reducing the applied voltage to, say, 90% of normal reduces the available torque to $(90\%)^2 = 81\%$ of normal. If the motor is carrying its normal full load this reduction in torque might well be sufficient to cause the rotor to stall. A limited range of speeds can be achieved by voltage reduction provided that the motor is lightly loaded.

The relationship between voltage, frequency and flux in a transformer was examined in Chapter 1. It was found that: $E = 4.44\, B_{max}\, A\, f\, N$ volts. From this we see that provided E and f rise or fall in the same proportion B_{max} is constant since 4.44, A and N do not change. This relationship is also true for the induction motor which is a special form of transformer in effect.

It is the flux in the air gap which is transferring the energy from the stator rotating field to the rotor which is driving the external load. If changes are made to voltage and frequency in step so that the flux is unaffected the torque is unaffected.

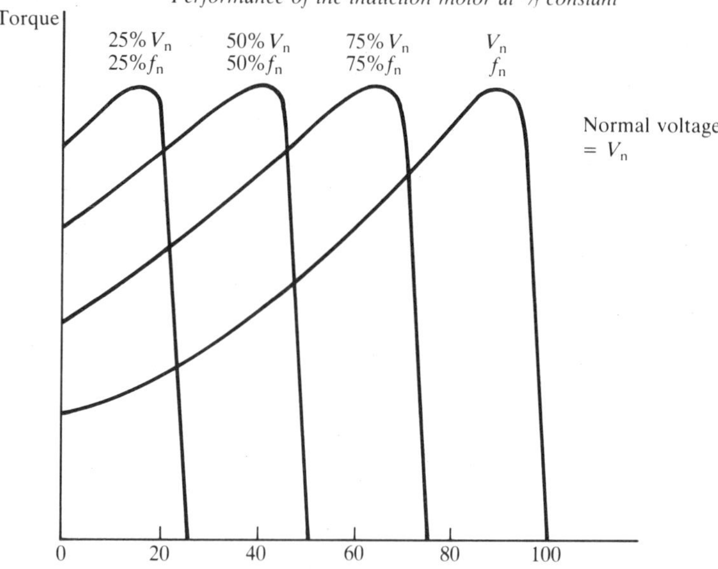

Figure 7.34

The effect of reducing frequency is to reduce the synchronous speed of the motor. At 50% of normal frequency, for example, the synchronous speed is only 50% of that at normal frequency. Thus by varying the frequency the motor may be made to run at any required speed. Varying the voltage in the same proportion maintains the torque for any particular speed. This effect is shown in *Figure 7.34*. Thyristors can be made to perform the necessary functions to achieve this method of speed control.

A schematic arrangement of such a system is shown in *Figure 7.35*. The basic arrangement is similar to *Figure 7.3* except that instead of simply amplifying the error signal it is necessary to cause the error to alter the firing angle of the associated thyristors. This is performed in the error processing network. The three-phase supply is rectified using a controlled rectifier to give a variable voltage

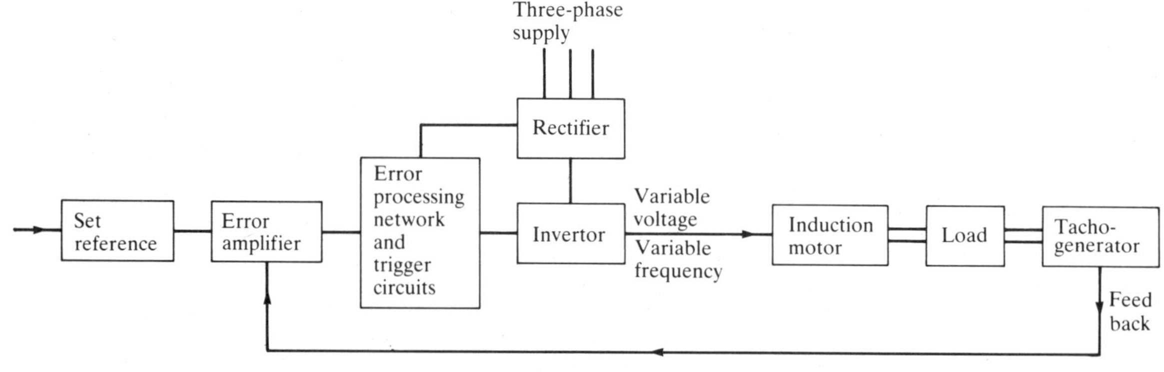

Speed control of induction motor

Figure 7.35

output the value of which is controlled by varying the firing angle this being controlled by the error processing network. This variable direct voltage is inverted using a chopper circuit to give an alternating output of the corresponding frequency. The variable voltage, variable frequency output from the invertor drives the induction motor. The speed of the induction motor is monitored by the tacho-generator which feeds back this information to the error amplifier.

One further possible arrangement is illustrated in *Figure 7.36.*

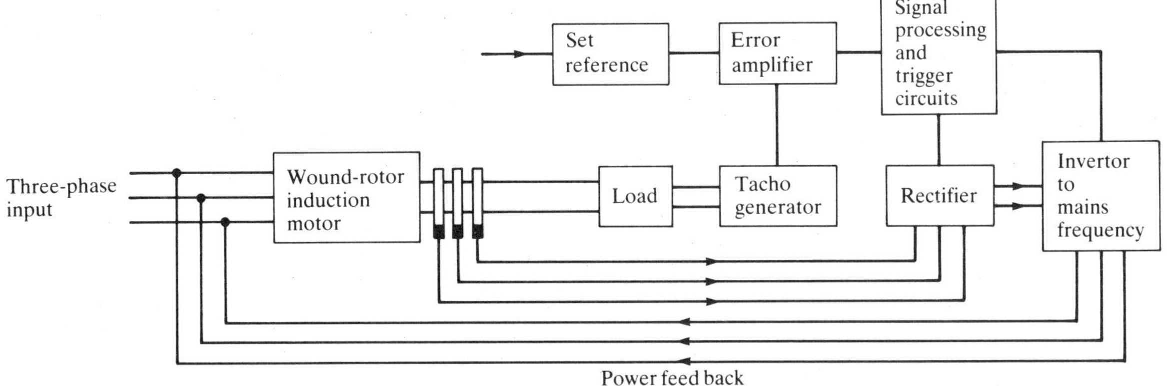

Figure 7.36

A normal three-phase, wound rotor machine is used. Instead of the power from the slip rings being burnt up in resistance banks, it is fed to a rectifier. The rectified output is fed to the thyristor invertor which changes it into alternating current at the correct voltage and frequency to feed it straight back to the motor input terminals. The invertor and rectifier are controlled by the error network as in *Figure 7.35*. The speed is controlled by changing the firing angle in the rectifier so changing the back e.m.f. applied to the rotor.

Control of d.c. motors

D.c. motors fed from an alternating supply may be operated at variable speed by feeding them from a controlled rectifier. The firing angle will be derived in the same manner as in *Figure 7.35*. The speed of the motor is directly proportional to the applied voltage provided that the field current remains constant. Generally this is fed from a separate rectifier.

PROBLEMS

1 What is a servomechanism?
2 In a servo system what is the function of (i) the amplifier and (ii) the damping mechanism?
3 Sketch the response of a servo system with (i) very little damping and (ii) an excessive amount of damping.
4 What is the function of a transducer in a servo system?
5 What is a cross-field machine? Why could such a machine be useful in controlling the run-up of a d.c. motor?
6 What is a magnetic amplifier? Why could it not be used to amplify signals at audio frequency?

7 What parameter of the magnetic amplifier core is changed by the direct control current?
8 Why is it desirable to use a core material in a magnetic amplifier which saturates suddenly?
9 What advantages has the three-limb magnetic amplifier employing two a.c. windings and one control winding (balanced winding type) over the two limb type with one a.c. and one d.c. winding?
10 What is meant by the term *regenerative* feedback as applied to a magnetic amplifier? What is its function?
11 Why is bias often necessary in a magnetic amplifier? Draw a schematic diagram showing how (i) regenerative feedback and (ii) bias are provided.
12 Draw a block diagram showing the elements in a control loop employing a magnetic amplifier to control (a) the speed of a d.c. motor and (b) the level of stage lighting using incandescent lamps.
13 Draw a circuit diagram of a single-phase bridge rectifier employing thyristors to obtain control of the output voltage across a resistive load. Sketch the associated waveforms of load voltage and thyristor gate pulses.
14 How may the speed of a d.c. motor being fed from a d.c. supply be controlled using thyristors. Explain the basic difference between the control of thyristors being fed from a direct supply and those being fed from an alternating supply.
15 Compare the use of the cross-field machine, the magnetic amplifier and thyristors for controlling (a) the speed of an induction motor and (b) the speed of a d.c. shunt-wound motor.
16 When controlling the speed of an induction motor why is it desirable to vary the voltage and frequency in step rather than vary the voltage from a fixed-frequency supply?

8 Measurements and fault diagnosis

Aims: At the end of this chapter you should be able to:

Describe the construction and operation of the d.c. potentiometer.
Discuss the use of the ohmmeter and the megger.
Measure inductance and resistance using bridge circuits.
Describe isolation and earthing procedures on an electrical system.
Discuss and evaluate the significance of errors which occur when measurements are taken.

THE D.C. POTENTIOMETER

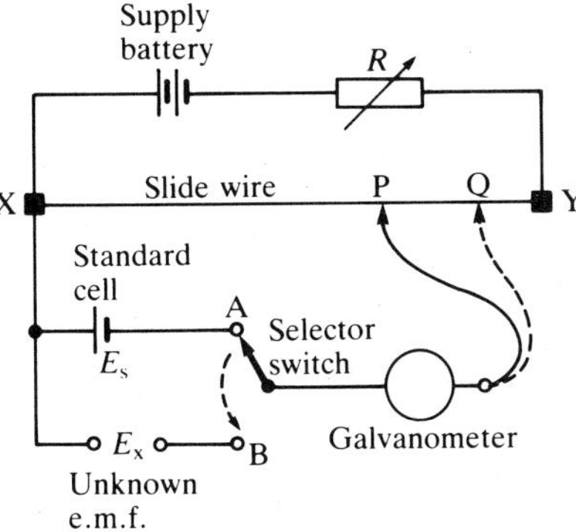

Figure 8.1

The potentiometer is a device for measuring potential difference by comparison with a standard e.m.f. derived from a source such as the Weston cadmium cell which has an e.m.f. of 1.01859 V at 20°C. The simplest form of potentiometer is shown in *Figure 8.1*.

With the selector switch on *A*, the standard cell is in circuit. The supply battery drives a current in a perfectly uniform slide wire which is generally slightly over 1 m in length. By sliding the slider along the wire a position is found for which the galvanometer current is zero (point P). At this point the potential difference between X and P due to the current in the wire is exactly matched by the e.m.f. of the standard cell. Since the wire is uniform, the voltage drop along the wire may be expressed as (E_s/XP) volts per unit length. To facilitate direct reading of voltage from the slider position, the slider is set on the slide wire at a point such that XP =1.01859 m and the wire current is adjusted by varying the rheostat R until the galvanometer current is zero, when:

$$\frac{E_s}{\text{XP}} = \frac{1.01859\ \text{V}}{101.859\ \text{cm}} = 0.01 \text{ volts per centimetre}$$

Changing the selector switch to B brings the unknown e.m.f. into circuit and provided that its value is less than that of the main supply battery, a new null point may be found on the wire at Q (XQ measured in cm). Then:

$$E_x = \frac{E_s}{\text{XP}} \times \text{XQ} = 0.01 \times \text{XQ volts}$$

Thus, if a balance point is found at, say, 79.54 cm, it can be deduced directly that the measured e.m.f. = 0.7954 V.

Using this potentiometer e.m.f.s up to 1 volt in magnitude may be measured. Some increase in range is obtained by using an arrangement similar to that shown in *Figure 8.2*.

The wire has been effectively extended by adding resistors XC, CD, DE and EF. Each of these resistors has a value exactly equal to that of 1 m of the slide wire and with the potentiometer calibrated as above, the potential difference across each will be 1 V. To measure a

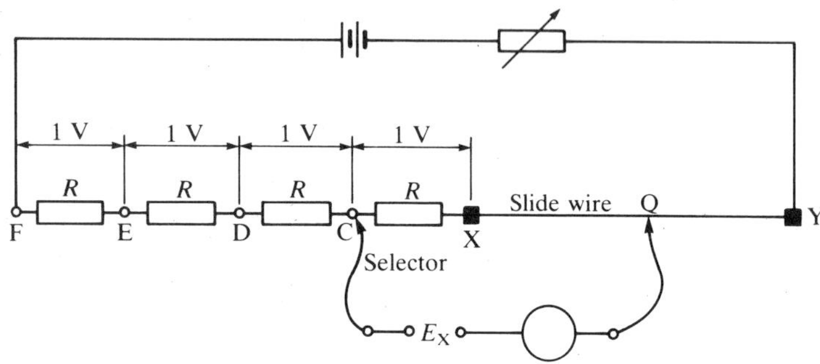

Figure 8.2

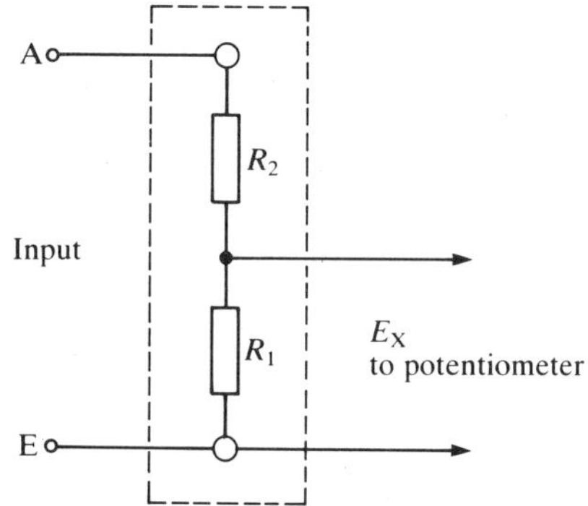

Figure 8.3

voltage between 1 V and 2 V the selector is plugged in at C and the slider moved to find a null point. E_x will have a value of 1 V plus $0.01 \times$ XQ. Setting the selector to F, an e.m.f. with a maximum value of 5 V can be measured using this particular potentiometer.

If larger voltages are to be measured a potential divider or volt-ratio box will have to be used.

In *Figure 8.3*, the large voltage to be measured is applied to terminals AE. The resistance ($R_1 + R_2$) is sufficiently large that only a very small current is drawn so as to minimise the loading effect. (Any current drawn from a source with high internal impedance will cause the terminal voltage to fall.) The potential across R_1 is fed to the potentiometer as E_x.

$$E_x = \frac{R_1}{R_1 + R_2} \times \text{voltage AE} \therefore \text{AE} = \frac{R_1 + R_2}{R_1} \times E_x$$

With commercial equipment it is not necessary to know the values of the internal resistances, the ratio of input to output will be quoted, say, 100:1 when the voltage being measured will be one hundred times the reading on the potentiometer.

Calibration of a d.c. analogue voltmeter

A variable direct supply is connected to the voltmeter to be calibrated and where the range is high, to a suitable range volt-ratio box. Where the voltmeter range is only up to about 5 V the arrangement in *Figure 8.2* may be used without reducing the voltage supplied to the potentiometer. If the voltmeter has no face markings the variable voltage is increased in small increments, a balance obtained on the potentiometer and the value of the input voltage

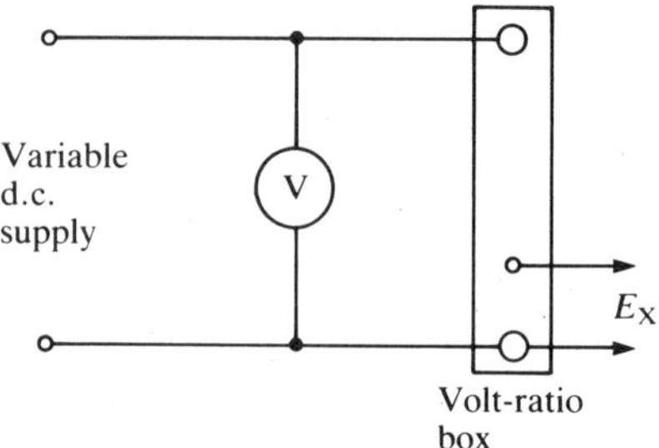

Figure 8.4

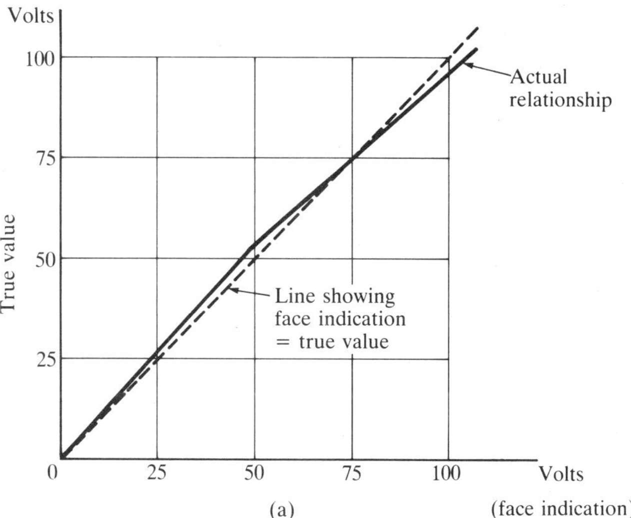

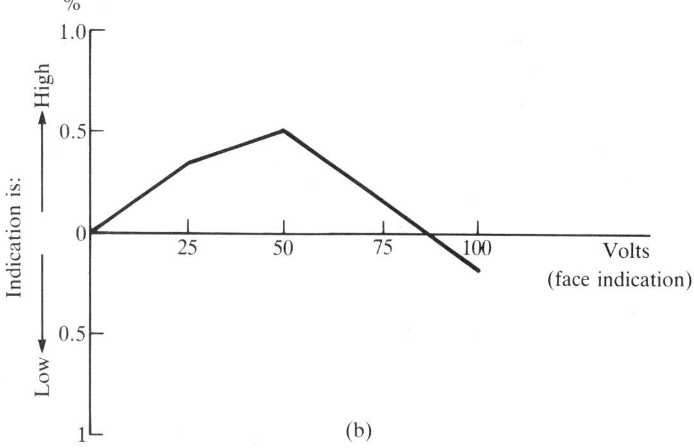

Figure 8.5

calculated. Marks will be made on the voltmeter face at each point and labelled with the corresponding value of voltage.

Where the voltmeter is already calibrated, the variable voltage is adjusted until the pointer is indicating a particular value. The actual voltage is determined using the potentiometer. A table is drawn up, or a graph drawn showing face indicated values together with the true voltages at these points (*Figure 8.5(a)*). Alternatively, the error at each indicated voltage may be calculated and plotted (*Figure 8.5(b)*).

Calibration of a d.c. analogue ammeter

A high precision resistor is connected in series with the ammeter and fed from a variable direct supply. The arrangement is shown in *Figure 8.6*. The value of the resistor is chosen to give a 1 volt drop when the full rated current of the ammeter flows in the circuit. The current is increased in steps, as was the voltage when calibrating the

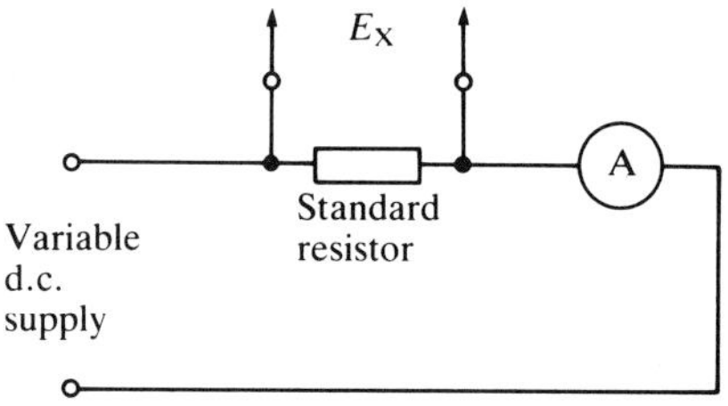

Figure 8.6

voltmeter, and the position of the pointer marked or graph plotted using current values calculated as follows:
Circuit current, $I \times R_{standard} = E_x$ (measured on the potentiometer)

$$\therefore I = \frac{E_x}{R_{standard}} \text{ A}$$

CONTINUITY TESTING AND THE OHMMETER

When using, for example, mineral insulated cable in which the cores are not marked, it is necessary to identify both ends of each conductor. The simple way to achieve this is shown in *Figure 8.7*.

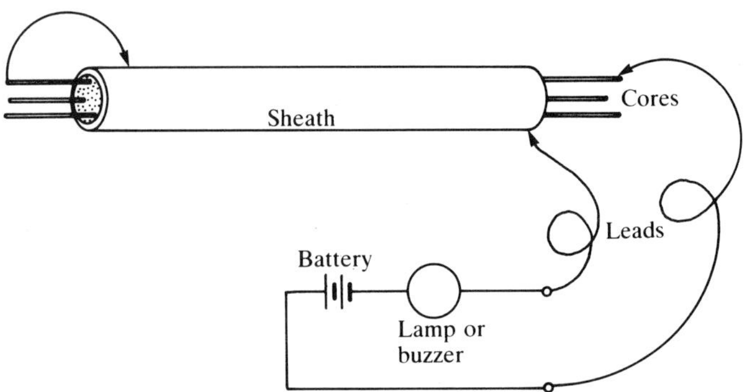

Figure 8.7

One core is connected to the sheath or to a good earth and a simple continuity tester formed from a battery and a lamp or buzzer. With one lead to the sheath (or earth) touching the other lead on to each of the cores in turn at the other end of the cable will cause the lamp to light or the buzzer to sound when the correct core is touched. This can then be labelled at both ends using coloured tape or ferrules. Where the connections are not good, the earth loop has too high a resistance or possibly when the length of cable being checked is long, the buzzer may not operate or the lamp will not visibly light up although it might be carrying some current. It is sometimes more satisfactory to know the actual resistance of the path being checked when an ohmmeter may be used to test continuity.

The ohmmeter comprises an ammeter with its face calibrated in ohms, a battery and calibration resistances. As an example let us assume a battery voltage of 4 V and the meter to give full-scale deflection for a current of 0.05 A.

To set up the ohmmeter, the external leads from the terminals P and Q in *Figure 8.8* are connected directly together. The resistance being measured is now zero. The ammeter is to indicate maximum current under these conditions. Since the battery e.m.f. is 4 V.

$$\text{Total circuit resistance including leads} = \frac{4}{0.05} = 80\,\Omega$$

Resistor R_y is adjusted until the meter indicates 0.05 A. This corresponds to zero external resistance and is marked 0 on the resistance scale. Disconnecting the leads results in zero current flowing and the ammeter scale zero is marked 'infinity' (∞) Ω.

The scale is calibrated in ohms between zero and infinity. For example, when 0.04 A is flowing, the total resistance = 4/0.04 = 100 Ω. Since all internal resistances and leads accounts for 80 Ω, the external resistance must be 20 Ω. 0.04 A on the ammeter current scale corresponds to 20 Ω on the resistance scale. *Figure 8.9* shows the complete scale. Note that it is not linear and the indication may be difficult to interpret when measuring high resistance values.

The meter ranges are altered in multi-range instruments by (a) changing the battery voltage and (b) fitting the meter with a shunt while at the same time changing the value of R_z.

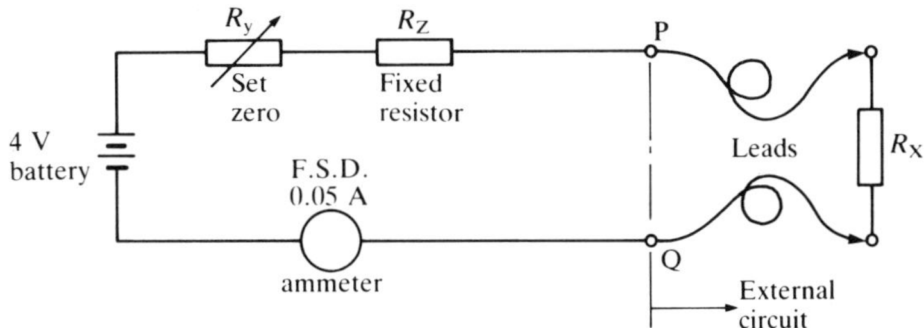

Figure 8.8

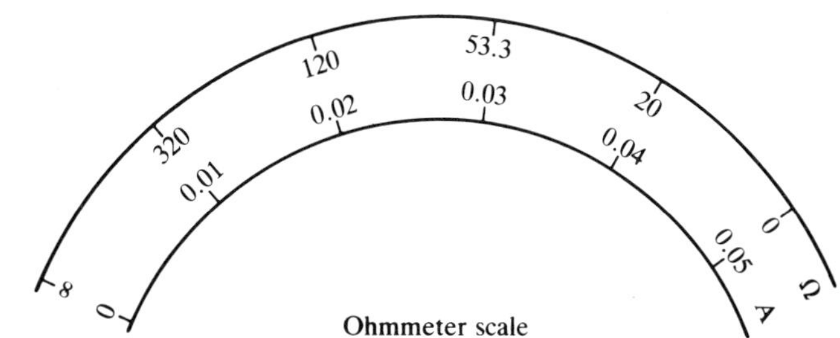

Figure 8.9

MEASURING BRIDGES

The Wheatstone bridge

In the potentiometer shown in *Figure 8.1* we saw how an unknown e.m.f., E_x, could be measured by balancing this e.m.f. against an identical voltage developed across a length of current-carrying wire. *Figure 8.10(a)* shows the balance point on the wire at C when the resistances from A to C and from C to B are R_1 and R_2 respectively.

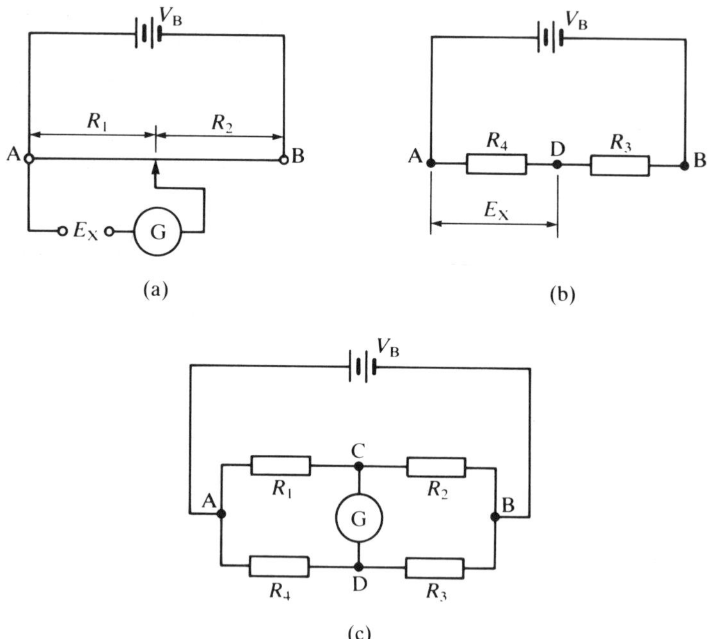

Figure 8.10

Now suppose instead of an external source of e.m.f. E_x, the same magnitude of voltage is developed using a potential divider as shown in *Figure 8.10(b)*. The voltage from A to D is given by:

$$V_{AD} = E_x = \frac{R_4}{R_4 + R_3} \times V_B \text{ volts}$$

If both sections (a) and (b) are assembled as in *Figure 8.10(c)* it is seen that the potential differences between A and C and between A and D are the same so that the potentials of points C and D are the same and there will be no galvanometer current. *Figure 8.10(c)* is known as a *bridge* circuit and with no galvanometer current the bridge is said to be balanced. This particular bridge which is used for measuring the values of resistances is called the Wheatstone bridge, after Professor Wheatstone.
Balance occurs when:

$$\frac{R_1}{R_4} = \frac{R_2}{R_3}$$

To measure an unknown value of resistance, this could be plugged into the bridge at position R_2. Transposing the balance formula we arrive at:

$$R_2 = \frac{R_1}{R_4} \times R_3$$

R_1 and R_4 may be pre-set and R_3 be in the form of a decade resistance box. By manipulating the decades in this box a balance point may be found and hence the value of R_2. If $R_1 = R_4$ then the value of R_2 may be read directly from the decade box. By changing the ratio of $R_1 : R_4$

by factors of 10, R_2 may be evaluated as for example, 1/100, 1/10, 10, 100 times R_3 allowing a wide range of resistance values to be measured with a single decade box.

The Maxwell–Wien bridge

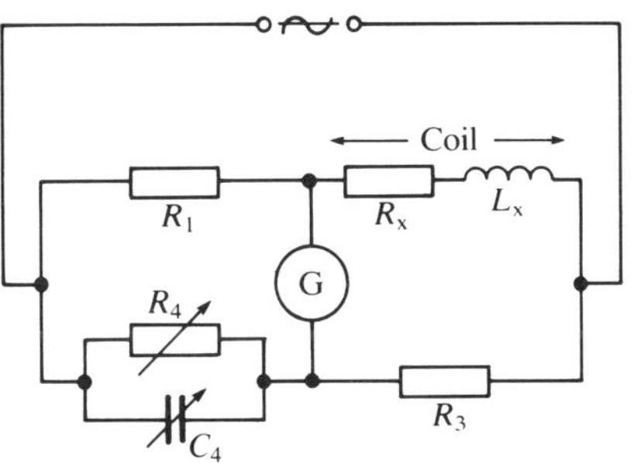

Figure 8.11

It is not necessary to use only resistors in the bridge arms and in *Figure 8.11* we see the Maxwell–Wien bridge which is used to measure the resistance and inductance of a coil. These are marked R_x and L_x respectively. Although R_x is shown as a separate component it is in fact the resistance of the inductive coil. Arms 1 and 3 are pure resistances as in the Wheatstone bridge but arm 4 comprises a decade resistance box connected in parallel with a variable capacitor.

The bridge is fed from an a.c. supply at the frequency at which the values for the coil are required to be known. The galvanometer has to be capable of responding to alternating current. Balance is found to occur when the following relationships are satisfied:

$$R_x = \frac{R_1 R_3}{R_4}\ \Omega \text{ and } L_x = R_1 R_3 C_4 \text{ H}$$

R_1 and R_3 are fixed so that the product R_1R_3 is a known quantity. R_4 and C_4 are varied progressively until zero galvanometer current is achieved. Then R_x is equal to the known product R_1R_3 divided by the value of R_4 on the decade box and the value of the unknown coil inductance is the product of R_1R_3 multiplied by the value set on the variable capacitor C_4.

The Owen bridge

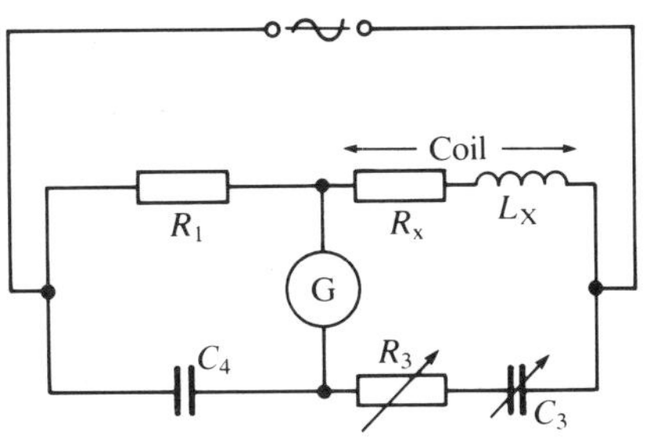

Figure 8.12

Another bridge serving the same function as the Maxwell–Wien type is shown in *Figure 8.12*. For this bridge balance occurs when:

$$R_x = \frac{C_4 R_1}{C_3}\ \Omega \text{ and } L_x = C_4 R_1 R_3 \text{ H}$$

The product C_4R_1 is known and the values of R_x and L_x found by varying R_3 and C_3 to achieve balance.

Suppose that the product $C_4R_1 = 1 \times 10^{-6}$, for example, and balance was obtained with a certain coil when $C_3 = 1000$ pF and $R_3 = 100$ kΩ.

$$R_x = \frac{1 \times 10^{-6}}{1000 \times 10^{-12}} = 1000\ \Omega \text{ and } L_x = 1 \times 10^{-6} \times 100\,000 = 0.1 \text{ H}$$

In commercial bridges the product terms are often allowed for in the markings on the knobs for the variable quantities. Balance is obtained in the above example when C_3 has a value of 1000 pF, when $R_x = 1000\ \Omega$. Therefore, instead of marking the travel of the C_3 adjusting knob in pF, it is marked directly in the value of R_x in ohms. Similarly, when $R_3 = 100$ kΩ. the corresponding value of $L_x = 0.1$ H. The travel of the R_3 adjusting knob is marked directly in henry. Thus a direct read out of values is obtained. There are many different bridges in use but the operating principles are the same in each case. As with the potentiometer, the outputs may be adjusted in decades by varying the product term. In the Owen bridge varying R_1 by factors 1/100; 1/10; 10; 100 etc. will change the range of the measurements possible. Where the coil resistances are very low it may be necessary to add external resistance to the bridge arm containing the coil and then subtract this from the final result. This can also be automatically allowed for in the calibration in commercial bridges.

$$\text{The Q-factor of a coil} = \frac{\omega L}{R} = \frac{2\pi f L}{R}$$

so that having found the coil resistance and inductance, the Q-factor may be calculated. It should be noted, however, that this will only be true for the actual frequency used to supply the bridge.

A number of instruments are available which give a direct digital readout of resistance, inductance or capacitance values. The component under test is connected between two terminals and the selector knob turned to '*R*', '*L*' or '*C*'. An arrow appears in the readout window indicating 'up' or 'down'. This refers to the range of readings, like changing the ratio in a bridge circuit. A second knob is turned in the appropriate direction changing the range by factors of 10. When the most suitable range has been selected the arrow disappears from the readout window and figures giving the value of the component show. The readout is valid for the frequency of operation of the device, which may be selected to typically 50 Hz or 10 kHz.

THE 'MEGGER' TESTER

For cable, switchgear and motor insulation resistance testing, a device which can measure millions of ohms while stressing the material with hundreds or even thousands of volts is required. The main limitation of the ohmmeter for testing insulating materials is the applied voltage. Consider a fault on an electric motor which allows a conductor to touch the casing. The resistance between the conductor and case with even the slightest amount of grease or dirt at the point of contact could be several thousand ohms when measured with the ohmmeter with its battery source. However, with normal working voltage applied to the conductor electrical breakdown of the dirt would occur causing the resistance to fall to a very-low value.

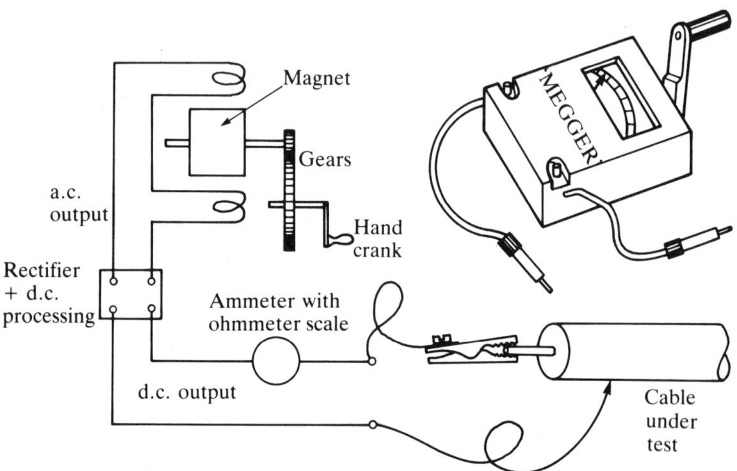

Figure 8.13

The insulation testing meter often used in the 'Megger' which now comes in two forms. The first type comprises a hand-cranked alternating current generator the output from which is rectified and smoothed to give a very nearly ripple-free direct output. Resistance measurements are read from an ammeter calibrated as described for the ohmmeter, the generator effectively replacing the battery. Models are available at 250 V, 500 V, 1000 V and 2500 V with the option to have them motor driven at the higher voltages (see *Figure 8.13*).

The second type generates its test voltage electronically using a 9 V 'dry' battery. Since the electrical capacity of such a battery is very limited this device is more suitable for testing small installations whereas the hand- and motor-driven types can be used for prolonged testing of long cable runs and large electrical machines.

EQUIPMENT TESTING

There are many tests which are carried out after installation of new plant and during commissioning. These are very specialised and not dealt with here. The following tests and inspections are carried out on plant during periodic checks or after a breakdown when its fitness for return to service is being considered.

Cable tests

The cable must first be disconnected from the supply. In the case of a cable feeding a piece of equipment, this will involve opening the circuit breaker and locking it in the open or isolated position. To test the cable alone, or the motor or equipment alone which the cable is feeding, the cable connections to the equipment must be unbolted and gently eased away so that there is no contact.

In the case of a feeder which can be fed from both ends, the circuit breakers at both ends must be opened and isolated.

Electrical tests are then made using the 'megger'. For circuits operating normally at 415/240 V, a 500 V megger is generally used. For higher voltage circuits the higher voltage test sets are employed.

On single-phase circuits tests are carried out between the two cores and between each core and earth. On three-phase circuits the tests are carried out between each pair of conductors; red to yellow, yellow to blue, blue to red; and from each of the cores to the earthed sheath. No absolute figures can be quoted for the insulation resistance since this will depend upon the length and type of cable, but the readings should generally be hundreds of megohms (1 megohm = 1 million ohms).

Visual checks should be made at the same time of the cable ends. Lead-covered, paper-insulated cables have their ends terminated in compound-filled boxes. There should be no oil seeping from the box and all should appear clean and in good order. Plastic-insulated cables are terminated in a screwed gland and it is necessary to generally check for cleanliness and appearance.

MOTOR TESTS

The supply is isolated and the motor disconnected from its cable at the terminal box.

On a single-phase motor the insulation resistance between one winding terminal and earth is checked. In the case of a three-phase motor the windings are separated by removing the links in the terminal box. The tests are then as for the three-phase cable, testing between each winding and its neighbour and between each winding and earth. With a d.c. motor the armature and field windings can be separated and the insulation resistance of each part to earth tested.

Visual checks should be made of the coupling between the motor and its load, the windings by removing either or both end covers, and the bearing grease or oil. A darkened grease with a bad smell often indicates trouble which would necessitate taking the motor to the workshop to fit new bearings.

Transformer tests

The input and output cables are isolated by opening the appropriate circuit breakers and locking them in this position. The cable ends are disconnected from the windings in the terminal boxes and the windings separated if there are available links. The insulation tests are then as for the motor on both primary and secondary windings separately.

Where a tap changer is fitted a visual check of the mechanism and contacts is advisable if accessible. With oil-filled transformers the cold oil level in the conservator tank is checked and a sample of oil taken for tests of electrical breakdown value, moisture content and acidity. Filtering or replacement may be required which, if suitable plant is not available on site, will be undertaken by the oil supplier.

Due to the inherent reliability of transformers the full range of tests is rarely carried out, a watch on the condition of the oil being considered adequate unless trouble is suspected.

Switchgear tests

The switch is isolated from the supply and a visual check made on the linkages, contacts and any operating coils, after removing the tank on oil-filled gear. The switch is closed manually to check contact movement and alignment. Any operating coils are isolated electrically and the megger used to check insulation resistance between the windings and the chassis of the switch.

With the switch open, insulation tests are made between the red and yellow, yellow and blue and blue and red terminals on both input and output sides. Finally insulation tests are carried out between the input and output terminals of the corresponding colours and each to earth.

With oil-filled gear a visual check for blackening of the oil is carried out. Similar tests can be carried out on the oil as for the transformer but colour and smell are usually good enough indications of condition.

ISOLATION AND EARTHING

When work is to be carried out on high and extra high voltage equipment, isolation from all sources of danger must be carried out and to prevent the potential of that equipment rising above that of earth due to accidental contact with live metal or inductive effects, it is solidly connected to earth. Generally a permit to work is issued stating the points of isolation and earthing and the precise limits of the safe area and equipment to be worked on. If the earth connection has to be removed for testing purposes, a special sanction for test document is required.

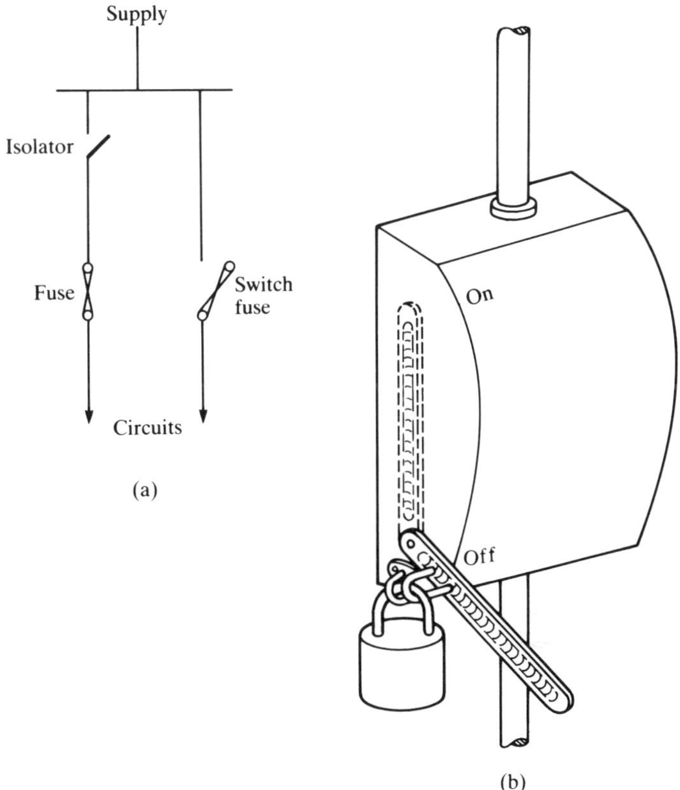

Figure 8.14

At low and medium voltages isolation from the supply is sufficient without earthing. Here again some form of permit to work is desirable.

For isolation at 415/240 V an isolator or switch fuse is often used. The schematic arrangement is shown in *Figure 8.14(a)* while a typical enclosure together with the method of locking is shown in *Figure 8.14(b)*.

Before work is commenced on a circuit the isolator or switch fuse is opened and locked in that position. The key is either held by the workman involved or in a lock-out box, a key to which he holds. A lock-out box has several different locks and keys so that other interested parties can each hold a key. They all have to come together before the box can be opened and the circuit re-energised.

On 11 kV and 33 kV circuits isolation is often achieved using withdrawable type switchgear.

Figure 8.15 shows two views of a bulk oil circuit breaker, for use up to 33 kV, with horizontal isolation. The circuit breaker is mounted on wheels which run on tracks. The contacts are of rose and poker type (see also *Figures 6.5* and *6.6*). In order to energise the circuit, the circuit breaker truck is pushed into its cubicle. The shutters are lifted at the last possible moment by small wheels on the side of the breaker engaging lifting levers attached to them. The

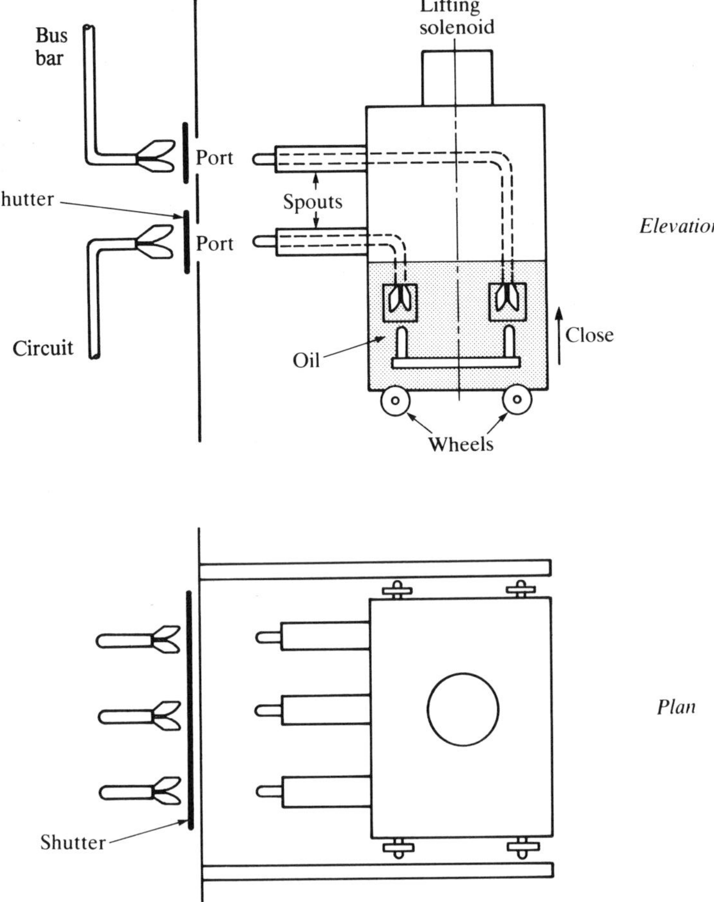

Figure 8.15

spouts enter the ports and make contact with the female rose contacts. The truck is locked in position. The circuit breaker may now be operated normally.

To isolate the circuit breaker it must be in the open position when it may be withdrawn from its cubicle. The metal shutters drop closing off the ports so that neither circuit or busbar roses may be touched. The shutters are locked in this position if work is to be done on the circuit breaker.

If work is to be carried out on the circuit cable or equipment, an extension piece is fitted to each of the circuit spouts as shown in *Figure 8.16*. A copper bar is screwed to the top (busbar) spouts and is solidly earthed. The circuit breaker is pushed into the cubicle when only the bottom shutters open allowing the earthing extension pieces to make contact with the circuit roses. The circuit breaker is closed so connecting the circuit to earth. If work is to be done on the busbars these must be disconnected from the supply transformer or generator and the positions of the extension pieces and earthing bar exchanged. The circuit breaker will now earth the busbars when racked in and closed.

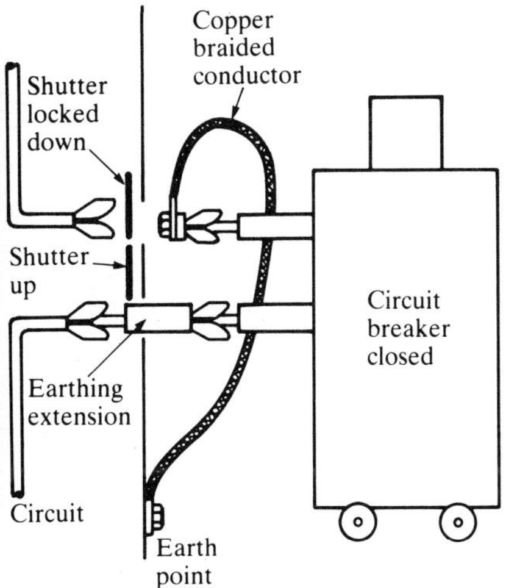

Figure 8.16

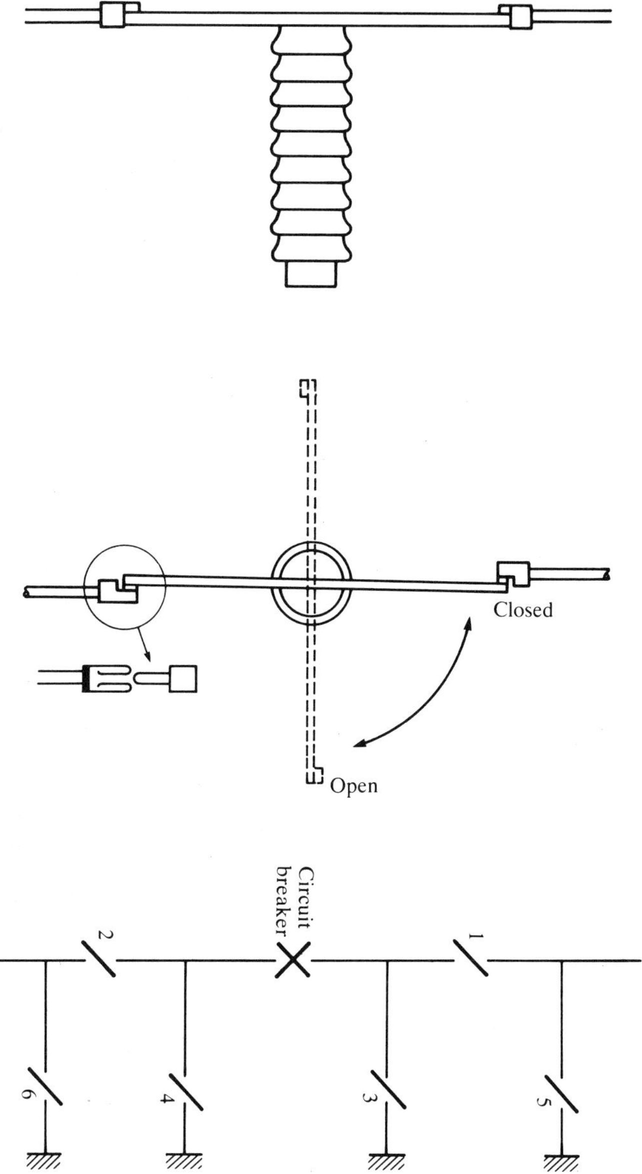

Figure 8.17

Vertical isolation is also common. This is virtually the same arrangement except that the circuit breaker is raised or lowered to give contact with the busbars and circuit the spouts being arranged across the top of the tank.

In open-air substations at 132 kV and 400 kV, isolators are used as shown in *Figure 8.17*.

To work on the circuit breaker it is first opened. Isolators 1 and 2 are opened. Isolators 3 and 4 are closed connecting the conductors to earth. Further isolators 5 and 6 are provided to earth the incoming and outgoing lines if these are de-energised by opening the circuit breakers at the far end of the lines.

The main danger involved is that a live circuit may be directly connected to earth. On withdrawable gear this may be brought about by connecting the extension pieces and earthing bar to the wrong sets of spouts due to a misunderstanding or carelessness. Where fixed isolators are used, as in *Figure 8.17*, an incorrect sequence of operations, closing the earthing isolators before opening the circuit breaker and its isolators 1 and 2 puts earths on to a live line.

When isolating equipment, working on, and diagnosing faults on pieces of equipment a clear plan of the method involved and the steps to be taken is absolutely essential. Intuitive working, relying on past experience to 'dive in' to check a particular component or section can lead to disaster if all the preparatory work has not been correctly carried out. This applies as much to repairing a television set as to a 400 kV circuit breaker. It is, however, much simpler to isolate a television set from the mains supply than it is the e.h.v. circuit breaker.

Now suppose that the circuit has been correctly earthed and that work in the cubicle itself or on one of the earthing isolators has to be done. The circuit breaker truck may have to be withdrawn or the isolator in question opened. To enable this work to be done, temporary earths have to be fitted. These are lengths of copper braid with a G clamp fitted to one end. The G clamp is screwed directly on to the busbar or circuit conductor while the other end of the braid is connected to earth. Inadvertently attempting to connect the G clamp to the wrong part of the circuit which is still alive will result in an explosion with possibly fatal results to the person concerned. To avoid this possibility a number of live-line detectors have been developed for use up to 33 kV. These sometimes indicate live conditions when the metal being tested is in fact isolated but is being charged inductively from an adjacent circuit. For this reason these testers tend to be distrusted. This is also true of the small screwdriver-type tester for normal mains work.

Accidents can of course occur due to incompetence or forgetfulness but where a proper system of safe working has been instituted and is enforced, these should be very rare.

Accidents occur at medium voltage in the main where electricians and others are allowed to perform their own isolations. A few examples will illustrate the point.

A fitter decides to make a small adjustment to a contactor without isolating the circuit since it is easier to test the circuit while alive. A flashover occurs when a screwdriver touches two live terminals.

Fuses are withdrawn from a fuse board which constitutes an isolation. Another person restores the supply unexpectedly by borrowing fuses from another way in the fuse board.

Painters decide to work in the path of a travelling gentry crane without having it locked off.

Work is carried out on electric heaters which happen to be cold and therefore thought to be switched off, but are in fact controlled by a thermostat which operates and energises the heaters while work is going on.

A safe system of working and a carefully thought out plan of action would avoid all such occurrences.

REQUIREMENTS FOR LOCKS AND WARNING NOTICES

When a circuit has been correctly isolated and earthed, the shutters are locked in position or on outdoor gear the isolator handles are locked off, the circuit-breaker operating mechanism is locked off and if earthing is through a circuit breaker, the mechanical tripping device is made inoperative and locked in that position. For medium voltage work, switch fuse handles are locked in the off position.

The locks are to prevent anyone from tampering with the isolation or removing earths by oversight or in order to do some unauthorised testing which may hazard someone else working on the equipment. Warning notices quoting any permit to work number and possibly the name of the issuing officer are placed at all control positions, at the circuit breaker and at the equipment upon which it is safe to work. If relevant, an area may be roped off within which it is safe to work. The rope is marked with flags and notices at regular intervals. The permit to work is issued as stated previously.

ERRORS

Relative errors

When measurements are made, ideally the results obtained would be exact. Unfortunately this is never possible, there is always some element of uncertainty in the measured values.

Let us consider the measurement of a voltage using, for example, a voltmeter. The measured result for reasons discussed later could be say, 1 V too large. Quoting the error as simply 1 V gives a totally inadequate idea of the significance of that error. Supposing we had been trying to measure a voltage with magnitude 1000 V, then a 1 V error would probably be quite acceptable. However if we had been trying to measure the e.m.f. of a lead-acid battery with an e.m.f. of 2.2 V, the 1 V error would be quite unacceptable. In the former case 1 V expressed as a percentage of the nominal 1000 V is 0.1% but in the latter case 1 V error on a nominal 2.2 V is 45.5%. These percentage values are known as the ***relative errors*** for each case.

The relative error for meter indication or value of components is usually quoted for the reason demonstrated. A particular grade of resistor used in electronic work has a relative error of ±5%. This means that a resistor marked with a value of 10 000 Ω can have an actual value which lies between 10 000 Ω + 5% of 10 000 Ω = 10 500 Ω and 10 000 Ω − 5% of 10 000 Ω = 9500 Ω. Quoting the relative error at ±5% gives a much better and immediate idea of the accuracy than quoting the range ±500 Ω.

In test equipment the relative errors of the components must be extremely small. In the potentiometer, for example, the accuracy of measurement depends on the original calibration using the Weston cell and on the slide wire having a uniform cross section along its length. The relative error of the voltage of the test cell and the variation in cross section of the wire expressed as a percentage of its nominal value must both be negligible for the device to be capable of producing worthwhile results.

Errors may be classified as (i) systematic errors and (ii) random errors.

Systematic errors Systematic errors are those which occur because of the nature of the equipment being used or the environment in which this finds itself. Some of these errors are:

(a) Those due to temperature changes
As temperature changes the physical dimensions of components change due to expansion and contraction, hence the capacitance of capacitors and the inductance of inductors change. The resistance of components will change, all materials having a temperature coefficient of resistance. The combined effects may cause the magnetic field strength of magnets, the restraining influence of hair springs, the resistance of current-carrying coils in meters all to change which will cause the meter indication to change. The frequency delivered by an oscillator may also change causing measurements which depend upon a specific frequency to be in error.

(b) Errors inherent in the method used
An example of this is in the voltmeter and ammeter method of determining load resistance and power.

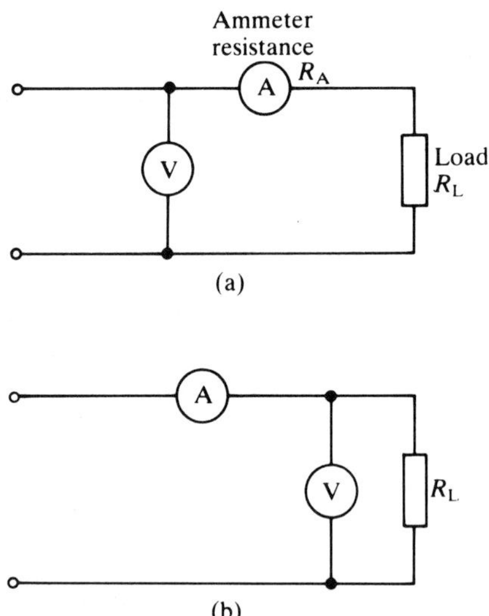

Figure 8.18

In *Figure 8.18(a)* the voltmeter indicates the supply voltage which is impressed on the ammeter and load connected in series. There will be a volt drop across the ammeter so that the full supply voltage is not applied to the load.

The resistance calculated from $\frac{V}{I} = R_L + R_A$ and not simply R_L.

Example 1. A circuit is connected as shown in *Figure 8.18(a)*. The resistance of the ammeter = 3 Ω. The supply voltage = 10 V and the circuit current = 0.5 A. Determine the true load resistance and power dissipated in the load.

Total circuit resistance = $(R_L + R_A)\,\Omega$.

$$I = \frac{V}{R},\ 0.5 = \frac{10}{(R_L + 3)}\ \therefore R_L + 3 = \frac{10}{0.5} = 20\,\Omega$$

$R_L = 20 - 3 = 17\,\Omega$

Had the resistance of the ammeter been ignored, the apparent load resistance = 10 V/0.5 A = 20 Ω.

An error of 3 Ω on a true value of 17 Ω = 17.6%

Load voltage = $I \times R_L = 0.5 \times 17 = 8.5$ V

Load power = $V_{load} \times I = 8.5 \times 0.5 = 4.25$ W.

Input power to the circuit = 10 × 0.5 = 5 W. (There would also be a power input to the voltmeter but because of the low voltage used the voltmeter current is assumed to be small and this power has been ignored. It should be realised, however, that this is one more reason why errors are present in measurements.)

In *Figure 8.18(b)* the ammeter not only indicates the current flowing in the load but that drawn by the voltmeter. Where the load has a high resistance and so draws only a small current, the current drawn by the voltmeter which was ignored in *Example 1* may be significant.

Example 2. In a circuit connected as shown in *Figure 8.18(b)*, the resistance of the load, $R_L = 15$ kΩ, the resistance of the voltmeter, $R_v = 50$ kΩ. The potential difference across the load which is indicated on the voltmeter = 210 V.

Calculate (i) the value of load current, (ii) the current in the ammeter and hence its indication assuming perfect accuracy and (iii) the error in assuming that the ammeter indication is in fact the current in the load.

(i) $I_{load} = \frac{210}{15\,\text{k}\Omega} = 14\,\text{mA}$

(ii) Voltmeter current $= \frac{210}{50\,\text{k}\Omega} = 4.2\,\text{mA}$

Current in the ammeter = 14 + 4.2 = 18.2 mA

(iii) Error = 4.2 mA on an indication of 18.2 mA = 4.2/18.2
= 0.2428 p.u.
= 24.28%

Similar considerations apply to the connection of wattmeters which have voltage and current sensing elements. If the wattmeter voltage element replaces the voltmeter in *Figure 8.18(a)* and the current sensing element replaces the ammeter, the power indication is that used by the load and the current sensing element. If connected as in

Figure 8.18(b) the power indication includes the power dissipated in the voltage element.

(c) The use of rectifier instruments

The deflection of a permanent-magnet, moving-coil instrument is proportional to the average current flowing in the movement. In a d.c. circuit, connecting the meter terminals correctly causes the pointer to move up the scale while reversing the connections results in the pointer being forced back on the zero stop.

If the meter is connected to a circuit carrying alternating current the meter indicates zero since the average value over a complete cycle of a symmetrical alternating current is zero. During the positive half cycle there will be a torque on the meter movement in one direction while during the negative half cycle the direction of the torque will be reversed.

In order to employ a moving-coil meter in an a.c. circuit it is necessary to connect it in series with a rectifier.

Assuming a perfect sinusoidal supply the average value of the current $= 0.636 \times I_{max}$.

The r.m.s. value of the current $= 0.707\, I_{max}$.

The r.m.s. value is therefore $1.11 \times$ the average value. 1.11 is the *form-factor* of a sine wave.

The deflection of the meter is due to the *average torque* which is a function of the *average current*. The meter must however indicate the effective or r.m.s. value so that it is necessary to rescale the meter face (or to use a transformer) to increase the readings by the factor 1.11. The scale markings are therefore only correct if the input to the meter is of pure sinusoidal form. Where iron-cored inductors, transformers or semiconducting devices are involved it may well be that waveforms are not sinusoidal so that the form factors are not equal to 1.11 and there will be errors in meter indication when using rectifier instruments.

(d) Frequency errors

The anode and cathode of any rectifying device make up a small capacitor since they are sections of conducting material separated by an insulator. At power frequencies and up to possibly 5 kHz the value of capacitive reactance is sufficiently high that very little charging current flows from the supply.

Capacitive reactance $X_c = \dfrac{1}{2\pi f C}\,\Omega$ and charging current $I_c = \dfrac{V}{X_c}$

At very high frequencies the falling capacitive reactance becomes significant since it allows charge to move into and out of a diode which shows up as an alternating current in the circuit and in the rectifier instrument when only unidirectional pulses (unsmoothed d.c.) are expected. As the frequency increases so does the alternating component of current and eventually, at a particular value of frequency, the meter reading will fall to zero. Care must be taken when selecting rectifier instruments to see that they are sufficiently accurate at the desired operating frequency. Rectifier instruments include most universal types such as the AVO meter.

The inductive reactance of coils is a function of frequency: $X_L = 2\pi fL\ \Omega$. The impedance of the moving-coil in moving-coil meters and the operating coils in moving-iron instruments will therefore change with frequency. In ammeters this change of impedance will not be particularly significant because the current is predominantly controlled by the load impedance for a fixed supply voltage. However, in voltmeters, the voltmeter current is determined by the impedance of the voltmeter and since this changes with frequency, the current and hence indication will vary.

Example 3. A voltmeter has a coil with inductance 20 mH which is connected in series with a series resistor with value 2 kΩ. It gives full scale deflection of 10 V when connected to a 10 V, 50 Hz supply. Assuming that the face indication is proportional to coil current, estimate the meter indication when the supply frequency is 5 kHz, the supply voltage remaining at 10 V. (Assume that the only effect to be considered is the change in inductive reactance of the coil.)

$$\text{At 50 Hz, } X_L = 2\pi fL\ \Omega$$
$$= 2\pi \times 50 \times 20 \times 10^{-3}$$
$$= 6.28\ \Omega$$

$$Z_{meter} = \sqrt{2000^2 + 6.28^2} = 2000.01\ \Omega$$

Meter current = 10/2000.01 = 5 mA
When the coil current is 5 mA, the meter is fully deflected and indicates 10 V.

$$\text{At 5 kHz, } X_L = 2\pi \times 5000 \times 20\ 10^{-3}$$
$$= 628.32\ \Omega$$

$$Z_{meter} = \sqrt{2000^2 + 628.32^2} = 2096.4\ \Omega$$

Meter current = 10/2096.4 = 4.77 mA

$$\text{Indication} = \frac{4.77}{5} \times 10\text{ V} = 9.54\text{ V}$$

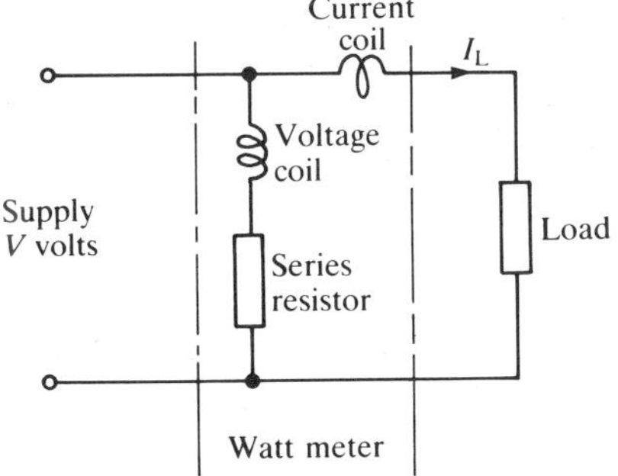

Figure 8.19

Frequency changes will also affect the indication of the dynamometer wattmeter.

The arrangement of coils in this type of wattmeter is shown in *Figure 8.19*. Due to the applied voltage a current I_1 flows in the voltage coil:

$I_1\ \alpha\ V$, the applied voltage

The current I_1 creates a magnetic field in which the current coil is situated. The current coil carries the load current I_L. A force is set up on the current coil due to the interaction between I_L and the magnetic field set up by I_1. This force operates against a restraining spring, causing the pointer to be deflected as in the case of the moving-coil ammeter, the difference being that the magnetic field is electrically produced in the wattmeter and by a permanent magnet in the moving-coil meter.

The phase angle between the applied voltage and the load current = $\phi°$

The power factor = $\cos\phi$

Power in the circuit = $VI_L \cos\phi$

Therefore, the wattmeter indication α $VI_L \cos\phi$

Now if I_1 is proportional to, and in phase with the applied voltage V the indication α $I_1 I_L \cos\phi$

$= kI_1 I_L \cos\phi$ where k is a constant of proportionality which takes into account the impedance of the voltage coil circuit, the numbers of turns on the two coils and the stiffness of the restraining spring.

If the voltage coil circuit were purely resistive I_1 would be a perfect analogue of the applied voltage V, i.e. I_1 would be directly proportional to V and would be in phase with V which is the required condition. However the coil has inductance and its inductive reactance will vary with frequency. Increasing the frequency of the supply while keeping the supply voltage constant will cause I_1 to fall since the impedance of the voltage coil circuit will be increasing. Additionally, as the inductive reactance increases, I_1 will lag the applied voltage by an angle which is frequency dependent so that the phase angle between I_1 and I_L will not be the same as that between V and I_L and the indication will therefore be in error.

Example 4. A dynamometer wattmeter has a voltage coil with inductance 40 mH and it is connected in series with a 4000 Ω resistor. The impedance of the current coil is small enough to be ignored. It is connected as in *Figure 8.19* to measure the power supplied to a load.

The supply voltage = 200 V

The supply frequency = 50 Hz

The load current = 5 A

The load power factor = 1.0 (the load is purely resistive)

The wattmeter indication = 1000 W.

Investigate the effect on the wattmeter indication of increasing the frequency of the supply to 2.5 kHz assuming that the circuit and meter resistances and the inductance of the voltage coil do not change with frequency.

At 50 Hz:

Voltage coil inductive reactance $= 2\pi fL = 2\pi \times 50 \times 40 \times 10^{-3}$
$= 12.57\ \Omega$

Voltage coil circuit impedance $= \sqrt{4000^2 + 12.57^2}$
$= 4000.02\ \Omega$

Figure 8.20(a) shows the impedance triangle from which it may be deduced that the current I_1 lags the circuit voltage by 0.18°. The phasor diagram for the wattmeter currents and voltage is shown in *Figure 8.20(b)*

$$I_1 = \frac{V}{Z} = \frac{200}{4000.02} = 0.05\ \text{A}$$

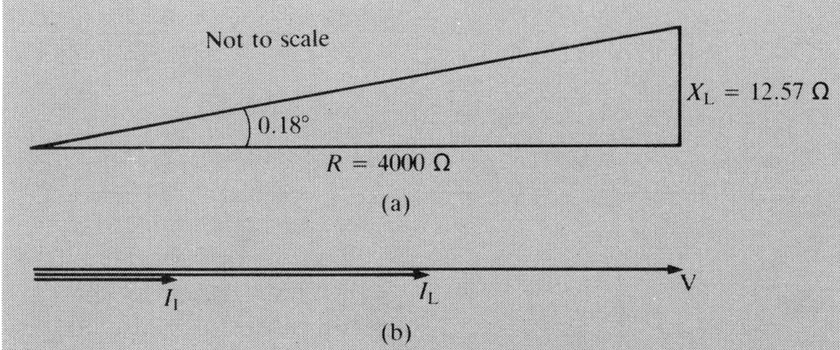

Figure 8.20

$$\text{Wattmeter indication} = kI_1I_L \cos \phi$$
$$\therefore 1000 = k \times 0.05 \times 5 \times \cos 0.18°$$
$$k = 4000$$

At 2500 Hz:

$$\text{Voltage coil inductive reactance} = 2\pi\, 2500 \times 40 \times 10^{-3} = 628.32\ \Omega$$

$$\text{Voltage coil circuit impedance} = \sqrt{4000^2 + 628.32^2} = 4049\ \Omega$$

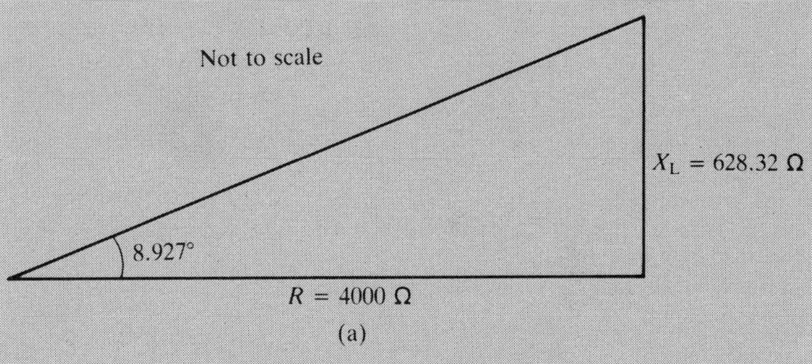

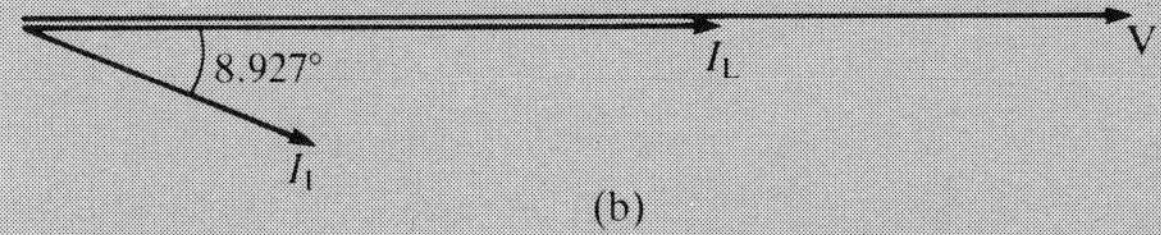

Figure 8.21

Figure 8.21(a) shows the impedance triangle from which it may be deduced that I_1 lags the circuit voltage by 8.927°
The phasor diagram is shown in *Figure 8.21(b)*.
Since we know the value of k from the original test at 50 Hz:

$$\text{Wattmeter indication} = 4000 \times 0.0494 \times 5 \times \cos 8.927° = 975.93\ \text{W}$$

Error 24.07 W on 1000 W = 2.407%
As the frequency is increased further the indication will fall

faster than is suggested by the above example due to the capacitance between the parts of the meter and between turns of each of the coils.

(e) Determination error

When using a bridge or potentiometer, often there will be no discernible change in the galvanometer indication while the circuit parameters are adjusted over a range. For example in the d.c. potentiometer, it might be possible to move the slider 0.2 cm either side of a mean position without any noticeable deflection of the galvanometer. This effect is often very pronounced in bridges where under certain conditions quite large changes in component values produce little obvious change in the balance condition. There is therefore some uncertainty in the final result.

(f) Reading errors

With analogue instruments errors occur due to:

(i) The scale length and linearity. The reading recorded is a matter of judgement when the pointer lies between two scale markings and this is particularly prone to error where the scale is non linear.

(ii) The actual width of the pointer.

(iii) Parallax (the angle at the scale and pointer are viewed). To assist in this case, some meters have a mirrored surface behind the pointer so that when the pointer and its image are in line, there is no parallax error.

(g) Time measurement

Whenever a stopwatch is used to measure time there are errors due to:

(i) The time taken for the operator to recognise that a particular phenomenon has occurred.

(ii) The time taken to push down the stop button and for the mechanism to stop.

The relative errors here can be large when short time intervals are considered. An analogy is that of the driver of a motor vehicle being confronted with a sudden hazard. It takes time for the driver to recognise the hazard and then to apply the brakes followed by the actual stopping time of the vehicle.

(h) Construction and adjustment error

However carefully meters are made and adjusted there is always some indication error. In a good grade instrument the error might be ±1% of the face reading over a specified range, say between 50% and 100% of full scale deflection (FSD). For a voltmeter with FSD of 100 V, when the meter indicates 50 V the actual voltage would lie between 50 V + 1% of 50 V = 50.5 V and 50 V − 1% of 50 V = 49.5 V. The error in voltage terms = ±0.5 V. At an indicated voltage of 100 V, the range is from 101 V to 99 V the error in voltage terms being ±1 V.

The hand-cranked megger is quoted as having an accuracy of

1.5 mm from any marked position on the scale (see *Figure 8.9*). This represents a fraction of 1 Ω at the low end of the scale to perhaps several thousand ohms at the high end.

Random errors

(a) *Errors of judgement.* These involve estimating readings from analogue meters when the pointer lies between scale markings. On one occasion a reading might be judged to be 3.4 and at another time, for the same pointer position, 3.5, say.
(b) *Random fluctuations of voltage or frequency.* During a set of readings, due to one or both of these fluctuations, results may be obtained which cannot be repeated.
(c) *Variable circuit parameters.* Contact resistances may vary, vibrations upset equipment, etc.
(d) *Slips and mistakes.* Scale factors may be forgotten, numbers written in the wrong columns, decimal points misplaced.

Estimation of the overall result of systematic errors

1 Where the overall result is to be the sum of several measurements

As an example consider three measurements, x, y and z
The overall result = x + y + z = A (the nominal Answer)
The error in the measurement of A = δA

so that the relative error in A $= \dfrac{\delta A}{A}$

Now x represents the fraction $\dfrac{x}{A}$ of the overall result

and y represents the fraction $\dfrac{y}{A}$ of the overall result

z represents the fraction $\dfrac{z}{A}$ of the overall result

The relative errors in each of the individual measurements are:

$\dfrac{\delta x}{x}, \dfrac{\delta y}{y}$, and $\dfrac{\delta z}{z}$ respectively

$$\frac{\delta A}{A} = \frac{x}{A}\frac{\delta x}{x} + \frac{y}{A}\frac{\delta y}{y} + \frac{z}{A}\frac{\delta z}{z}$$

The relative errors of each component is 'weighted' according to the proportion of the whole that the component represents. If a particular component only represents a very small fraction of the total then it has little effect on the overall result if it has say 50% error in its determination. This is demonstrated in *Example 5*.

Example 5. A resistance with total value nominally 1600 Ω is to be fabricated by soldering three individual resistors together in series. The details of the three resistors are:
(i) Nominal value 1000 Ω, relative error ±2%
(ii) Nominal value 500 Ω, relative error ±5%
(iii) Nominal value 100 Ω, relative error ±10%

What is the worst possible relative error of the final 1600 Ω resistor?

Resistor (i) represents nominally $\frac{1000}{1600}$ part of the total.

It has relative error ±2%. Its contribution to the total error

$$= \frac{1000}{1600} \times \pm 2\%$$

$$= \pm 1.25\%$$

Similarly for resistor (ii), $\frac{500}{1600} \times \pm\ 5\% = 1.5625\%$

and for resistor (iii), $\frac{100}{1600} \times \pm 10\% = \pm 0.625\%$

Total relative error = ±(1.25 + 1.5625 + 0.625)% = ±3.4375%
If all resistors are at the limit of their permitted errors and are all high, the maximum error will be +3.4375%. Similarly, if all resistors are low by their full tolerance the figure will be −3.4375%. If one is high and two low or vice versa the final relative error will be smaller.

Example 6. Re-assess the relative error in *Example 3* using the same resistance values but with the relative errors reversed. Resistor (i) 1000 Ω, relative error ±10%, resistor (ii) 500 Ω, relative error ±5% and resistor (iii) 100 Ω, relative error ±2%.
(*Ans* ±(6.25 + 1.5625 + 0.125) = ±7.9375%)

2 Where the result is to be a product or quotient of two or more quantities

Let the quantities be x, y and z. Then the required result is A = xyz, xy/z or any other combination forming a product or quotient.

$$\frac{\delta A}{A} = \frac{\delta x}{x} + \frac{\delta y}{y} + \frac{\delta z}{z}$$

Example 7. The power in a d.c. circuit is determined using the result:
$P = V \times I$ watts
The voltage is measured using a voltmeter which indicates 175 V and which has a relative error of ±1.5%. The current is measured using an ammeter which indicates 2.75 A and which has a relative error of ±1%.
Determine the relative error in the value of power and the upper and lower limits of that power.
Power (P) = 175 (V) × 2.75 (I) = 481.25 watts (nominal)

$$\frac{\delta P}{P} = \frac{\delta V}{V} + \frac{\delta I}{I} = \pm(1.5\% + 1\%) = \pm 2.5\%$$

$$\therefore \delta A = A \times \pm 2.5\% = 481.25 \times \pm 2.5\% = \pm 12.03\ \text{W}$$

The relative error = ±2.5% and the upper and lower limits are 481.25 ± 12.03 W or from 469.22 W to 493.28 W.

Example 8. A bridge used to measure the resistance and inductance of a coil balances when:

$$R_x = \frac{R_1 R_3}{R_4} \text{ and } L_x = R_1 R_3 C_4$$

If the relative errors on the components are: $R_1 \pm 1\%$, $R_3 \pm 2\%$, $C_4 \pm 4\%$ and $R_4 \pm 0.5\%$; determine the maximum relative errors in the measured values of R_x and L_x.

$$R_x = \frac{R_1 R_3}{R_4}: \qquad \frac{\delta R_x}{R_x} = \frac{\delta R_1}{R_1} + \frac{\delta R_3}{R_3} + \frac{\delta R_4}{R_4}$$

$$= \pm(1 + 2 + 0.5) = \pm 3.5\%$$

In order for the relative error to have a maximum positive value R_1 and R_3 need to be high, adding to the error; and R_4 needs to be low so increasing the number of times it divides into the top line, again increasing the error. Alternatively the two top quantities could be low and the bottom one high leading to the maximum negative error.

$$L_x = R_1 R_3 C_4: \qquad \frac{\delta L_x}{L_x} = \frac{\delta R_1}{R_1} + \frac{\delta R_3}{R_3} + \frac{\delta C_4}{C_4}$$

$$= \pm(1 + 2 + 4) = \pm 7\%$$

It should be observed that where a result is obtained by multiplying or dividing quantities, these individual quantities need to have very low relative errors if the final result is to be acceptable.

Example 9. A resistor with precisely-known resistance of 2000 Ω is connected to a 200 V, 50 Hz supply using an ammeter and voltmeter as shown in *Figure 8.22(a)* to measure the input. Determine the effects of the instrumentation on (i) load voltage, (ii) load current, (iii) load power and (iv) the power drawn from the supply as compared with connecting the resistor directly to the supply as shown in *Figure 8.22(b)*.

Redrawing the circuit as shown in *Figure 8.23*, we see that the voltmeter and load are in parallel and have an effective resistance given by:

$$R_{\text{effective}} = \frac{2000 \times 20\,000}{2000 + 20\,000} = 1818.2\,\Omega$$

Total circuit resistance = 1818.2 + 2.5

$$I_{\text{in}} = \frac{200}{1818.2 + 2.5} = 0.10985 \text{ A}$$

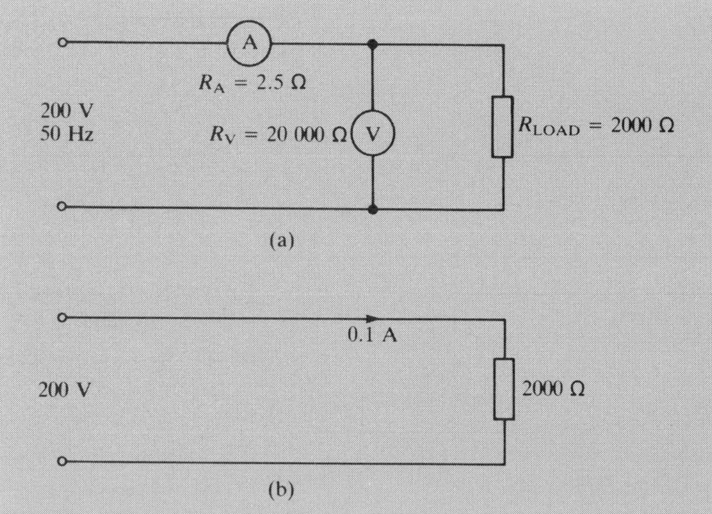

Figure 8.22

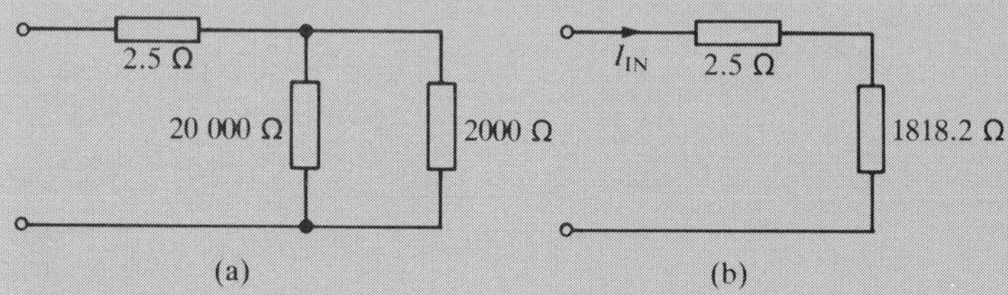

Figure 8.23

Volt drop across the ammeter = 0.10985 × 2.5 = 0.2746 V

Load voltage = supply voltage − drop across the ammeter
= 200 − 0.2746
= 199.725 V

$$\text{Load current} = \frac{199.725}{2000} = 0.099863 \text{ A}$$

$$\text{Load power} = I_{load}^2 R_{load} = 0.099863^2 \times 2000 = 19.945 \text{ W}$$

Quantity	*Without instrumentation*	*With instrumentation*	*Difference*
V_{load}	200 V	199.725 V	−0.1375%
I_{load}	0.1 A	0.099863 A	−0.1375%
Load power	20 W	19.945 W	−0.275%
Power drawn from supply	20 W	200 × 0.10985 = 21.97 W	+9.85%

Example 10. The energy supplied to a circuit is measured using a voltmeter, an ammeter, a power factor meter and a stop watch.

The relative errors of the measuring instruments are:

Voltmeter ±0.5%

Ammeter ±0.25%
Power-factor meter ±0.4%
The stop watch is correct to ±1 second in 1 hour. The response time of the stop watch and operator is ±0.2 seconds at the beginning and end of each timing period.
Determine the maximum relative error in the value of energy input to the circuit timed over periods of (i) 1 minute and (ii) 15 minutes.
(i) Energy timed over a period of 1 minute.
Consider first the stop watch. It is accurate to 1 second in 1 hour.
±1 second in 60 minutes is ±1/60 second in 1 minute.
At the beginning and end of the timing operation the operator and the start/stop mechanism of the watch may introduce an error of ±0.2 seconds.
Total timing error is therefore ±1/60 + 0.2 (starting) + 0.2 (stopping)
= ±0.41667 s
Over a period of 1 minute, this represents a relative error of

$$\pm\frac{0.41667}{60} \times 100\% = 0.69444\%$$

Power = $VI \cos\phi$ watts
Energy = power × time = $VI \cos\phi \times t$ joules
Where quantities are multiplied to obtain the required answer, the relative errors are added.
Total relative error = ±(0.5 + 0.25 + 0.4 + 0.69444)
= ±1.844%
This is a maximum value and it may well be that with the starting and stopping of the stop watch, the starting error will be negative, i.e. late starting, so that the time count tends to be too small, but that a similar error when stopping, a positive error, will give a time count which is too long. The two errors could tend to cancel each other.
(ii) Energy timed over a period of 15 minutes.
Again consider the stop watch. ±1 second in 1 hour = 0.25 s in 15 minutes
The starting and stopping errors are as before.
Total timing error = ±(0.25 + 0.2 + 0.2) = 0.65 s

$$\text{Relative time error} = \frac{0.65}{15 \times 60} \times 100\% = 0.0722\%$$

Total relative error = ±(0.5 + 0.25 + 0.4 + 0.0722)
= ±1.222%

This example demonstrates the importance of ‘end effects’. These are fixed error quantities which only occur at the start and finish of something. Here it is a fixed time error at the beginning and end of the interval being measured. 0.4 seconds as a proportion of 1 minute represents quite a large error. However when compared with 15 minutes or even longer, say, 1 hour, it becomes insignificant.

Another example of end effect is relevant to the measurement of current using a standard resistor and a potentiometer. When current enters and leaves a resistor it does not immediately disperse itself uniformly across the cross section of the resistor material. Since, at the ends the current only flows in part of the conductor, its resistance here is higher than further along the material. The resistance of the resistor is not uniform along its length. Where high precision is required, tap off points to the potentiometer are made a short distance from each end. At these points the current distribution in the material has become uniform and between the two tap off points the resistance per unit length is uniform and precisely known.

If the resistance of the resistor were being calculated from the formula:

$$R = \frac{\rho l}{A} \Omega$$

There would be relative errors in all the quantities as for V, I and $\cos\phi$ in *Example 10*, together with specific end errors concerned with the working length l of the material and the area over which the current is spread in the end sections of the resistor. With a very long wire the end effects can be ignored, but with a very short wire, where precise results are required, the end effects could be very significant.

PROBLEMS

11 A d.c. potentiometer is standardised at 0.01 V/cm. It is used to measure an unknown voltage with the aid of a 50:1 volt ratio box. Zero galvanometer current is achieved when the slider is at 50.47 cm from the end of the wire. (Distance XQ in *Figure 8.1* = 50.47 cm.) What is the magnitude of the unknown voltage?

12 A standard resistor with value 5 Ω is connected into a circuit as shown in *Figure 8.6*. In order to determine the circuit current the potential difference across the standard resistor is measured using a potentiometer, standardised at 0.01 V/cm. Zero galvanometer current is achieved when the slider is 89.35 cm from the end of the wire. (XQ = 89.35 cm in *Figure 8.1*). What is the magnitude of the circuit current?

13 The power in a d.c. circuit is determined using a potentiometer. The following readings were obtained:

(i) The load voltage is applied to a volt ratio box with a 250:1 ratio. Zero galvanometer current occurs when the slider is at 29.82 cm from the end of the wire (Distance XQ in *Figure 8.1* = 29.82 cm).

(ii) The load current is measured using a 0.5 Ω standard resistor connected as in *Figure 8.6*. Zero current flows in the potentiometer galvanometer when the slider is at 68.83 cm from the end of the wire. (XQ in *Figure 8.1* = 68.83 cm.)

What is the value of the circuit power?

14 Describe the construction of a simple ohmmeter. Explain how the effect of low battery voltage is compensated for during use.

15 Why is the simple ohmmeter inadequate when testing for earth and short-circuit faults on cables and motors? What device is available and more suitable for these applications?

16 Describe the range of tests which are applied to (i) a three-phase induction motor and (ii) a bulk-oil circuit breaker, to determine their state of health and to ensure, as far as possible, that they will continue to perform satisfactorily.

17 A coil is tested to determine its Q-factor using a bridge. At 5 kHz the results obtained are:

$L = 45.3\,\text{mH} \quad R = 12.3\,\Omega$

What is the Q-factor of the coil?

18 (a) A coil with a Q-factor of 125 at 3.4 kHz has a resistance of 15.6 Ω.
What is the value of its inductance?
(b) If the resistance and inductance of the coil remained constant with changing frequency, what would its Q-factor be at 400 Hz?

19 The circuit breaker controlling the power input to an oil-impregnated paper insulated cable feeding a 3.3 kV, 50 Hz, three-phase induction motor is reported to have tripped causing the motor to stop. It is necessary to establish why the circuit breaker tripped and to take remedial action. Carefully explain *all* the steps which should be taken to establish the nature of the fault starting with the obtaining of the necessary permit to work.

20 Routine maintenance work is to be carried out on a 440 V, d.c. shunt-wound motor which drives a conveyor system in a factory. Describe the necessary procedure to ensure that the work can be carried out safely. What tests and inspections would be carried out to ensure, as far as possible, the health of the motor.

21 When measurements are made there is always some uncertainty in the results obtained. Discuss briefly some of the errors which may be present when making measurements.

22 Discuss the systematic errors which are associated with rectifier instruments.

23 When using instrumentation on circuits working at frequencies above a few hundreds of hertz care has to be taken in the selection of suitable instruments and in the evaluation of the results obtained. Discuss why this is so.

24 When using a multi-range analogue instrument to measure a quantity, why is it advisable to select the range which gives the largest deflection consistent with not over-driving the pointer?

25 When performing tests in which timing plays a part, why is it better to run a longer rather than a shorter test where there is a choice?

26 A 200 Ω resistor with relative error ±5% is connected in parallel with a 500 Ω resistor with relative error ±2.5%. What is the relative error in the value of the parallel pair?

Hint: $R_{\text{equivalent}} = \dfrac{R_1 R_2}{R_1 + R_2}\ \Omega$

Evaluate the relative error in the denominator using the 'weighting' method. Then follow *Example 8*: care with the sign of the relative error of the denominator.

27 A distance of 25.36 m is to be measured out in a straight line along the ground. A 25 m steel measuring tape and a 30 cm desk ruler are to hand. The total length of the steel measuring tape is guaranteed to within ±3 cm. The desk ruler has relative error ±0.25%.

With the measuring tape fully extended and the desk ruler placed at its end the nominal distance from start of the tape to end of the ruler is 25.3 m. The final 6 cm (0.06 m) is guessed with an error of ±20%. What is the relative error on the whole measurement and what are the overall limits on the measurement?

28 A wattmeter used to measure the power supplied to a resistive load has the arrangement as shown in *Figure 8.19*. The voltage coil has an inductance of 20 mH and it is connected in series with a resistor which has a value of 2500 Ω. When the supply voltage is 50 V at a frequency of 50 Hz the coil draws its design current and the wattmeter indication is correct (within its specification).

For frequencies of (a) 1 kHz and (b) 5 kHz: determine the percentage error which occurs in the indication due to (i) the change in magnitude of the impedance of the voltage coil circuit and (ii) the phase change which occurs as the voltage coil circuit inductive reactance changes.

29 The inductance and resistance of a coil are measured using a commercial instrument which uses a frequency of 5 kHz.
The inductance measurement has a nominal value of 42.5 mH with a relative error of ±5%
The resistance measurement has a nominal value of 8.65 Ω with a relative error of ±1%
The frequency is stable to within ±25 Hz.
(a) What is the nominal value of the Q-factor of the coil?
(b) What is the relative error of the value in (a)?

30 A voltmeter and ammeter are connected into a circuit as shown in *Figure 8.22(a)*. The supply voltage = 200 V.
The resistance of the ammeter = 2 Ω.
The resistance of the voltmeter = 2500 Ω.
The load resistance = 500 Ω.
If the load resistor were connected directly to the supply with no instrumentation included, it would draw 0.4 A and dissipate a power of 80 W.
(a) With the circuit connected as in *Figure 8.22(a)* determine (i) the load voltage (ii) the current in the ammeter and (iii) the load power.

(b) If the voltmeter is disconnected from its present position and reconnected directly across the supply terminals, recalculate the values (i) to (iii) in part (a) above.

Solutions to problems

CHAPTER 1

11 (i) 3303, (ii) 72

12 (b) (i) high grade transformer steel
(ii) laminate core

13 Hysteresis loss $\alpha\, f$ New loss = 44 W
Eddy current loss $\alpha\, f^2$ New loss = 42.35 W

14 (i) $R_T{}^p = 0.785\ \Omega$ ($Z_T{}^p = 2.5\ \Omega$) $X_T{}^p = 2.374\ \Omega$
$R_o = 400/0.144 = 2778\ \Omega$, $X_o = 400/1.5935 = 251\ \Omega$
(ii) $R_T{}^s = 0.0491\ \Omega$ $X_T{}^s = 0.148\ \Omega$

15 (i) 1.186 A, (ii) 0.179 A, (iii) 0.1496 A

16 (a) 11.92 A, (b)(i) 13.45 A, (ii) Cos 38.32° = 0.7845 lagging

17 (a) 0.0654 Ω, 0.286 Ω, 0.278 Ω.
(b) I_{FL} = 208.2 A Efficiency = 89.3%.

18 57.6 A 0.71 lagging.

19 (a) $Z_T{}^{480} = 0.1485\ \Omega$, $R_T{}^{480} = 0.0496\ \Omega$, $X_T{}^{480} = 0.14\ \Omega$
(b) (i) I_{FL} = 208.33 A
$\phi = 31.78°$: $\sin\phi = 0.527$

$$\text{Regulation} = \frac{208.33 \times 0.0496 \times 0.85 + 208.33 \times 0.527 \times 0.14}{480} \times 100\%$$

$$= 5.03\%$$

(ii) 455.85 V, (iii) 95.34%

20 I_p = 27.18 A

$$\text{Efficiency} = \frac{27.18 \times 440 \times 0.9}{27.18 \times 440 \times 0.9 + 96 + 96} \times 100$$

$$= 98.25\%$$

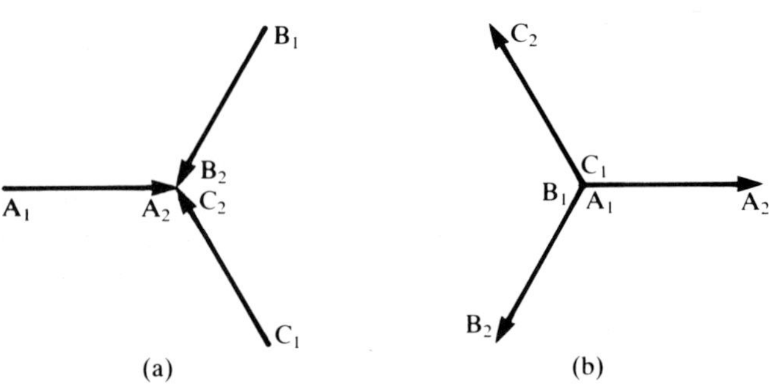

21 (a) yY 0 (b) yY 6

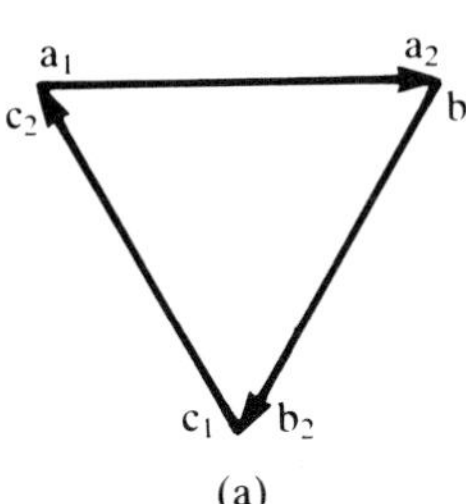

(a)

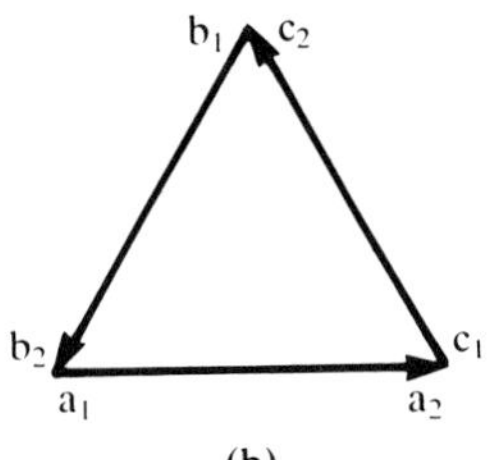

(b)

22 (a) Dd 0 (b) Dd 6

CHAPTER 2

9 (a) 8 1/3 rev/s, (b) 10 rev/s
10 72 slots
11 1199 V/phase, 2076 V line

CHAPTER 3

7 12 rev/s
8 4%
9 5% of 60 Hz = 3 Hz
10 (i) 5550 W, (ii) 5384 W
11 (i) T_{max} at 0.25 p.u. slip, (ii) T_{max} at 1.0 p.u. slip
(iii) T_{max} at 0.417 p.u. slip
15 (i) 0.967, (ii) 62.7 Nm
16 (i) 48.7 Nm, (ii) 119.2 Nm

CHAPTER 8

11 0.5047 × 50 = 22.235 V
12 $I = 0.1787$ A
13 $V = 74.55$ volts
$I = 1.3766$ A
Power = 102.6 W
17 Q = 115.7
18 (a) L = 91.28 mH
(b) Q = 14.7
26 Numerator: relative error = ±7.5%, Denominator: weighted relative error = 3.21%, Max. relative error 4.29%
27 $\pm(0.11 + 2.957 \times 10^{-3} + 0.0473) = \pm 0.1686\%$
28 (a) $I_1 = 19.9747$ mA Error 0.126%
Phase angle = 2.877°, Cos 2.877° = 0.9987 Error 0.126%
(b) $I_1 = 19.397$ mA, Error 3.02%
Phase angle = 14.1°, Cos 14.1° = 0.9698 Error 3.02%
29 $Q = 154.36$
Relative error of f = 0.5% Total relative error 6.5%
30 (a) (i) $V_L = 199.04$ V, (ii) $I = 0.48$ A, (iii) 79.234 W
(b) (i) $V_L = 199.203$ V, (ii) $I = 0.3984$ A, (iii) 79.364 W

Index